THE HOLT CHEMISTRY PROGRAM

ACTION CHEMISTRY
Matter • Energy • Change
Bolton • Lamphere • Menesini • Huang

LABORATORY EXPERIMENTS in ACTION CHEMISTRY
Matter • Energy • Change
Complete
Separate Units 1–9

ACTION CHEMISTRY Matter • Energy • Change
Complete
Separate Units 1–9

ACTION CHEMISTRY MAGAZINE UNITS 1–9

Tests

Teacher's Edition to ACTION CHEMISTRY Program

FOUNDATIONS OF CHEMISTRY *Toon and Ellis Second Edition*
Laboratory Experiments for FOUNDATIONS OF CHEMISTRY
Teacher's Edition for FOUNDATIONS OF CHEMISTRY
Teacher's Edition for Laboratory Experiments for FOUNDATIONS OF CHEMISTRY
TESTS for FOUNDATIONS OF CHEMISTRY

MODERN CHEMISTRY *Metcalfe, Williams, and Castka*
MODERN CHEMISTRY Teacher's Edition
Laboratory Experiments in Chemistry
Exercises and Experiments in Chemistry
Exercises and Experiments in Chemistry Teacher's Edition
Tests in Chemistry
Alternate Tests in Chemistry
Key to Tests

Ruth P. Bolton
Elizabeth V. Lamphere
Mario Menesini
Paul C. Huang

ACTION CHEMISTRY
Matter · Energy · Change

HOLT, RINEHART and WINSTON, INC.

New York   ·   Toronto   ·   London   ·   Sydney

RUTH P. BOLTON, Teacher of Chemistry in Northview High School, Covina, California

ELIZABETH V. LAMPHERE, Science Department Chairman in Norwich Senior High School, Norwich, New York

MARIO MENESINI, Director of Educational Consulting Service, Orinda, California

PAUL C. HUANG, President of Onoma Productions, Inc., New York—a film company/design studio. Mr. Huang is a writer, film producer/director.

Credits for unit opener photographs:
Units 1, 2, 3, 5, and 7 (Felix Cooper)
Unit 4 (H. Foote, Shostal Assoc.)
Unit 6 (Dr. E. R. Degginger)
Unit 8 (Grant Heilman)
Unit 9 (J. Alex Langley, dpi)

Illustrations on pages 5/**6–7**, 5/**13**, and 5/**20** are from the CHEM Study films named. The illustrations are used with the permission of the Chemical Education Material Study, University of California, Berkeley. Credits for other photographs and art appear in captions.

Cover photograph: Oxygen torch heating test tube. (*Dr. E. R. Degginger*)

ISBN: 0-03-086072-5

3456   039   987654321

Preface

ON ENTERING A NEW WORLD . . .

It is as if you were Columbus, an astronaut or any explorer reaching out for exciting new events. True, your name will not grace the pages of history because you decided to study chemistry. But your excitement will come from discovering new things about the world you have been feeling, smelling, and seeing all of your life. Your discoveries will not shock the world because the findings you will make are discoveries which scientists have already made. Your adventures will be personal discoveries of chemical truths.

The laboratory will be your world of experiences. You will answer many questions by using the tools and materials provided in the chemistry laboratory. The questions you answer will create new questions: What is this material called matter? How much material will do what? How can you change matter from one form to another? How can you change one kind of material into another kind of material?

You will answer questions and find a new security because you will understand better the world in which you live.

Mario Menesini
Orinda, California
April 15, 1972

The authorship team of Mrs. Bolton and Miss Lamphere designed the course of ACTION CHEMISTRY. Mrs. Bolton is responsible for the major section of the laboratory activities and Miss Lamphere is responsible for some student activities, the teacher materials, and student testing program.

Dr. Menesini has been mainly responsible for the reader-text. Mr. Huang is the writer of the magazine.

Acknowledgments

Special thanks are due to the consultants who have helped us in the manuscript stage of the program.

Dr. Richard C. Anderson, Professor of Educational Psychology and Psychology, University of Illinois. Dr. Anderson reviewed the manuscript of the laboratory manual and the reader-text for educational appropriateness.

Dr. Stephen R. Baig, Assistant Professor of Chemical Oceanography, Nova University, Oceanographic Laboratory, Dania, Florida. Dr. Baig reviewed the magazine.

Dr. R. E. Gaensslen, Assistant Professor of Biochemistry, John Jay College of Criminal Justice, City University of New York. Dr. Gaensslen provided content criticism and suggestions for the magazine. He also wrote sections of the reader-text on photosynthesis and rubber.

Mr. H. Richard Gerfin, a science teacher in Somers Central School, Lincolndale, New York, is the author of Unit 5, "Chemical Reactions" of the reader-text, and Chapters 20, and 25 of the reader-text.

Mrs. Marilyn Noeltner Smith, a teacher of chemistry in the Beverly Hills Unified School District, Beverly Hills, California. Mrs. Smith is the author of Unit 4, "The Why of Chemical Behavior" and Unit 6, "Organic Chemistry and Biochemistry" of the reader text. Mrs. Smith also reviewed all laboratory materials and the accompanying teacher materials.

Dr. I. Walerstein, Professor Emeritus, Purdue University, Visiting Professor, Tel Aviv University. Dr. Walerstein reviewed the manuscript of the laboratory manual and the reader-text for science content.

Mr. Elbert C. Weaver, former Chairman of Chemistry at Phillips Academy, Andover, Massachusetts. Mr. Weaver offered suggestions and criticized the last units of the reader-text for science content.

We wish to thank the following for their contributions to the program:
Norwich Central City School System, Norwich, N.Y., for the use of their facilities for taking special photographs; the staff of Onoma Productions, Inc. for the design of the Magazine and the layout of the Laboratory Manual with special thanks to Frank Spinks for his cartoon artwork; the cartoons were conceived and written by Paul Huang; Felix Cooper for his artwork in the laboratory manual and in the reader-text; Diana Bourdrez and Linda Lindroth for obtaining photographs; Ruth Riley for the layout of the reader-text; Mary Mundy-Editor.

Special Acknowledgments

There have been many people who have taken part in the building of this program. Among them are the students and teachers who field tested Unit I of the ACTION CHEMISTRY Program: Laboratory Experiments; Reader-text; Magazine; and Testing program. This test took place in the Autumn of 1971 in schools around the country. The foresight of the supervisors, the dedication of the teachers, and the patience of the students helped us learn the strengths and weaknesses of our proposed products. Using the results of this test program we have developed the finished ACTION CHEMISTRY Program.

Many thanks to the teachers and supervisors who tested Unit I and helped us with their criticisms and comments:

Mr. Carl Conrad, Lorain Southview High School, Lorain, Ohio
Dr. Harvill F. Dean, Lower Cape May Regional High School, Cape May, N.J.
Mr. Stephen W. Dolak, Altoona Area High School, Altoona, Pa.
Mr. Harold D. Yoder, Science Supervisor, Altoona Area School District, Altoona, Pa.
Miss Nell Garland, Bearden Senior High School, Knoxville, Tenn.
Mr. Robert Molkenbur, Johnson High School, St. Paul, Minn.
Mr. Harley R. Murchie, Mattanawcook Academy, Lincoln, Maine
Mr. Daniel Petrucelli, John F. Kennedy Memorial High School, Iselin, N.J.
Mr. Howard B. Richard, Mt. Desert Island High School, Mt. Desert, Maine
Mr. Arthur E. Rondeau, White Plains High School, White Plains, N.Y.
Mr. Raymond Smith, A.S. Johnston High School, Austin, Texas
Mrs. Carla Winslow, Hoboken High School, Hoboken, N.J.

Contents for the Reader—Text

ACTION CHEMISTRY

Matter · Energy · Change

Contents

UNIT 1 MATTER

Chapter 3   *READER TEXT*   **Chapter 3**   *LABORATORY MANUAL*

MATTER: ITS PHASES AND PHYSICAL PROPERTIES

Chapter 4   *READER TEXT*   **Chapter 4**   *LABORATORY MANUAL*

THE CLASSES OF MATTER

Discovery, By Chance or By Design

1

THE MEANING OF CHEMISTRY

It's the Use That Counts

Put salt on your breakfast cereal and it becomes a pollutant. Put salt on meat and it tastes good because that's one place it belongs. If you add one thing to another, both things might change. Cook some meat and there is a difference in the appearance, taste, and feel. Gold is different from copper, and something in aspirin makes your headache feel better. If it's breakfast cereal, gold, or aspirin, and you want to know what it is or how it changes—the science of chemistry can help you. *CHEMISTRY is the study of materials and how they change.*

You live in a world of many different kinds of materials or chemicals. Many materials like water you use for living, work, or play. Other chemicals are not so familiar. You do not use them often and have no need to understand them. But every chemical, familiar or strange, has its own character. As you study chemistry you will learn about the materials in your surroundings and how they affect your life.

"O.K.! Who's the wise guy that put the salt in the sugar bowl?"

Discovery? Invention?

Discoveries often lead to inventions. Once it was *discovered* that liquids expand and contract, the thermometer could be *invented*. Once it was *discovered* that a mixture of potassium nitrate, carbon, and sulfur was explosive, gunpowder could be *invented*.

The reverse is also true. Inventions also lead to discoveries. Thomas A. Edison *invented* the electric lamp. From his lamp came a *discovery* about electric current. A feeble current could pass from a thin wire, called a filament, through empty space to a metal plate. This, in turn, led to the invention of the vacuum tube.

What does this mean to you? Well, for example, the vacuum tube brought the radio, television, and HiFi! Next came the transistors which give you "mini" radios, portable televisions, and desk-top computers. The need for improvements on inventions brings more discoveries. These bring changes in the way you live.

Thomas Edison and Dr. Irving Langmuir discussing the vacuum tube at the General Electric Research Laboratory. (The Bettman Archive)

Discovery of gunpowder in Europe. (New York Public Library)

Looking Back and Looking Ahead

Long ago people thought that they could change metals like lead, tin, or copper into valuable gold and silver. People who tried to do this were called alchemists. They never succeeded. Only in modern times have men been able to change one metal into another, but there is still no practical way to make gold.

Alchemy probably started with the Greeks who were living in Egypt. Then it was taken up by the Arabs. Soon it spread into the western part of Europe.

As we look back upon history, we find it hard to believe that so many people spent so much time with so little success. But we know now that their facts were wrong. Now it is easy for us to be Monday morning quarterbacks. Once the facts are known it is easy to see mistakes.

How will future generations look at our scientific efforts?

Tomorrow's experts may be amused that we used big rocket boosters to lift spacecraft off the earth. They may ask something like: "Why did the people of the twentieth century use brute force to launch their space vehicles? Why didn't they use anti-gravity machines?" Or some other method may be known to them.

This is what is exciting about science. It does not stay the same. It is always changing with new discoveries—some by chance, some by design!

QUICK QUESTION?

Tell how the definition of chemistry applies to an experience you have had today. (Chemistry is the study of materials and how they change.)

THE BEGINNINGS OF CHEMISTRY

Chemistry—A Detective Story

Some materials are known as substances. *A SUBSTANCE is a variety of material which has the same makeup throughout.* Chemical elements are the building substances of nature. These basic substances have been found, one by one, through the ages by patient searchers in many lands. The chemical elements known to the ancient world were the metals: gold, silver, copper, iron, lead, tin, and the nonmetals: sulfur and carbon. Now we know of 105 elements.

Imagine a detective story with 105 characters. Each character has his own style of operation. What is the mystery? To find out who the characters are, and how each is involved in the story. What a job!

Chemical mysteries do involve 105 characters, called elements. Unlike the case of a giant detective story you will have no trouble keeping track of the characters. Each "character" or element plays a role according to a script. The script was written by nature and was discovered by a few great scientists, super-detectives. These great scientists devoted their lives to finding out how elements behave. That behavior does not change.

Your laboratory experience questions the change of a nail. A nail is placed in a blue solution called copper sulfate. By comparing the product of Experiment 1.1 *Changes* with known substances in Experiment 1.2 you are able to determine the identity of the main elements. You also find that the elements change places. By following leads you can discover more about this same mystery in Experiment 1.2-A. By your detective work you also can solve a chemical mystery.

People Have Learned about Chemistry by Playing Detective

For centuries, people have studied the earth's elements. Dmitri Mendeleev was one of the early scientists. He was a kind of detective. He saw that elements seemed to belong in groups from the way they reacted. So he made up a kind of a crossword puzzle. He wrote in the name of elements where they seemed to belong. This was the first time that the elements had been arranged in an orderly manner. Their placement showed their similarities and differences.

But Mendeleev could not finish his puzzle. He left some blank spaces. Some elements had not yet been discovered. He predicted that these elements would be found. He even predicted what they would be like, based upon his system. These elements were found, and they were almost the same as he had predicted. Today, chemists are using Mendeleev's work called the Periodic Table.

Natural gold. (Dr. E. R. Degginger)

Liquid oxygen. (Dr. E. R. Degginger)

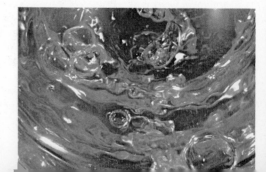

(left) Copper in three forms: block, pellets, and sheet. (Dr. E. R. Degginger) (right) Bromine vapor. (Dr. E. R. Degginger)

Cro-Magnon artists in a cave. (Courtesy of the AMERICAN MUSEUM OF NATURAL HISTORY)

Detectives through the Centuries

Who were the first detectives to investigate the nature of materials? No one really knows. Cavemen were probably the first ones to figure out how to use different kinds of materials. Certain stones could be used as weapons. Certain rocks could be chipped to form sharp axes.

Early men discovered that certain materials mixed together could be used to make lasting pictures on cave walls. They also discovered ways to build shelters. They mixed soils together with straw. Then they baked the mixture to form bricks. Though, we have improved the methods since then, we still bake clay to make bricks.

Through the ages, many scientific detectives have worked to unravel the mysteries of what is around us. Others have worked to discover ways to produce a more efficient and productive way of life. Chemists have developed drugs which have saved millions of lives. Unfortunately, some discoveries have led to destructive devices like the atom bomb. Chemists made materials like gasoline and detergents which also polluted our environment. Now scientists are working on ways to prevent pollution yet still provide the comforts of modern living.

Entertainment and art have progressed from cavewall paintings to the TV set which brings living drama to everyone. Science has also progressed. Every day new discoveries are coming out of the research chemical laboratories. Many of these new findings will provide a safer and more comfortable life for you.

QUICK QUESTION?

Have you ever used any of the elements shown on page 6? Explain.

A FAMILY TREE OF THE CHEMICAL SCIENCES:

There is more than one kind of chemistry. Each branch of chemistry has the same objective: to study materials and how they change. Many people work as chemists or technicians in one or more of the branches of chemistry.

Gas analysis lab test of lunar rock. (NASA)

QUALITATIVE ANALYSIS: this study, a branch of analytical chemistry, includes tests for the *kinds* of materials present in a sample. For example: what are the substances found in moon rocks? So far no new elements have been found that do not exist on earth.

INORGANIC CHEMISTRY: the study of substances largely those which were never a part of living things. Moon rocks are inorganic. No trace of living materials has been found within them.

NUCLEAR CHEMISTRY: the study of the smallest particles which make up matter. Radioactivity is an important subject which concerns the study of the moon rocks. Such a study of nuclear chemistry can tell the scientist about the history of the moon.

QUANTITATIVE ANALYSIS: this study, also a branch of analytical chemistry, includes tests for *how much* of different kinds of chemicals are present in a sample. A scientist, who studies moon rocks, tests to find out what amounts of substances are in the rocks. How do the amounts of substances in these rocks compare to various rocks from earth?

Plants exposed to lunar material 35 days before photograph was taken. (NASA)

BIOCHEMISTRY: the study of materials and their changes in a living creature. So far, no living organisms have been found on the moon. Scientists have, however, grown plants in moon dust and find that these plants thrive. No one yet knows exactly why.

ORGANIC CHEMISTRY: the study of substances which contain carbon, for the most part, the study of materials left from once-living organisms. Scientists who study moon rocks would be excited to find an organic substance on the moon. It might prove that life once existed on the moon.

CHEMISTRY: the study of materials and how they change. A rock from the moon is studied. The object is to find out what it is and how it can be used.

Apollo 14 Lunar sample nicknamed "Big Bertha." (NASA)

THINK POWER

THE SCIENTIFIC METHOD

Crossing the avenue against roaring traffic would be a dumb decision to make. Other problems are not that easy to solve. These decisions require thinking through the possibilities and perhaps deciding on a "best bet" or an "educated guess." Such a course of action requires that you know all the facts available about the situation. It requires that you think clearly through the problem. Your answer or solution should show that you are sharp and aware of the results of the decision. Thinking clearly through problems and testing the decisions are what the scientific method is all about.

Scientists usually think in an orderly way. But they sometimes have sudden "brainstorms." Many of the great discoveries in science come as a bright idea when the scientists least expect them.

Identification of the Problem: You are driving in your car. Suddenly your engine develops a strange "knocking" sound. Just as you identify that something is wrong with your engine, you must know something about a problem you are dealing with in chemistry. In the laboratory you may be given a problem. It may be to find out what an unknown chemical is. At other times you may have to figure out what the problem itself is.

Observation and Data Recording: You take your car to a mechanic. He asks you questions about the development of the noise. He observes the nature of the exhaust. Perhaps he makes a few adjustments. He records the data.

In chemistry you will make observations and collect data. You will write down what you observe. As a result of these observations, you will then collect data.

You observe your unknown—a clear liquid. At what temperature does it boil? The boiling temperature of 100°C is data. Because you record the data, at another time you can check your information and use the results.

Hypothesis: By putting his recorded observations and data together the mechanic is able to make an "educated guess" about the condition of your car. Something may be wrong with the valves or the cylinders of the engine.

In the laboratory, after studying what you observed, you too will be able to make an "educated guess" about your clear liquid. You will determine what needs to be done so that you can test your guess. Your guess may be that the clear liquid is water.

An alchemist follows directions. He did not follow the scientific method, however. He guessed, but did not *test* his guess. (Culver Pictures)

Students learning to be technicians in a biochemistry laboratory. (Shostal)

Testing the Hypothesis: In order to find out if it is a serious problem with the engine, the mechanic will probably use some instruments. He may attach a gauge to measure various characteristics of the engine, such as pressure, firing of the spark plugs, and the timing of the engine. The results indicate burnt valves and a need to replace the rings of the cylinders.

In the laboratory, once you have established a hypothesis, you will perform certain tests to see if your hypothesis is correct. It is just as important to find out if your hypothesis is incorrect. The results of the tests may provide an answer to your problem. In the laboratory you decide to freeze the clear liquid to see if it freezes at 0°C. The liquid does freeze at 0°C.

Generalizations and Conclusions: The mechanic puts together his observations, data, and test results. He finds that the results point to a complete motor overhaul.

Likewise your answers in the chemistry laboratory may all point to one answer. Water has all the properties you discovered in the laboratory. This is the answer to the problem. Your clear liquid is water.

Communications of Results: When the mechanic decides what repair the car needs, other people must know about it. You need to give permission for the repair, perhaps new parts must be ordered, and you may have to consult your bank account to find out if you can pay for the repairs.

You will communicate the results of your experiment. Your teacher, and the other students you may be working with, will have to know what you found out. You will need to put your answers down in an orderly and understandable way. How else can you or others know what you have learned?

QUICK QUESTIONS?

1. Prove that the superstition, "Walking under a ladder brings bad luck," is true or false by using the scientific method.
2. A friend pulls a reddish-gold colored object from a tub of blue solution. He claims that he has changed an iron object to one made of gold. How would you prove or disprove your friend's claim?
3. Name one profession or job for each branch of chemistry. Tell how you think the branch of chemistry could be used in the job.

Why Think? Why Not Act?

This is a very logical question. We can go on to ask, "Why didn't the early chemists abandon their wrong beliefs and see the plain truth?" (Truths, of course, are only plain when they are known.)

The important thing is not *what the ancient chemists thought.* They often came up with wrong answers. The important thing is, *that they thought.* Now we can use their ideas and test them. You will never find an answer unless you think and research. Even a wrong answer may be a step toward the solution.

All the questions in chemistry have not been answered. There are many problems left to think about, to try to solve. Students have answered important questions repeatedly throughout the history of chemistry. Students may still think about, and possibly solve, the remaining problems.

It Is Important to Develop "Think Power"

"Why should I bother to learn to think? Why not let someone else do it, and I can just get the answers?" This is an understandable question.

As long as you live, you will find yourself in situations that you have never learned about. Unless you know how to think your way out of them, you will be lost and bewildered. Throughout this course in chemistry you will be involved in "think training."

An athlete trains to stay in shape for the game. Many of the skills the athlete acquires can be used in his daily life. Much the same is true of the study of chemistry. You will find many uses for your understandings and skills learned in chemistry.

To understand how you can live more comfortably may well depend on your knowledge of chemical reactions. How chemical materials are involved with your life can be important in many different ways. For example, look at the family dinner scene. Chemistry is important in the field of agriculture to produce the foods being served. New products such as the dishes being used were developed through chemistry. Even the wash and wear clothes the family is wearing had their start in the chemistry laboratory.

Not all of the secrets of chemistry have been uncovered. New problems related to chemistry are being solved every day. Among important current problems facing the chemist are:

1. the chemistry of the body
2. the reactions of chemicals in the atmosphere
3. how to make an unlimited power source like the sun

There are many social problems as well as scientific ones that can be solved through chemistry. Anyone who wants to start solving them—here is the chance!

Family dinner scene. (De Wys)

SALES
CHEMICAL EQUIPT

At least one year of high school chemistry or equivalent required. Person chosen will be trained on the job to sell to hospitals, schools and industrial laboratories. Expense account, company paid health and life insurance, company car. Good advancement possibilities. Paid vacations and holidays.

Environmental Technologist-
WANTED

Trainee opportunity for expansion program. High school chemistry and one year of advanced chemistry desirable. Qualified applicants will learn new technologies in air and water pollution analysis. Good chance to learn the science most needed TODAY.

ASSOCIATE EDITOR

Chemistry

We have an opening in Editorial Department for an Associate Editor — chemistry. This is a challenging position with responsibility. Candidates should have a background in chemistry and English.

SENIOR AGRICULTURAL CHEMIST

CHANCE TO TRAVEL

Knowledge of fertilizers, pesticides and production methods for low-cost, high-potency, food production. Consultant to State Department. Develop methods for disadvantaged countries. Advanced degrees in agricultural chemistry and knowledge of foreign language desirable.

HIGH SCHOOL STUDENT
Summer Job!

Some understanding of chemistry desirable. Industrial laboratory needs summer help. Laboratory assistant to work with and help technicians.

TOXICOLOGIST
– Research for Humanity

Excellent opportunity for an experienced chemist to assume responsibility for testing of drugs. A doctorate in pharmacology or related field is preferred; experience in industry will be an added asset.

Food Service
DIRECTOR

National Company needs person to direct all food service operations. Understanding of diets and food chemistry necessary. Send resumes. Good opportunity to advance to managerial position.

SENIOR CLINICAL LABORATORY TECHNOLOGIST

NEEDED

Large hospital needs competent, trained technician in biochemistry to supervise medical tests in modern medical laboratory. Experience and ability to communicate with staff necessary requirements. Salary open. Health insurance.

CHF
WA

Crime Detection Lab
needs CHEMIST

TO COMPLETE STAFF

Excellent opportunity for capable individual to develop and perform techniques for industrial hygiene and crime detection programs in a modern progressive public health laboratory. Experience in laboratory necessary. High salary.

NE

Chapter 1

ACTION POINTS

CHEMISTRY is the study of materials and how they change.

DISCOVERIES in chemistry lead to **INVENTIONS** which make your life better.

ALCHEMY, a pursuit of medieval times, led to chance discoveries.

INORGANIC, QUALITATIVE ANALYSIS, QUANTITATIVE ANALYSIS, ORGANIC, BIOCHEMISTRY, AND NUCLEAR are important branches of chemistry.

The **SCIENTIFIC METHOD** is a logical process for solving problems.

The **SCIENCE OF CHEMISTRY** can solve many problems, social as well as scientific.

The Evidence for Matter: What and How Much? 2

You Are Matter
. . . and that's because
YOU TAKE UP SPACE
AND HAVE MASS!

Can you see anything in the room that doesn't take up space and doesn't have mass? Everything that you see, and some things that you cannot see, like air, take up space and have mass. So all of the things or objects in your surroundings are forms of matter.

Weight depends on the downward pull of the earth, called the pull of gravity. The pull of gravity gets weaker as you move away from the surface of the earth. As a result, weight may vary. *MASS is the amount of matter contained in an object.* Mass does not depend on the pull of gravity, and therefore is always the same.

For example, on the moon where gravity is less you weigh less. An astronaut, who weighs 180 pounds on earth, weighs about 30 pounds on the moon. Your mass is the same on the earth, on the moon, or anywhere else in the universe.

The basic material with which the chemist works is matter. In chemistry you will learn about the nature of matter and how matter can be changed from one kind to another.

Everything you see in this photograph is matter. (Mickey Palmer from DPI)

The spring scale measures the pull of gravity on an object. It measures weight.

The pan-type balance, when balanced, indicates the mass of the object on the left has the same mass as the known mass on the right.

MOON

EARTH

MOON

EARTH

Home Lab

Developing Your Own 'Thing'

In Experiments 2.1 and 2.2 size and weight relationships were a matter of guessing. Your experiences with other objects served as a standard of comparison to judge similar weights and volumes. The experiment gave you some notion of your ability to sense standards of weights and volumes.

If King Henry *I* could use the width of his thumb (inch) and the length of his feet (foot) to set standards, then certainly you should consider the possibility of inventing your own system.

Use a full length of your paper as the new standard unit. Call this unit, a 'RAP.' If the long edge of your paper is one rap, then how many raps in width is the top of your desk? Did it come out an even number of raps? If it didn't, you may need $\frac{1}{2}$ or $\frac{1}{4}$ raps. Fold the paper four times so that you have a series of 16 folded divisions along the edge of your paper. Now you can describe the length of your desk in 1/16th rap units.

Is there something wrong with using your rap system of measurement? If you were a king, you could demand that all of your subjects use your thumb and your foot as a standard. The law would be set up. But think of the problems and confusion if everyone could establish his own system of measure. There are too many problems now with two different standards: the ENGLISH SYSTEM and the METRIC SYSTEM.

(Photo by Joan Menschenfreund)

Optical Illusions—Do You Need to Measure?

Why should you bother with balances, rulers, or graduated cylinders? Can't you tell by your senses which is heavier, longer, or of greater volume?

Don't be too sure! The senses can be fooled. If you doubt this, look at the drawings and decide.

The mark of a true scientist is that he never guesses when he can be sure. He makes the exact measurements.

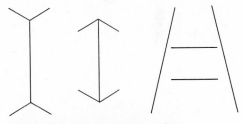

Measure these lines with your ruler. Can you believe your eyes?

QUICK QUESTIONS?

1. Select a stick of any size for your unit of measure. Name it after yourself.
   (a) What would you need to consider if you were measuring large distances with your unit of measure?
   (b) What would you need to do with your unit of measure if you wished to measure the length of your pencil?
2. An astronaut traveling in space is said to be weightless. Does he have any mass? If the astronaut lands on the moon does his mass change? Does his weight change?
3. How would you increase the mass of an automobile tire?

MEASURING BY TENS

Science depends on accurate (correct) measurements. It is important to use the simplest ways to make measurements. The simple and easy ways of working help to eliminate errors. The metric system is used by most scientists because it is simple and easy.

The English system of measure which uses feet, pounds, and quarts is much more awkward to use. Changing 12 inches to 1 foot, 3 feet to a yard and 5280 feet to 1 mile requires us to remember a lot of numbers.

The metric system is based on divisions of 10. No matter what you are measuring in the metric system, the basic number to remember is 10.

Our money system is a good example of measuring by tens. There are 100 cents in one dollar. The same thing is true of 100 centimeters in one meter. So just as a penny is 1/100th of a dollar, a centimeter is 1/100th of a meter. The prefix "centi" means 1/100th. When it is used in front of a unit, you are taking 0.01 or 1/100th of that unit. Don't be confused about changing English units to metric units or the reverse. When you are in the laboratory get a good idea about the size of the metric units. Use the metric system. Think in the metric system. Many people hope that we shall all one day use the metric system for our everyday measurements. Much of the world does now!

In the Metric System, How Was the Length of a Meter Determined?

Originally, the measurement of a quarter-way around the earth was taken. Then, this was divided into ten-million parts. One of these parts equalled one meter. One meter was marked on a bar of platinum.

Today, the meter is very slightly different in length.

It is no longer determined by the marks on the bar of platinum, but is determined by wavelengths of orange-red light. This is much more accurate but more complicated than marks on the bar.

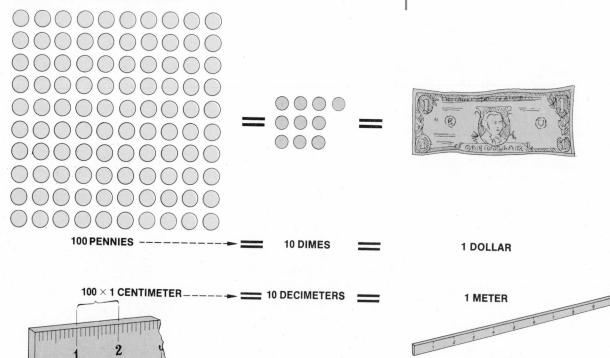

100 PENNIES   - - - - - - - - - - ▶   =   10 DIMES   =   1 DOLLAR

100 × 1 CENTIMETER - - - - - ▶   =   10 DECIMETERS   =   1 METER

The Volume of Matter

When you are thirsty you ask for a *glass* of water. You want an *amount* of matter. You ask for the matter by the *amount of space* it takes up. *VOLUME is the amount of space matter takes up.* You know that the glass will hold less than a pitcher and more than an eyedropper. That's not exact enough in the laboratory.

If you know just how much a container holds, you can use it as a standard. This is similar to the use of a measuring cup in cooking or of a teaspoon for taking medicine. In the laboratory we use standards for measuring volumes. The one we use most is the graduated cylinder. The metric unit of volume is the liter. It is about the same size as a quart. The liter is divided into 10 parts just like the meter. But, we use a much smaller unit, the MILLILITER. The prefix "milli" means one thousandth. *The milliliter is 1/1000th of a liter.* The graduated cylinder is marked off in milliliters. Use the graduated cylinder in Experiment 2.2. Find out how to measure the volume of liquids.

If you lived in Germany, for instance, you would buy milk by the liter instead of the quart. A liter and a quart are about the same.

How do you measure the volumes of solids? We will learn how to do this two ways. In Experiment 2.2 we measure the volume of a regular solid with sides we can measure with a metric ruler.

$$\text{Height} \times \text{width} \times \text{length} = \text{volume}$$
$$\text{cm} \quad \times \text{cm} \quad \times \text{cm} \quad = \text{cm}^3$$

The reason the "3" is written above the cm to the right is simply to indicate the number of times you multiplied cm. A cm^3 is called a cubic centimeter.

In Experiment 2.2 we measure the space an irregular solid takes up by the amount of water it displaces. There we have two ways to measure the volume of a solid.

Volume is measured in *milliliters* (ml) or *cubic centimeters* (cm^3). In the United States the metric system is used only in science. The liter contains 1000 ml or 1000 cm^3. Small quantities of liquids are usually measured in the laboratory in ml or cm^3.

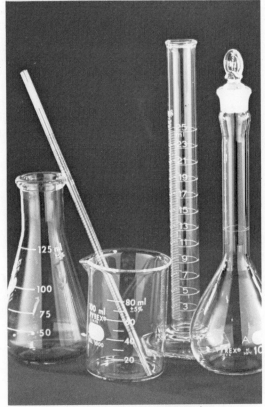

You might use a gallon jug or a measuring cup to find the volume of liquids at home. In the laboratory, careful measurements can be made by using the laboratory containers pictured above. The pieces of apparatus are: Erlenmeyer flask, beaker, graduated cylinder, volumetric flask, and the long tube is called a pipette. (Dr. E. R. Degginger)

Home Lab

Obtain a quart milk carton. Measure the volume of the container using a metric ruler. Fill the carton with water. Measure the volume of water in a graduated cylinder. How does the number of cubic centimeters compare to the number of milliliters of water?

QUICK QUESTION?

What measurements of quantities are important in locating and designing a city street?

HOW HEAVY IS HEAVY?

Consider three boxes. All are exactly the same size or have the same volume. One box is made of wood, another of cardboard, and the third is of lead. No problem. The lead box is the heaviest. While in this situation you have little difficulty in determining differences, in the laboratory it is not always so easy. The use of the laboratory balance is needed really to tell differences in mass.

By knowing the volume of an object and using the balance to determine mass you can determine differences in materials. *The amount of mass in a substance divided by the volume it occupies is called the DENSITY.* Density is expressed as a simple fraction or ratio. You use such fractions quite often: number of hits per times at bat; miles per gallon of gasoline; pounds of sugar per bag. So why not a ratio of mass per volume? If you think of pound per bag (the volume) then pounds per one bag is a way of expressing density. Density in chemistry is expressed as the mass in grams (g) in one volume, cubic centimeter (cm^3).

Measuring the Mass of Matter

You have learned that there is a difference between mass and weight. Weight can differ from place to place, but mass remains the same no matter where it is. At the supermarket, butcher shop, or post office spring scales are used to measure weight. There is no need to find out exact amounts of matter. In the laboratory a balance which measures mass is used. A balance operates like a see-saw with the masses to be measured placed in the left pan of the balance. Weights of known mass are placed on the right pan. By comparing the weight, the mass is automatically found.

The GRAM is the metric unit of mass. Measurements are discussed as grams and fractions of a gram, as 1/10th or 1/100th of a gram. There are times in the laboratory when very small quantities are weighed. The unit 1/100th of a gram, CENTIGRAM, or the smaller unit 1/1000th of a gram, MILLIGRAM, is used. When very large amounts of mass are measured, the KILOGRAM, which contains 1000 grams is used.

Your laboratory balance can probably weigh to 1/10th of a gram with accuracy. This is about the mass of an ordinary pin. A fine research balance however can weigh to the nearest 0.000001 of a gram. This type of balance would have little difficulty in weighing the dot over the letter "i."

WHO HAS THE HEAVY ONE?

Modern analytical balance. (Mettler Instrument Corporation)

Density and Specific Gravity

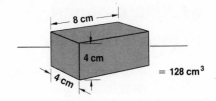

Density: *The mass of one cubic centimeter of pure water at 4°C is one gram—DENSITY.* This is an important observation. Using water as a standard for relative "lightness" and "heaviness" is a very convenient tool.

$$density = mass/unit\ volume$$

A cube of butter has a mass of 105.4 grams (M).

The volume is 128 cm³ (V).

$$D = M/V$$

The density of butter = 105.4 g/128 cm³
                    = 0.82 g/cm³

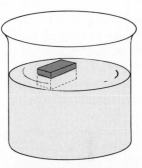

BUTTER FLOATS ON WATER

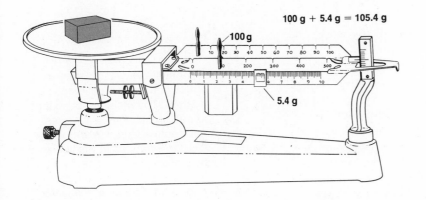

100 g + 5.4 g = 105.4 g

100 g

5.4 g

$$D = \frac{105.4\ g}{128\ cm^3} = 0.82\ g/cm^3$$

Specific Gravity: The arrangement of "light weights" to "heavy weights" in the comparisons at the right shows a very handy characteristic of water.

If a certain piece of iron weighs 7.4 times as much as an equal volume of water, you have the SPECIFIC GRAVITY of iron, which is also its density.

$$Specific\ Gravity = \frac{mass\ of\ a\ given\ volume\ of\ a\ material}{mass\ of\ an\ equal\ volume\ of\ water}$$

Specific gravity is just a number. It has no measurement units. For liquids and solids it has the same numerical value in the metric system.

MATERIAL	DENSITY (g/cm³)	
Cork	0.2	
Gasoline	0.75	These float on
Wood (Oak)	0.8	water because
Butter	0.82	they are lighter.
Ice	0.99	
WATER	1.00	
Aluminum	2.58	The density of
Zinc	7.1	these materials is
Iron	7.4	greater than that
Gold	19.3	of water. They
Platinum	21.4	sink in water.

NATURE'S ORDER

On Being the Right Size

Nature has an order of remarkable beauty. The patterns are definite and precise. Because of this precise and definite order in nature, you can predict what will happen if the order of nature is changed. For example, scientists have found that the lack of extremely small amounts of certain substances will cause plants to die.

Man is so sure about some of his measurements and observations that he has stated laws which describe the certainty of natural events. In your study of chemistry some of the laws which have been discovered will become your working tools. You can apply these laws of nature to your laboratory work as well as to your everyday surroundings. The laws which describe nature work everywhere.

Man has discovered the beautiful organized ways of nature by using measurement. He knows about huge bodies of matter trillions of miles away from earth. He also knows about the particles of matter too small for even the most powerful microscopes to bring into view. He can measure and describe in great detail the workings of his own body. He can count the number and kind of cells in blood. He can measure the pressure of the blood and the electric charges in the muscle of the heart.

We can say that the history of man's technology can be traced by the degree to which he has been able to measure. Today man is using technology and systems of measurement to correct some of the bad effects man has had upon the environment. Measurement of pollution in the air, on land, and in the water has become a vital concern. Scientists have measured the amounts and kinds of pollution in the streams and lakes. They have been able to set standards of safety for drinking water and for swimming. There have been too many of the wrong kinds of materials deposited in the wrong places. Because we know about measurements, we can take steps to guard the future of our environment.

Topaz, an example of order in nature. (Dr. E. R. Degginger)

Archimedes

Archimedes was a Greek scientist with an eye for practical matters. The most famous story about Archimedes is his great bathroom scene. Hieron, the king of Syracuse in Sicily, had a new crown. There was doubt in his mind that it was made of pure gold. The king suspected the goldsmith of cheating him by mixing cheaper silver in with the gold. The king asked Archimedes to find out if his crown was pure gold. Archimedes probably talked to himself about this problem. How was he to find out if the crown was pure gold?

QUICK QUESTIONS?

1. The density of ice is 0.9 g/cm³. Because the density of ice is 0.9 g/cm³, it floats. Why is it important that the density of ice is not greater than 1.0 g/cm³?

2. Arrange your own table of densities. Rearrange the listed materials so that they range from least dense to most dense—gasoline, ice, wood, water, platinum, gold, and cork.

One day, Archimedes filled his bathtub to the very brim. As he got into the tub water overflowed onto the floor. The farther he got into the tub, the more water he displaced. If he completely submerged himself, the overflow would have been the space or volume occupied by his whole body. Then he thought of the crown. It was difficult to measure its volume because it was such an odd shape. If he completely submerged the crown into a full container of water, the overflow of water would be the volume of the crown. Taking an equal weight of pure gold, he also submerged it in a container full of water. If the volumes were the same, the crown would be pure gold. Archimedes was so excited by this discovery that he ran home naked through the streets shouting "Eureka, Eureka!" (I have found it! I have found it!) Later he found out that the goldsmith cheated.

Chapter 2

ACTION POINTS

MATTER is anything that takes up space and has mass.

All measuring systems require a **STANDARD UNIT** that compares the object to be measured to a given quantity.

The **METRIC SYSTEM,** universally used in science, measures in multiples of tens:

   Mass is measured in **GRAMS.**

   Volume is measured in **LITERS.**

   Length is measured in **METERS.**

DENSITY is the comparison of mass to volume or mass divided by volume.

Everything in the universe has an order or property that is an important characteristic of its nature.

Matter: Its Phases and Physical Properties

3

You live in a huge universe of matter. Because you cannot live without a sense of order, we sort matter into categories. The sorting is often based upon what we can detect with our senses. *The characteristics of substances we can note with our physical senses are PHYSICAL PROPERTIES.* In this chapter you will learn about different physical properties and try to group matter by using them.

Can you sort all matter into three physical forms? There are, for example, three different physical phases of water: ice, which is SOLID; water, which is LIQUID; and steam, which is the GAS phase. See water in its various forms in Experiment 3.1 *Water—No Quick Change Artist!*

Here is a table which classifies some of the objects in your surroundings into three groups, called the three phases of matter—solid, liquid, and gas.

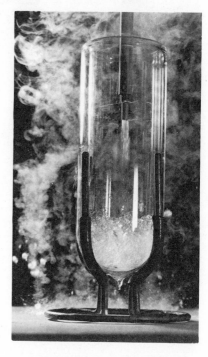

Hydrogen is shown here in the liquid and gaseous phases. The liquid hydrogen changes to a gas at a very low temperature. (Rapho Guillumette)

	OBJECTS	DEFINITIONS	PHASE
	ice rock book penny	Each of these occupies a definite volume. Each has a definite shape.	All of these objects are SOLIDS.
	water gasoline milk alcohol	All have a definite volume but none have a definite shape. They take the shape of the container into which they are poured.	These objects are all LIQUIDS.
	steam automobile exhaust neon air	They have no definite volume. They have no definite shape.	These materials are all GASES.

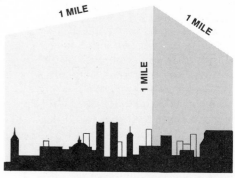

How small is a molecule? Under standard conditions one milliliter of gas contains many molecules. If each molecule were as large as a grain of sand, the pile would be 1 mile high, 1 mile deep, by 1 mile long.

Particles Called Molecules

There should be a reason why one thing is a solid, one a liquid, and another a gas. Chemists base the idea of phase on the theory that all matter is composed of very tiny particles. In gases, and some liquids and solids, these particles are what chemists call MOLECULES. *A MOLECULE is the smallest possible part of the substance that is still that substance.* If you keep breaking apart a drop of water, you will get the smallest quantity of water possible—a molecule of water. Split the molecule and you no longer have water. You have the substances of which water is made (oxygen and hydrogen).

How small are these tiny molecules? So small that you could fit many millions on the point of a pin. You see molecules only by using special techniques. Some pictures of them have been taken by using modern instruments.

Home Lab

Here are experiences and evidence that support the idea that molecules exist.

If molecules are far apart, then you should be able to squeeze other molecules between them. Fill a glass with water to the point where one more drop will make it overflow. Now carefully add a very small quantity of sugar—the water will not overflow.

Try the same thing with a spoonful of salt; again with a spoonful of water; and now try a spoonful of alcohol.

A small amount of food dye placed in the bottom of a glass of water will eventually spread throughout the water. There must be some explanation of this "self-mixing." There must be something in motion. Could it be molecules?

(Photos by Joan Menschenfreund)

QUICK QUESTIONS

1. There are patterns of objects and people in your classroom. You need only to invent a definition or system and you can make up a classification system. For example all of the people in the class will fit into two groups: male and female. Another example: all of the objects would fit into animal, mineral, or plant. Try the following and tell how you would put them into a classification order:
   (a) all of the materials used for writing
   (b) the furniture in the classroom
2. How does classifying matter into three phases help you to understand more about matter?
3. Explain how an automobile depends on three phases of matter.

A MODEL FOR MOLECULES

Dancing Molecules

What makes one substance different from another? It is the arrangement and energy of the molecules within the substances.

Sometimes scientists use comparisons to show or demonstrate how they think nature works. Comparisons are particularly useful when you cannot see the objects about which you are thinking. The scientists call these comparisons, models. Some models are entirely mathematical. The models or comparisons may not be exact or true to the actual situation. In the case of the Dancing Molecule comparison, understand that molecules neither dance nor enjoy the rhythm of a good tune. In thinking of molecules as dancers, you are considering a very distant relationship between what happens to dancers dancing to fast or slow music, and what happens to molecules of the same substance at different temperatures.

Solid: In the solid phase of a substance think of the molecules as bunched together vibrating to the slow beat of music. The molecules are in a fixed position. They do not move about one another. Look at the pattern of dancers in the square dance. The dancers move back and forth, but do not move out of their pattern.

Liquid: In the liquid phase of the same substance, the temperature is above the melting point. Think of the beat of music as being faster. The dancing molecules are twirling and spinning about each other. This condition is something like a snake dance. There is still contact among the dancers, but there is more freedom of movement than in a solid.

Gas: In the gaseous phase of the substance the temperature is above the boiling point. The beat of the music has increased. The dancers are flying about wildly in great confusion. They bounce against the walls of the dance hall, hit the ceiling and strike each other with great force. As in a modern rock dance each individual molecule is doing "its own thing." The faster the music, the faster the dancers move.

Changing Phase

Ice is the solid phase of water in which the molecules are set in a pattern. ENERGY is supplied in the form of heat. As the ice melts the molecules start to move out of their pattern. They start tumbling around each other. The solid phase of water is turning into the liquid phase. When more heat energy is applied, the water

Square dance patterns can give an idea of structure in a solid. The contact and movement among the dancers cause the pattern. The "holding forces" among the molecules in a solid give it definite shape and definite volume. (Caplin and Thompson from FPG)

These dancers can give an idea of the molecules in a liquid. They have some contact between them. The molecules can flow, but the "holding forces" gives the liquid definite volume. (Culver Pictures)

There is little contact among these dancers of rock music. They are similar to gas molecules which are very independent of each other. Gases do not have a definite volume, nor a definite shape. (Hugh Rogers from Monkmeyer)

QUICK QUESTION?

What does what you have just read have to do with Experiment 3.1 *Water—No Quick Change Artist?*

boils. Steam results. The liquid phase becomes a gaseous phase with the molecules moving so rapidly that they no longer stick together. The water vapor escapes from the liquid. The molecules fly off to mix with the molecules of air. Some other substances can be made to go through the three phases of matter.

Traveling Molecules

DIFFUSION is the mixing of molecules caused by the movement of molecules in liquids or gases. Molecules always move away from the point where there is the most molecules. If you cut a clove of garlic in the kitchen, gaseous garlic particles causing the odor will diffuse throughout the air in your house. Soon the odor-causing molecules of garlic will diffuse through all the rooms in the house.

Escaping Molecules

Molecules in a liquid do not all move at the same rate. Some of them may have enough energy to dash out of their liquid phase into the air. This process is EVAPORATION. Some liquids such as gasoline and alcohol, evaporate more rapidly than water. Sometimes rapid evaporators may be recognized because of their odor. They are called VOLATILE. *A VOLATILE substance is one which readily changes from a liquid to a gas and evaporates quickly.* Some volatile substances do not have strong odors, but they may be dangerous if flammable or toxic.

In the case of evaporated gasoline, a highly volatile material, there is a danger of explosion. Other volatile liquids are highly poisonous if inhaled over long periods of time.

The Sun Works for Man

The energy from the sun may be used in many ways. It is a source of power that requires no bill at the end of the month.

One use of the sun puts an important substance on your dinner table. At the end of San Francisco Bay there are evaporation ponds. The ponds are alternately flooded and allowed to dry. As the sun's heat evaporates the water, a thin film of a white material is left behind. The white material contains the salt you shake over your food.

QUICK QUESTIONS?

1. If the smallest possible part of a substance is a molecule what happens to a molecule of water
   (a) when it becomes steam?
   (b) when it becomes hydrogen and oxygen?
2. Why does it help you to know that gasoline vaporizes more rapidly than water?
3. How is weather in your community affected by changes of phase?
4. Describe a laboratory procedure that depends on change of phase.
5. How does the motion of molecules differ in ice, water, and steam?

(left) Piles of salt are raked from an evaporation pond in Thailand. (Van Bucher from Photo Researchers)

(right) **CAUTION!** *VOLATILE* MATERIAL FUMES ARE DANGEROUS. Use only in well-ventilated room (Dr. E. R. Degginger).

THE GO POWER! HEAT ENERGY

ENERGY is the ability or capacity for doing work.
The sun is our chief source of energy. There are many
forms of energy: mechanical energy as a pile driver that
can ram a pole into the ground; electric energy that can
do work in running motors, operate T.V. sets or light
lamps. Heat energy, released from tiny molecules, can
move trains, fly airplanes. Changes in energy are related to the weather we experience.

One source of energy is of particular importance to
the chemistry student—the heat that is generated
by chemical activity. Burning fuels such as wood, gas,
and oil are chemical actions which produce heat energy.
Perhaps you don't think of chemical activity in your
day-to-day living, but heat is also generated in the body
by chemical reactions. All of this energy once came
from the sun.

Energy in Action

*When energy is stored up and has the ability to do
work, it is POTENTIAL ENERGY.* A rock poised on
the edge of a cliff has potential energy. So does a stick
of dynamite! *Action energy, or the energy that matter*

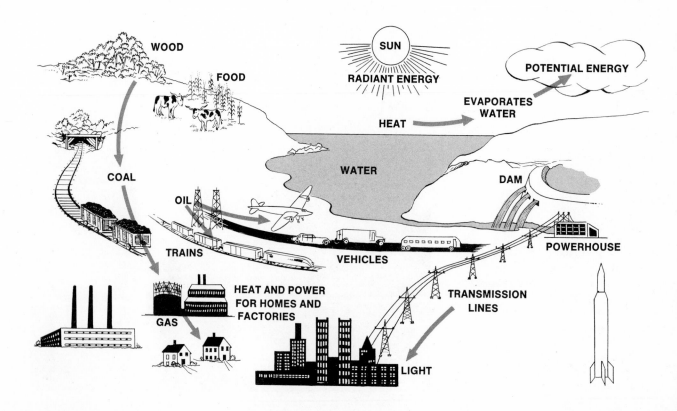

has when in motion, is KINETIC ENERGY. The falling rock pushed over the edge of the cliff and the exploding dynamite are examples of kinetic energy.

The model of dancing molecules supports a very important idea about kinetic-molecules or molecules in motion. The KINETIC MOLECULAR THEORY indicates that heating a substance makes the molecules move faster. Therefore, the kinetic energy of the molecules is increased. The temperature of the substance is a measure of the average kinetic energy of its molecules. Molecules also have potential energy which helps them to overcome the "holding forces" in some phases.

Rich and Poor Molecules

Some molecules have more energy than others. These are energy-rich molecules. Others, energy-poor molecules, haven't had the chance to pick up heat. Energy-rich molecules in water may have enough kinetic energy to zoom out of the liquid phase into the air as vapor. This process was described as evaporation. The energy-poor particles remain behind in the liquid phase of water.

The phase of matter depends on the energy of molecules in the body. If you rob more and more energy away from the liquid phase of water what do you think will happen? In your laboratory Experiment 3.2 *Project Deep-Freeze,* you observe the effect of the gradual decrease of kinetic energy in the molecules of water. The molecules of water finally lose enough heat energy so that they freeze in their path. They no longer move about freely. Ice, the solid phase of water, is formed.

QUICK QUESTIONS?

1. When does a football player demonstrate potential energy? Kinetic energy?
2. Describe potential and kinetic energy in a match.
3. What is meant by energy-rich and energy-poor molecules?

Plan for a satellite to collect solar energy. (Peter E. Glaser—Arthur D. Little, Inc.)

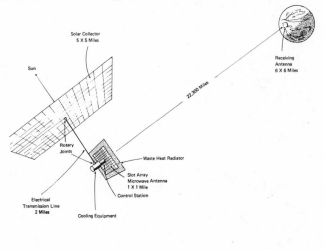

MOLECULAR SPEEDOMETERS

The energy or motion of molecules in matter can be measured. A convenient way of describing the average energy of molecules is to take a temperature reading. A thermometer can be used to find at what temperature the average speed of molecules will cause a given substance to be in a solid, liquid, or gaseous phase.

"What's the freezing temperature of water?"

Look at the illustration. It depends upon the thermometer used.

The Fahrenheit thermometer is used to describe temperature in weather reports. It is also the thermometer used in cooking foods. It is based on the boiling point of water at 212°F and the freezing point of water at 32°F.

The Celsius thermometer is a valuable tool for the chemist. It is based on water as a standard; freezing at 0°C and boiling at 100°C.

Lord Kelvin based his thermometer on the decrease in the volume of a gas as the temperature decreased. He calculated that all kinetic energy, molecular motion, would cease at −273°C or ABSOLUTE ZERO. Absolute zero is 0°K. On the Kelvin thermometer, the freezing point of water is 273°K. The boiling point of water is 373°K. Add the number 273 to any Celsius temperature, and you will have degrees in the Kelvin system. The degrees are the same size on both Celsius and Kelvin.

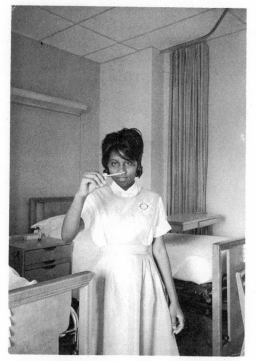

Hospital aide learning how to read an oral thermometer. (Sybil Shelton from Monkmeyer)

Normal Boiling Points and Normal Freezing Points of Water

FAHRENHEIT	CELSIUS	KELVIN
212°F	100°C	373°K
32°F	0°C	273°K

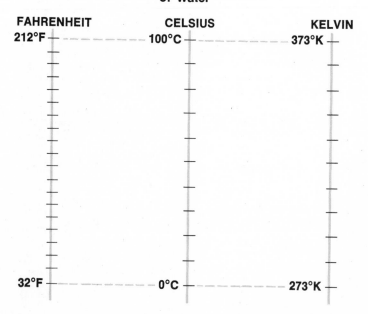

Student reading weather thermometer at high school weather station. (Hays from Monkmeyer)

NEW MERCURY THER- MOMETER INVENTED

HOLLAND, 1714—Today, the announcement came from Holland that a German physicist, Gabriel Daniel Fahrenheit, has developed a new kind of thermometer using mercury. Up to this time alcohol has been used as the expanding liquid inside thermometers. The inventor demonstrated that the mercury expands more regularly over a wide range. It has a high boiling point. He indicated that the mercury thermometer would prove more dependable and accurate than the alcohol thermometer.

Fahrenheit said that a mixture of ice and water registers 32° on his thermometer. It registers 212° in boiling water. The scientist had no comment when asked if it were true that he used his wife's temperature to record human temperature. One of the original readings for humans was 100°. It is now recorded that humans register 98.6° on the new thermometer. There is speculation that Mrs. Fahrenheit may have had a fever.

The scientist-inventor was quick to point out that other scientists contributed much to his success. He said that discoveries of different kinds of materials that expand at different rates led him to the development of his mercury thermometer. It is predicted that Fahrenheit's name will be linked to his new thermometer.

Fahrenheit was born in Danzig, Germany. He has worked for some years in Holland developing new and improved weather instruments. It is possible that because of his scientific contributions, the scientist will be elected to the Royal Society of London.

The invention of the Fahrenheit thermometer is written here as a modern news release. Fahrenheit was elected to the Royal Society of London in 1724 for his many contributions to science. That honor is similar to the winning of the Nobel Prize today. Fahrenheit was 50 years old when he died in 1736.

QUICK QUESTIONS?

1. Why is the term "molecular speedometer" used to describe a thermometer?
2. What makes Kelvin's thermometer different from a Celsius thermometer?

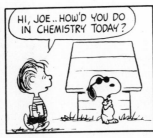

HEAT AS A QUANTITY

Heat and temperature are frequently confused. Temperature describes the average kinetic energy of the molecules. Heat takes into account the quantity of matter, and, therefore the total amount of heat energy. For example, one kind of wood burns at 1091°C. The temperature of a burning wood match and a wood house on fire may be the same temperature. *Is the amount of heat the same?*

Degrees are used to measure temperature. CALORIES are used to measure heat quantities. The common wood match liberates 500 calories of heat. Five common wood matches for example produce five times as much heat as one match. If one burning match releases 500 calories of heat, then five wood matches produce 2,500 calories of heat. The temperature of one match or of five matches is the same—1091°C.

If you could transfer the entire 500 calories of heat from one match to 5 grams of water at 0°C, you would raise the temperature of the water to 100°C. To bring the molecules of water up to the energy level at which they vaporize takes some extra "go power" calories. The boost in energy to change liquid water to gaseous water is 540 calories per gram of water at 100°C. Thus five grams of water at 100°C need 2700 calories before they become steam. *How many more matches would this take?*

We calculate 5.4 matches. It is not practical, however. You can't capture all the heat from a match just by holding it under a container of water. Much of the heat is lost to the surrounding air and much goes to the container holding the water. That's why a calorimeter is used.

Calorimeter

Calorimeters are instruments used to measure the amount of energy in the form of heat. The material in the container is insulated from the surroundings. This instrument is widely used by science and industry. It is commonly used to determine the amount of heat contained in coal oil and natural gas.

To use a calorimeter it is necessary to observe the effects produced by heat such as:

(1) the rise in temperature when heat is added to a substance
(2) the change in the phase of the substance
(3) the transformation of energy (chemical, electric, or mechanical) into heat.

Calorimeter.
(Sargent-Welch)

Two Kinds of Calories

The calorie that scientists generally use is the small calorie. *One CALORIE is the quantity of heat required to raise the temperature of one gram of water 1°C.*

Do you know someone on a diet? If so, you will hear frequent references to "calories." These Calories are the large Calories, indicated by C. They are equal to 1000 calories.

The Temperature Game

Base your guess on what you have just learned. That water is a great storehouse of heat. Coastal cities have warmer winters and cooler summers. Match up the temperatures with the cities:

All of these cities are at about 36° or 37° latitude. Match each city with its correct temperature reading:

1. San Francisco, California
2. Nashville, Tennessee
3. Las Vegas, Nevada

Low 41.4°F
High 91.1°F } 50° variation

Low 32°F
High 79.2°F }. 47.2° variation

Low 53.3°F
High 65.4°F } 12.1° variation

QUICK QUESTION?

Why can't you use only a thermometer to measure the quantity of heat?

Nuclear generating plants are a modern source of energy. (Westcott for USAEC)

About Water and Heat

The exhaust from rockets during testing will grow so hot that it will burn up the pad, unless some measures are taken. Many of the rocket test stands are cooled by great amounts of water during the critical moments of the rocket firing.

Nuclear plants that manufacture power are often located on the seacoast. There large amounts of water are available to absorb the large quantities of heat generated.

TELLING ONE THING FROM ANOTHER

Color

The color of a material is usually the first characteristic you notice. It is an important part of our lives. The chemistry of color is part of your study. You will use color to find out about "what's happening" and "how much" by noting the speed and amount of color changes.

Ductility

The particles that make up some solids have a very useful property. They can be stretched out into long, thin objects, like wires. Copper, gold, and silver are substances which have molecules that will permit this re-arrangement. These materials can be used as wires to conduct electricity, as decorations, and as cables for a bridge. *This wire-forming ability is called DUCTILITY.*

Malleability

If you can pound a metal into a sheet, it can then be used to form containers or coverings. *This property of a substance to be pounded into a sheet is called MALLE-ABILITY.* Molecules of gold are particularly adaptable to being pounded into flat shapes. One ounce of gold can make a sheet that will cover 100 square feet of area. Quite often the gold decorations you see on furniture or walls are from a material called "gold leaf" which is super-thin gold. Aluminum can be made into foil because it is malleable.

Hardness

Some substances are very hard. A diamond drill, for example, can bore through the hardest rocks or steel. Diamonds are considered the standard for the hardest material. Some substances are so soft that you can scratch them with your fingernails.

We should know that among substances there is a great range for each of these properties.

Silver is both malleable and ductile. (Jones from Monkmeyer)

Diamond is a very hard substance. It is used to cut other substances. (Steve and Dolores McCutcheon)

Elasticity

A special form of ductility and malleability is ELAS-TICITY. Molecules of a substance can be stretched out and still return to their original shape (if not stretched beyond their limits). This is the reason steel springs can bounce you up and down over long periods of time.

Brittleness

Things are brittle if they break readily. Usually we think of materials such as glass, some plastics, and chalk as substances that break apart readily. Non-metals are brittle materials. Metals, on the other hand, are difficult to shatter.

Automobile coil spring makes use of the elasticity of metal. (General Motors)

Everybody has broken a dish. The china is brittle. (Dr. E. R. Degginger)

Good News About Television Sets

The picture on your color television set will, in the future, be brighter. Scientists have found that they can get a redder red by using YTTRIUM, a rare metallic element. (Although yttrium is classed as a rare-earth element, the name is misleading. It has been found in such abundance that it is now more plentiful than lead.)

Up to now, the red phosphor used in color television tubes has not been as bright as it should have been. The other colors have had to be held down accordingly, so that they would not overpower the red.

Now with yttrium, a brighter red, the other colors can be brighter, also.

THOSE THAT DO AND THOSE THAT DON'T

A Chemical Disappearance

In Experiment 3.4 *A Chemical Disappearance,* you observe another characteristic of matter. It's no surprise to you that salt or sugar seems to "melt away" (dissolve) when put into a glass of water. Other substances do not disappear. They just fall to the bottom of the container. Lime or calcium hydroxide partially disappear into the water. Most of the lime makes the water cloudy and eventually settles out.

When a substance seems to disappear into water, it is said to DISSOLVE and to form a SOLUTION with the water. The water is called the SOLVENT because it does the dissolving. A material dissolved into water, such as the sugar, salt, or lime, is called a SOLUTE.

Metals and Nonmetals

Certain characteristics of matter can help you tell the differences between substances that are metals and substances that are nonmetals. In Experiment 3.3 you test the properties of both metals and nonmetals.

Metals are not difficult to identify. Metals have a certain shine or luster. They are hard and hold together. Metals can be pounded into different shapes and drawn into wires. You would have little difficulty in recognizing a chair made of metal from a chair made of wood.

The elements sulfur, carbon, and oxygen are nonmetals. Oxygen is a gas so there is little difficulty distinguishing oxygen from a metal. But how can you tell sulfur and carbon from a metal? They are both solid nonmetals. The nonmetals are quite brittle. They do not have a shiny luster, nor can they be drawn into wires or pounded into various shapes.

There is still another way to tell a metal from nonmetals. A current of electricity will pass through a metal, but a nonmetal does not conduct electrical current.

To avoid contact with electricity it is well to have a nonconducting nonmetal between you and the source of the electrical current.

Later, you will study more about the particles responsible for the characteristics of metals and nonmetals. Then you will realize even more the importance of dividing these two great groups of elements into separate classifications.

QUICK QUESTIONS?

1. What is the solvent you use in making lemonade? Name two solutes in lemonade.
2. How do you tell that a material is a metal?
3. How would you tell the physical difference between two metals (copper and iron for example)?
4. How would you tell the difference between a metal and a nonmetal (sulfur and iron for example)?

Molten sulfur being sprayed onto storage vat.
(Farrell Grehan from Photo Researchers)

Fascinating Sulfur

Sulfur was discovered in prehistoric times. It has interested
men through the ages. The name
"brimstone" means "burning
stone." Ignited sulfur was used
in early times in many countries
for religious ceremonies, for
smoking out buildings, and for
bleaching cloth.

Today, most of the world's
supply of sulfur comes from deposits in the coastal regions of
Texas and Louisiana.

The manner in which sulfur is
mined is interesting. The Frasch
process is used. This process
takes advantage of the low melting point of sulfur, 116°C. Water
at high pressure can be heated
above this temperature. The
water is pumped into the deposit. Melted sulfur, almost
chemically pure, drips down and
is then pumped to the surface
in another pipe.

Chapter 3

ACTION POINTS

There are three **PHASES OF MATTER,**
solids, liquids, and gases.
A **MOLECULE** is the smallest particle of
an element or compound that can exist by
itself.
ENERGY, the ability to do work, can be
either potential (stored) or kinetic (active).
Molecules have both kinetic and potential
energy. **KINETIC ENERGY** gives them
motion. **POTENTIAL ENERGY** allows
them to overcome "holding forces."
HEAT ENERGY can be absorbed by molecules which then move faster. Heat energy
can also be involved in phase change.
DIFFUSION is the mixing of gases or liquids resulting from the motions of their
molecules.
EVAPORATION occurs when molecules in
a liquid gain enough energy to leave the
liquid as a gas.
TEMPERATURE measures the average
kinetic energy of the molecules in a substance.
The quantity of heat is measured in **CAL-
ORIES.**
**COLOR, DUCTILITY, MALLEABILITY,
ELASTICITY, BRITTLENESS,** and
HARDNESS are all characteristics which
differ from one kind of matter to another.
These characteristics are used to identify
substances.
A **SOLUTION** is made up of a **SOLVENT**
(that which dissolves) and a **SOLUTE** (that
which is dissolved). It is of uniform composition but the amounts or proportions
may vary within wide limits.
METALS and **NONMETALS** differ in
their physical characteristics and react
differently in chemical combinations.

The Classes of Matter 4

LIKENESSES AND DIFFERENCES

How the Chemist Sorts the Universe

You live in a world of many kinds of things. If you recognize likenesses and differences in objects around you, then you are able to put them into groups. For example, take automobiles. Suppose you know the make, model, year, and the horsepower of a lot of cars. You can tell immediately that a 1926 Maxwell convertible with a 50-horsepower engine is an unusual car. Similarly classifying matter helps you to understand matter.

You have already classified matter according to phases: solids, liquids, and gases. You noted other properties of matter such as density, ductility, malleability, and solubility. They tell little, however, about the chemical makeup of different kinds of materials.

Chemists classify matter according to physical characteristics. In addition, they have other important ways of classifying matter. For instance, they classify matter according to the questions:

Of what are materials composed?

How can materials be changed?

WHO CARES IF WE CONTROL THE SECRET OF THE SUN? YOU DO!!!

The element hydrogen is the fuel of the universe. It is what gives our sun its "go power." If we can harness this fantastic power, your bill for energy will be cut 90%. (Bob Nemser)

What materials give whole milk its flavor? This analytical chemist sorts out the materials in milk to find the answer. Her work will aid in the manufacture of dry milk. (USDA)

The Big Three

One way to study what materials are composed of is by the process of analysis. *ANALYSIS is the study of materials by breaking them down.* By using analysis the chemist can determine what a material is made of by breaking it apart. He can test the parts of materials by finding out how they change under different conditions. You analyze and test household products in Experiment 4.3.

By using analysis chemists have found that all the materials in the universe can be grouped into three big classifications:

ELEMENTS
COMPOUNDS
MIXTURES

The science of chemistry is concerned with what goes into these three groups.

WHO CARES IF A PARAKEET BREATHES UNDER WATER? YOU DO!!!

You can't use the oxygen in the water molecule. It is locked to hydrogen in the *compound*. But you CAN use the oxygen dissolved in a *mixture* with water. Industry is working on a membrane which acts like the gills of a fish. One day with its help man may be able to breathe under water without an outside source of air. (Photo Courtesy of General Electric)

WHO CARES ABOUT GROWING METAL WHISKERS? YOU DO!!!

Out of a mixture of chemicals these tiny metal whiskers grew. These bits of metal threads will be able to support fantastic weights in small areas. You could hang your television on the wall by a slender thread! (Photo Courtesy of General Electric)

QUICK QUESTION?

Explain the statement, "KNOWLEDGE IS ORDERED INFORMATION." Use the following in your answer.

(a) Our money system is based on ordered information.
(b) What order or grouping of information will help you to find a certain address in your town?

ELEMENTS, THE SIMPLE SUBSTANCES

What Is an Element?

An ELEMENT is a simple substance that cannot be broken into simpler substances. For example, when, by analysis, a chemist tries to break copper or iron into simpler substances, he finds that he cannot do it by ordinary chemical means. Copper and iron, then, are elements.

The early Greeks believed there were only four "elements": earth, fire, air, and water. Later experiments showed that each of these "elements" was made up of other materials. Rather than just four elements, modern scientists have discovered 105 simple substances called elements. There are probably more elements not yet discovered.

There are 92 natural elements. Some are found as gases in the atmosphere. Other elements are found in the waters of the earth or as solids in the earth's crust. A dozen or so elements do not occur in nature. They have been made by man.

You are already familiar with some of the common elements which are metals: copper, iron, silver, gold, lead, aluminum, and tin. You know the nonmetals: sulfur, carbon, chlorine, and oxygen. Separating metals from nonmetals is a way of grouping or classifying elements.

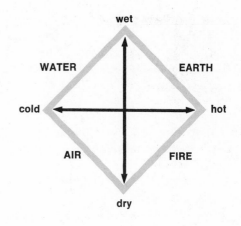

LIST OF COMMON ELEMENTS AND THEIR SYMBOLS

aluminum	Al	magnesium	Mg
barium	Ba	mercury	Hg
bromine	Br	nickel	Ni
calcium	Ca	nitrogen	N
carbon	C	oxygen	O
chlorine	Cl	phosphorus	P
copper	Cu	platinum	Pt
fluorine	F	potassium	K
gold	Au	silver	Ag
hydrogen	H	sodium	Na
iodine	I	sulfur	S
iron	Fe	tin	Sn
lead	Pb	zinc	Zn

Interesting Names

The names of the elements are often clues to whether they are metals or nonmetals. Generally, the names of metals end in "um" or "ium." The names of nonmetals end in "n" or "ne."

Elements are named to honor people, places, and things:

For scientists—
    einsteinium for Einstein
    curium for Madame Curie
For places—
    californium for California
    germanium for Germany
For heavenly bodies—
    plutonium for Pluto
    uranium for Uranus
For Mythological characters—
    thorium for Thor
    vanadium for Vanir
For properties—
    bromine for the Greek word for stench, "bromos"
    chlorine for the Greek word for greenish yellow, "chloros"
    hydrogen for the Greek words for water and producer.

Biobriefs of Some V.I.E.'s (very important elements)

Bronze was made from copper and tin as early as 3700 B.C. (The Bettman Archive)

Oxygen—The Most Common Element

Oxygen was discovered in 1774 by Priestley and Scheele independently of each other. You cannot see oxygen or taste it, but we all need it to live. Humans and animals breathe it in and plants give it off. We use it to burn the food we eat which gives us energy. Fuels combine with oxygen to make our cars go. In fact, common burning requires oxygen and is called rapid oxidation. *OXIDATION is the combining of oxygen with other substances.* You will learn later that oxidation has another meaning.

Where do we find oxygen? Oxygen is found as an element in the air, the earth's crust, and in air bubbles in water. It is combined with most other elements. For example, in every water molecule oxygen is combined with hydrogen. It combines with carbon to form the carbon dioxide of the air. Oxygen is indeed a very common element.

Diamond, a form of carbon. (Ward's Natural Science Establishment)

Carbon—The Element of Life

You might think the element carbon has many disguises. Girls admire diamonds. What are they? Pure carbon. Fellows use graphite as a lubricant on their cars. What is it? Carbon. We all use "lead" pencils. The marks made by the pencil? Carbon. It is in the form of graphite. The soot that you get in your eye? Carbon.

There are over a half million known substances with carbon in them. So many that there is a special branch of chemistry to study them—Organic Chemistry. These substances are found in the air, in the earth's crust, and in every living cell.

Think of all the people on earth. They and all of the plants and animals have carbon in every cell. Test a common plant cell. Heat some sugar. What do you get? Carbon.

Copper—The Element with a History

During Prehistoric Times men found copper. They made crude knives and hammers of it. Copper is a very malleable metal, so it can be beaten easily into different shapes. This is important because hammering also causes it to be harder. Later men found that they could melt copper over fire and cast it into any shape they wanted. By 5000 B.C., the Egyptians were using copper to make weapons. These weapons were discovered when the ancient tombs were opened.

Why do people still work at finding copper today? For one thing, our electric systems depend on it. Miles and miles of copper wire carry electricity across the country. Hundreds of miles of copper wire are used in the circuits of a single airplane.

Due to its properties, copper is extremely useful and very beautiful. You will see it often in art exhibits as metal sculptures. It is a truly versatile element.

Oxygen in use in the hospital room. (The Bergman Associates)

QUICK QUESTION?

What is wrong with this statement? "If you've seen one element, you've seen them all."

THE UNIVERSE OF CHANGE

Physical and Chemical Changes

Tear a piece of paper in half and you have made a physical change. *The change in the size, shape, or phase of a substance is a PHYSICAL CHANGE.* No new substance is formed by the actions of a physical change. When you melt iron or boil water into steam, you have changed the phase of the substance but not the substance itself.

Burn a piece of paper and you have made a chemical change. *A change which results in the formation of a new substance is a CHEMICAL CHANGE.* If the substances such as gasoline, wood, or water could not be changed into other substances, there would be no science of chemistry. But they can be changed and chemistry deals with such changes.

Most of the materials that you see around you are the result of some chemical change. There is no escaping from chemical activity. Take something as central to your life as eating, for example. Your stomach changes food chemicals into other kinds of chemicals. The new chemicals are used in various parts of your body to keep you alive and functioning. You are able to think because chemical changes are taking place in the cells of your brain. How well we understand and control chemical changes is directly related to how well we live.

The pepper is still pepper after it has been ground. Is this a chemical or a physical change? (Joan Menschenfreund)

The materials in the barn are not the same after burning. Is this a chemical or a physical change? (Ray Atkeson from DPI)

"You've just ruined my black cherries flambé!" (Don Orehek)

This is a sad chemical change, but rather the cherries than a forest fire.

Compounds, the Not-So-Simple Substances

You will find very few "pure" or uncombined elements in nature. To be sure, there are elements which are found in the uncombined state, but most elements are always ready to combine with other elements. They have certain properties which make them active in an uncombined state.

The elements in a chemical reaction generally release energy to form a compound. Two or more elements may react to form a new substance with new properties, called a COMPOUND. *A COMPOUND is a substance that can be broken down into elements by chemical means.*

Two examples of the formation of a compound with tremendous release of energy are the following:

Suppose you mix two gases together, the element hydrogen and the element oxygen. Give them a spark. "Boom"—you have a violent chemical change. After the excitement, you could find that a very familiar compound was formed, hydrogen oxide, H_2O, more commonly known as water.

Another violent reaction occurs when you put a poisonous metal, sodium, together with a deadly gas, chlorine. After this violence you would notice that some white matter had formed. The sodium and chlorine joined together to form a compound, sodium chloride, otherwise known as table salt. But you don't eat poison. The poisonous qualities of both elements disappear. The new qualities of salt remain.

These are rusted derelict's chains. Is rusting a chemical change or a physical change? (Dr. E. R. Degginger)

Do the Same Elements Always Make the Same Compounds?

No. They only make the same compounds if they are in the same proportions and put together in the same way. For example sugar is made of: carbon, hydrogen, and oxygen. But these same elements in different proportions and in different arrangements can make many other very different compounds such as: alcohol, vinegar, and starch.

A Compound or a Mixture?

If you mix salt and pepper, do you have a compound? No. Why? There is no chemical change between the two materials. They simply mix. The mixture is still salt and pepper. Each can still be identified.

How can you tell when a compound is formed?

1. The reacting substances must lose their own identity.
2. Evidence of a chemical change must be present during the reaction such as light or heat.
3. The substances present in the compound have a definite amount by mass.
4. It must not be possible to break the new substance down by physical means, such as filtering, using a magnet or pounding.

QUICK QUESTIONS?

1. A lawn mower produces a physical change. Its power is produced by a chemical change. Explain.
2. A physical change takes place in the engine of an automobile when air is mixed with gasoline.

What chemical change takes place to make the engine run? What compounds are produced as a result of the chemical change? Why would you call the exhaust from an automobile a mixture?

THE PLANNED CHEMICAL MERGER

The Right Conditions

Getting two elements to react and combine is much like planning a party. To plan a party you need the right kind of food and the right kind of entertainment. If you do not have the right conditions the party will be a failure. The same is true in combining chemicals; the conditions have to be suitable. To form copper oxide in the laboratory, for instance, you need certain amounts of oxygen, copper, and heat. Or, if you intend to form water, hydrogen and oxygen will not combine without a spark.

The Right Symbols

To have a successful party you also have to invite people who get along. The same is true when putting elements together. Not all elements react with each other. Usually a metal reacts with a nonmetal.

Each of the 105 elements has a symbol. Not only does the symbol stand for the element, but it is a shorthand way of writing the name of the element. It can take the place of the name of the element and stand for the element in a chemical formula.

The symbol also stands for one ATOM of the element. *An ATOM is the smallest particle of the element that can react with another substance.* Later you will find that the symbol stands for many other things.

The Right Formula

There is another condition necessary for the formation of a compound. The right amounts of the substance must combine. You can have more or less of a substance present, but only certain amounts will react and be present in the compound. A formula indicates the definite amounts of materials or proportions which make up a compound.

In Experiment 4.2 you measure the mass of the copper wire. The correct amounts by mass of copper and oxygen are needed to form a compound. You do not have to weigh the oxygen. All the oxygen you need for this union is available in the atmosphere. It is easy to determine the mass of the oxygen used by weighing the final product and subtracting the mass of the copper.

How much of the elements is required to form a unit of a compound? To answer you must have a recipe or a FORMULA. The formula tells you how many units of

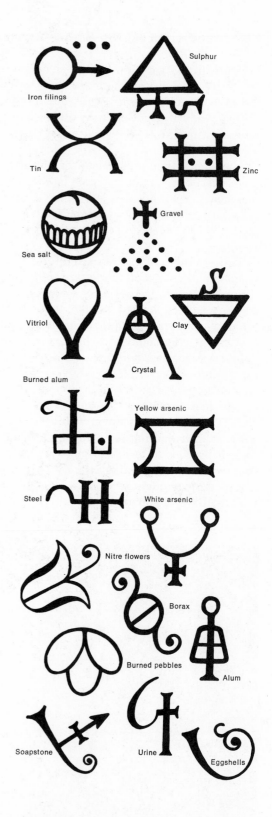

Symbols used by the alchemists. (New York Public Library)

Iron filings
Sulphur
Tin
Zinc
Gravel
Sea salt
Vitriol
Clay
Burned alum
Crystal
Yellow arsenic
Steel
White arsenic
Nitre flowers
Borax
Burned pebbles
Alum
Soapstone
Urine
Eggshells

what elements are in a compound. For example, in the formula for water, H_2O, the "H" and "O" indicate the presence of hydrogen and oxygen. The small "2" below the letter H, means there are two units (atoms) of the element hydrogen. The symbol "O," indicates that there is only one unit of oxygen. Thus, you have the formula for a molecule of the compound water, written H_2O.

The Right Names

Another essential for a good party is knowing the right names of the people. Of course, it's always good to know the characteristics of the people and how they will mix together. Knowing the names of all the elements and their symbols is rather difficult, but you probably know a few of the more common ones. By now you are familiar with some elements like sulfur (S) and oxygen (O) which are nonmetals and copper (Cu) and iron (Fe) which are metals.

You may have noticed that when you write the names of the compounds made from a metal and a nonmetal, the metals are written first. Examples are: copper oxide, copper sulfide, iron oxide and iron sulfide. The—"ide" is added at the ends of the nonmetals partners in the formulas of compounds of only two elements.

In writing a formula for the compound containing two nonmetals, the number of atoms of each element is indicated in the name. For example, carbon dioxide in which the "di" means that there are two atoms of oxygen in the molecule.

So, the right name is important. From it we can write the right formula using the right symbols which gives the relative number of atoms of the elements in the molecule.

These students are learning to use symbols, formulas, and equations. (Rogers from Monkmeyer)

QUICK QUESTIONS?

1. What ending is used in naming a compound that contains two elements? Give four examples.
2. The 2 in H_2O is called a subscript (written under). What does a subscript mean in a formula?

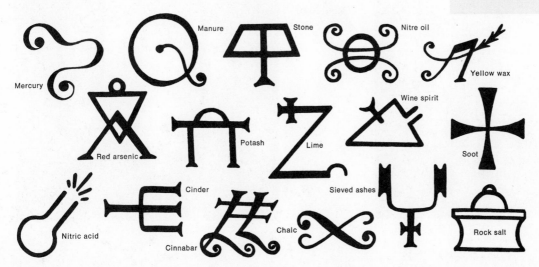

WRITING CHEMICAL SENTENCES

What happens when two substances come together? The answer could be expressed in a long paragraph. The chemist prefers a simple sentence. The chemical sentence has two parts. The first part tells you what was used. The second part tells you what was formed. The two parts of the sentence are connected by an arrow (———→). This horizontal arrow means "yields" or "produces."

An example:

> hydrogen   +   oxygen ——→ water
>   (combines with)   (yields)

The arrow can also mean "equals." *Why does the arrow also stand for an equal sign?* The fact that these chemical sentences can also be called "equations" may give you a hint. An equation represents a mathematical quantity separated by the equal sign. Both sides have the same amounts or quantities. Two plus three equals five in an equation. You would simply write: **2 + 3 = 5.**

$$2$$

$$2+3$$

$$2+3=5$$

Iron. (Fundamental Photographs)

Chlorine.

The same is true of chemical equations. Iron plus oxygen equals iron oxide. You would write this equation:

$$\text{iron} + \text{oxygen} \longrightarrow \text{iron oxide}$$

The weight of iron and oxygen on one side of the equation is the same as the weight of the combined oxygen and iron in iron oxide.

Therefore, the two parts of the equation are equal. Another chemical word equation:

$$\text{zinc} + \text{sulfur} \longrightarrow \text{zinc sulfide}$$

Later you will substitute the chemical formula for the words of each sentence. Then the chemical equations will be even simpler.

The chemical equations you have been writing are called "direct union word equations." The "direct union" means that you are combining two simple substances. These simple substances are elements which produce their combined form or compound. Later you will find out about other kinds of chemical reactions.

QUICK QUESTION?

Describe the following experiments by writing chemical word equations.

(a) oxygen is combined with the metal, lead

(b) a substance called calcium oxide is made from elements

(c) hydrogen sulfide is produced from elements

Iron and chlorine reacting to form Iron(III) chloride. (Fundamental Photographs)

Iron(III) chloride. (Fundamental Photographs)

THE WORLD OF MIXTURES

Some of the things you use in your everyday life are **MIXTURES.** Ice cream, cosmetics, ginger ale, hair oils, glass, and air are all mixtures. *MIXTURES are materials that are put together but are not chemically combined.* The mixture can be groups of elements or compounds in any amounts that you may wish to use. In chemistry you cannot consider a compound or a molecule a mixture. For example, water is always in a definite proportion of two atoms of hydrogen and one atom of oxygen. The hydrogen and the oxygen are also combined chemically. If you put hydrogen gas and oxygen gas together without exploding them in a reaction, these gases remain a mixture. Once the explosion (the chemical reaction) has taken place, then the compound water is formed. There is no longer a mixture of oxygen and hydrogen. There are molecules, now, of the compound H_2O.

Air in a room containing many people will differ from air outside on the street or air at the top of a hill. The crowded room will contain more carbon dioxide and more water vapor than the street or the hilltop. Air can also contain varying amounts of smog, chemicals from factories, and automobile exhausts. So air is a mixture. The gases that make up air are not in chemical combinations with each other or the other gases that might be added.

Water in the sea contains many different kinds of particles and also can be described as a mixture. Even drinking water would be described as a mixture. It contains many minerals and even some gases. Gases such as chlorine are mixed with water in various quantities to eliminate germs.

Mixtures can be separated mechanically. Some are separated more easily than others. Muddy water from a creek, for instance, will settle after a few days. The mud and other particles will fall to the bottom of the container. Some of the lighter particles may still be clouding the water. Passing the water through charcoal or fine sand could remove the finer particles in the water. In your laboratory experiment you separated particles by:

1. sifting the mixture through a screen to remove large particles
2. removing metallic particles with a magnet (iron particles)
3. dissolving particles in water
4. passing the mixture through a filter
5. having the liquid in the mixture evaporate

These are all mechanical means of separation.

Mixing is an activity you perform in many ways and in many places. The girl above is using the blender in her kitchen to mix nuts, a solid, with a liquid. (Joan Menschenfreund)

Home Lab

Mix some salt and sand together. Which would you say is the best way of mixing these two substances? You may even invent a new method of mixing salt and sand. Does it matter how much or little salt or sand you use? It depends on how you would use a salt and sand mixture. Since there would seem to be no real use for such a mixture it probably doesn't matter how much you use of either. Are there chemical changes in the two substances? The salt will still taste salty, and the sand will still be as gritty as ever. There would appear to be no change in a chemical way.

Can you recover the sand and salt? Dissolve the mixture in water, and filter out the solid particles of sand. Then let the water evaporate away, and you will recover the salt.

You discovered that you could recover the materials from your mixture. Each substance retained its original properties. No chemical change took place in the substances added to the mixture. They changed only in physical appearances, not in chemical composition.

Mixtures can be made by merely adding things together. You may stir or shake the mixture to get an even distribution of the materials. How much do you put in? That depends upon what kind of mixture you want. A cake batter, for example, can be mixed with more or less sugar depending on how sweet you want the cake.

EXAMPLES OF MIXTURES

From the grocery store
  Mushroom soup contains a mixture of:
    water, milk, mushrooms, vegetable oil, enriched wheat, flour, cream, salt, tomatoes, starch, sugar, margarine, monosodium glutamate, and flavoring.
From the drugstore
  Some tablets for relief from colds or hay fever contain a mixture of:
    Phenylephrine hydrochloride 5 mg., phenindamine tartarate 10 mg., aspirin, caffine, and aluminum hydroxide-magnesium carbonate co-dried gel.
From a mountain
  A piece of granite may contain:
    Quartz, mica, and feldspar.

QUICK QUESTIONS?

1. "French dressing is a mixture." How would you prove this statement?
2. Describe how you would separate a mixture of finely powdered iron, sulfur, and salt. Would the same method work if you had finely ground plastic instead of the iron in the mixture?

Lavoisier and his wife in the laboratory. (Culver Pictures, Inc.)

Lavoisier, Founder of Modern Chemistry

A great triumph in Lavoisier's life was the discovery of how things burned. Until his time it was thought that there was a mysterious substance involved in burning called phlogiston. It was believed that all burnable materials contained phlogiston, which was given up during burning. Lavoisier experimented with burning, weighing the material before burning and afterwards. There was an increase in the weight of the material after burning. He determined that burning was the chemical combination of the material with oxygen. The weight of the oxygen from the air which combined with the material was the reason for the extra weight.

Lavoisier had one of the best chemical laboratories of the time. He was well prepared, having studied under some of the best French scientists of his day. He read about the works of others before designing and forming his own methods of experimentation. He did not leave things to chance discoveries. He tested for the results that he thought would prove his ideas. He was using the scientific method in most ways, but he was unsuccessful in telling others about his work.

Unfortunately, as is the case for many public figures today, Lavoisier had a problem in communications. He was unable to publish some of his results immediately. There were many discoveries by Lavoisier. However, because of difficulties in letting others know about them, he did not always get the credit.

Chapter 4

ACTION POINTS

An **ELEMENT** is a substance that contains only one kind of matter.

A **COMPOUND** consists of two or more elements held together chemically. A compound has properties which are different from those of its constituents and its constituents are difficult to separate.

A **MIXTURE** can be separated into its parts by simple mechanical means.

All elements can be represented by **SYMBOLS.**

PHYSICAL CHANGES are caused by such activities as breaking, freezing, or vaporizing. In a physical change the chemical identity of the substance is not lost.

CHEMICAL CHANGES take place when new substances are formed. Such changes may take place when new molecules are put together or when molecules are broken apart or rearranged.

A **FORMULA** is the representation of the molecule of an element or compound by chemical symbols. Each formula has its own chemical name.

A **CHEMICAL EQUATION** is a short method of describing a chemical reaction. It tells what chemicals were used to produce other substances.

A **MIXTURE** is an association of two or more materials which retain their identity. A mixture may contain solids, liquids, gases, or any combination of these phases. Many mixtures are essential to life, such as blood, and many mixtures are used in day-to-day living.

SOLUTIONS

Unit 2

Contents

UNIT 2 SOLUTIONS

Chapter 5 *READER TEXT*   **Chapter 5** *LABORATORY MANUAL*

WATER IN SOLUTIONS

Chapter 6   *READER TEXT*   **Chapter 6**   *LABORATORY MANUAL*

MAKING SOLUTIONS

Water in Solutions 5

WATER, WATER EVERYWHERE

Pointing toward the porthole, the captain said, "As we get closer, you can see that the earth is covered with clouds."

The navigator added, "There seems to be a lot of blue stuff, too. What is it?"

"The deep blue part is probably some kind of liquid," the captain answered. "The spaceship chemist says that the oceans of blue liquid and the clouds are a compound of oxygen and hydrogen.

This conversation might take place between two spacemen approaching earth from another planet. Of all the features of earth, the liquids and gases they observe are the most outstanding. The liquid they see is a compound we call water. At least three-quarters of the earth's surface is covered with this liquid.

If they landed on our planet, they would find water exists in different ways. We have already discussed the phases of water as ice, water, and steam. In this unit we shall discuss water as a substance and water in solutions.

Water can dissolve and form solutions with many different kinds of materials. If water were not a solvent, many life-giving chemical reactions could not take place. You will find here on our planet that every organism from the smallest microscopic blob to humans themselves depends on water in some way. Earth is truly a water world!

Earth as seen from space. (*NASA*)

Your Work with Water

The travelers from outer space would surely notice the importance of water to us earthlings. But how often do you think of the importance of this compound? Why should you notice it? Water is common and used for many purposes. You accept the fact of water without thinking much about it. Yet, seventy percent of your body is water. Although man can survive about two months without food, he can die within a week without water. This makes it important to everybody.

Think of some of the things that you do with water. Much of the time you use it as a solvent. When you wash, water is the solvent that dissolves the soap and carries away the dirt particles. When you cook, water is often the solvent for the seasonings and spices. When you water plants, the solvent water dissolves minerals from the soil so that the plants can make use of them. As a matter of fact, knowing about solutions may give you better ideas about using water in your daily life.

QUICK QUESTION?

Look at the picture of the earth and imagine that you are a space traveler from another planet. How would you describe your first impressions of the earth to the folks back home?

(above) Irrigation. (below) Using water for recreation. (*Jack Fields from Photo Researchers*)

Watering turkeys. (*Van Bucher from Photo Researchers*)

PROPERTIES OF SOLUTIONS

If you dissolve a crystal of copper sulfate in water, a clear, blue color will spread uniformly throughout the liquid. A solution is a uniform mixture of a solute (in this case copper sulfate) and a solvent (in this case water).

You can have a little or a lot of a substance in a mixture. There is also no need to have definite amounts of either the solute or the solvent in solution. For example, you may dissolve a little salt in a lot of water, or you may dissolve a lot of salt in a very small amount of water. In either case, it is still a salt solution. A solution is, therefore, one kind of a mixture. Like other kinds of mixtures, a solution can be separated into its parts by purely physical means. If a salt water solution is poured through filter paper, salt cannot be collected. But, if the water is evaporated the salt remains.

A solution is uniform. What about a cup of coffee with a lot of sugar lying in the bottom of the cup? The sugar that is not dissolved in the bottom of the cup is not in solution. If you stir it, the sugar and coffee will become a solution. The same amount of solute will be found in every part of the solution. Test it. The coffee should be equally sweet throughout. The solute in a solution does not settle. If there is a settling out, as in muddy river water, then there is not a solution.

A solution is clear. Ocean water is clear. The many salts in ocean water do form a true solution with water.

(Mimi Forsyth, Monkmeyer)

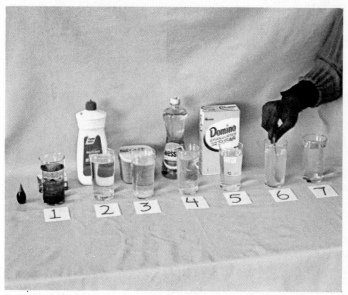

Home Lab

It is possible to make different kinds of water solutions in the kitchen. You might think of your experiment as polluting water.

For mixing containers, use anything from drinking glasses or paper cups to simple bottle caps. If you use bottle caps, measure the solutes by the amounts that can be placed on the tip of a toothpick. If you use glasses for the water, you can use teaspoons for the solute.

In each container of water, place a measured amount of one of the following solutes:

1. food dye
2. some detergent
3. the white of an egg or powdered egg
4. salad oil
5. sugar
6. salt
7. only water

Observe the contents of each container. Record your observations. Let the containers stand overnight. Are there any changes in the smells, appearance, or other properties of the combinations? How do the combinations compare with your observations of them when the solutes were first added? Place a drop of each combination in a separate spot of a frying pan. Keep track of what you put where. Heat the pan very slowly at the lowest possible temperature.

Describe the appearance of the residues after the water has been evaporated.

From your observations and what you know about the properties of solutions, were all of the combinations solutions? Explain.

HAPPENINGS IN SOLUTIONS

Chemical Dropouts

Mix two dry chemicals together and there will be little reaction. Chemicals in solution, however, usually do a bit of reacting. You could compare the two by mixing two substances together, for example, potassium iodide and lead nitrate. Both are white, crystalline, salts. If these white salts are kept dry, the two chemicals will show little change when mixed together. Now suppose you add lead nitrate to water in one container to form a solution, and potassium nitrate to water in another container. The scene is set for action. If the two clear solutions are poured together, a chemical change can be observed. The clear solutions become a clouded mixture of a different color. The parts can be separated by filtration.

What has happened? There has been a change of chemical partners. When potassium iodide in solution reacts with lead nitrate in solution, the iodide partner switches places with the nitrate partner. Two new chemicals are formed. One is the compound potassium nitrate which dissolves in water to form a solution. The other is the compound lead iodide which does not form a solution with water.

Here is the chemical sentence which describes this reaction:

lead nitrate + potassium iodide $\longrightarrow$

potassium nitrate + lead iodide $\downarrow$

Lead iodide is a chemical dropout. In the language of chemistry two terms describe this type of dropout. First, it is called a PRECIPITATE. *A PRECIPITATE is a chemical that falls out of solution when it is one of the products of a reaction.* Second, it is said to be of LOW SOLUBILITY. *LOW SOLUBILITY describes substances that dissolve very slightly in a given solvent, usually water.* Very often these substances are shown to be of low solubility in equations by the arrow, $\downarrow$, following the formula.

When two compounds react to form two new compounds, double-exchange reactions occur. Not all reactions of this type produce precipitates. Some produce two soluble substances. You write equations for some of these reactions in the Exercise. Some double-exchange reactions produce a gas. We will study these in a later chapter.

$$\text{I} \quad \text{II} \quad\quad \text{III} \quad \text{IV}$$

$$2+4 + 1+5 = 2+5 + 1+4$$

$$AB+CD \longrightarrow AD+CB$$

Double replacement reactions are represented here by numbers and letters. Notice that the sides are equal to each other. The combinations are different.

QUICK QUESTIONS?

1. Why do reactions take place faster in liquids than in solids?
2. How do double-exchange reactions differ from direct union reactions?
3. What is meant by the following?
   (a) precipitate
   (b) low solubility
   (c) $\downarrow$
4. In Experiment 5.1 you work with precipitates for the first time. Describe the difference you observe in the test tubes with precipitates and those with solutions only.

WATER: A TWO-WAY STREET

The Big Chemical Soup

Just be thankful that you weren't there. The action was hot, fast and furious a billion or so years back in the earth's history. Everyone could have a volcano in his own backyard. The air was made up of gases so poisonous that one breath could be your last. Hydrogen and oxygen were exploding to form water by the ton. Down into the craggy steaming depressions of the earth, torrents of water poured. The water, gathering into large lakes and steaming pools, made a foul smelling solution. Gases spewing out of volcanic craters and chemicals forming on the earth's surface dissolved in the water and formed a chemical soup. Chemical reactions took place in these huge water solutions, as the earth began to calm a bit. Life was a product out of the chaotic beginnings of the earth according to some theories. Some chemical reactions produced the first molecules needed for life.

But how did the clean, clear, blue waters of the present day come about? It took many more millions of years, but it happened. *A systematic process of evaporation and condensation of water started what we now call the WATER CYCLE.* The sun evaporated the water. The vapor went up into the atmosphere, cooled and fell as rain. The water that was left in the seas was a solution of many different chemicals. The water which was evaporated left its nonvolatile impurities behind, which settled to the bottom. After awhile there was more pure water and the seas were much clearer and cleaner.

Varieties of Water

When a chemist says water he means hydrogen oxide, H_2O. A pool of pure water molecules is difficult to find. Water is a good solvent. It is so good that we call it the universal solvent. The majority of chemicals are soluble in water. As a result, when we talk about water in general we include drinking water, rain water, seawater, river water, ground water, well water, spring water, and perhaps a few other kinds. The difference between one kind of water and another is often the kind of solutes found in the solution. In Experiment 5.2 you test some varieties of water.

Dissolved gases in water are often major reasons for the differences in the taste of water. Gases in the atmosphere dissolve into the drops of rain as it falls. Mountain streams, churning through rapids, dissolve great

(George Leavens, Photo Researchers)

(Alexander Lowry, Photo Researchers)

(Ross Kinne, Photo Researchers)

Water becomes a solvent as it comes in contact with other substances which dissolve into it.

quantities of air. Every gas forces its way into solution. *The greater the pressure of the gas above the liquid, the more gas dissolves into a liquid.* This statement is a natural law called HENRY'S LAW. There are many minerals which also dissolve into water. The salt, sodium chloride, in sea water is an excellent example. Besides sodium chloride, there are many other minerals which dissolve in water. When water passes through soil, it picks up solutes of calcium and magnesium compounds. When these salts are dissolved in great quantities, we may speak of the water as being HARD. *HARD WATER contains substances which make it difficult for soap to make suds.* Magnesium and calcium compounds react with the soluble soap to form compounds of low solubility which do not form suds. The hard water also clogs boilers and pipes. Test different kinds of water for hardness in Experiment 5.3.

What goes into water can also come out of water. Water is a two-way street. The study of purifying water has become an important public issue. Water pollution is cutting down on our pure water supplies. People are now demanding higher quality water. We shall study some of the ways to purify water. In Experiment 5.4 you actually purify some impure water.

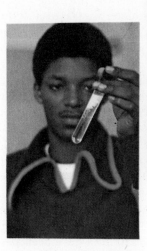

(left) Hard water. (right) Soft water. (*Mimi Forsyth, Monkmeyer*)

Water is constantly moving through a cycle. The sun evaporates the water. It is cooled and condenses to fall as rain or snow.

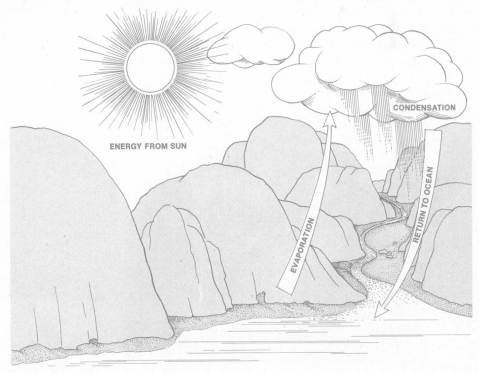

ENERGY FROM SUN

CONDENSATION

EVAPORATION

RETURN TO OCEAN

HARMFUL IMPURITIES IN WATER

Billions of dollars is the price tag for clean water. In the United States alone we use over 400 billion gallons of water a day. At such a rate of water usage there is a need to conserve water and to rid it of pollution. This is a big job.

In the experiments for this chapter you work with: 1. water in solution; 2. different kinds of water to make solutions; 3. purifying water to make it more useful in the chemistry laboratory. In the series of experiments you observe what happens in nature on a larger scale.

Nature, itself pours some solutes into streams and oceans. Man, too, has managed to pour a great variety of pollutants into streams, lakes, and oceans. Fortunately, scientists are finding out more about the nature of pollutants, and more about their effects. As a result of this research, laws have been passed which restrict the dumping of waste into water. As you observe in your experiments, chemicals can change water from clear and clean to cloudy and murky. Chemicals can also reverse the process. They can help clean water.

Besides minerals and gases dissolved in water, harmful microbes in water such as typhoid and dysentery germs cause a major problem. You can get sick and die from drinking water that contains dangerous germs. Technicians and bacteriologists test drinking water for such germs. Every large city in the world purifies its drinking water. Most of them use chlorine to kill germs.

There are five basic steps to purification of drinking water: sedimentation, filtration, aeration, lime-soda treatment, and chlorination. When the process has been completed, the water should be clear, soft, free from objectionable odor and taste, and also free from harmful germs.

Polluted water. (*Larry Nicholson from Photo Researchers*)

Portable laboratory for testing drinking water. (*Vincent J. Lopez—Dept. of Water Resources*)

QUICK QUESTION?

Do some research. Find out where your water comes from. How is it treated by your water supply agency? What testing is done to determine the purity of the water you drink? Outline the testing process.

Sedimentation

Water is run into large tanks where aluminum sulfate is added. This chemical reacts in the water to remove the fine silt and bacteria. A jellylike mass, which carries the impurities, settles with the impurities to the bottom of the tank.

Sedimentation pond. (*USDA*)

Filtration

From the sedimentation tanks, the water is filtered through layers of gravel, coarse sand, and fine sand. More of the impurities of the raw water are captured in these filters. Each day the filters are 'back washed', a process in which water is forced through in the opposite direction to clean the filters.

Aeration.
(*Vincent J. Lopez—Dept. of Water Resources*)

Aeration

Water is cascaded over an artificial waterfall or shot up into fountains. In this way the water is exposed to air and sunlight. Substances causing disagreeable tastes or odors are oxidized and thus removed from the water.

Lime-Soda Treatment

Water can be softened by the addition of lime, (calcium hydroxide) and soda (sodium carbonate). By using these chemicals in just the right amounts, compounds of calcium and magnesium, which cause hardness, can be removed from solution. But water made soft with lime and soda is not satisfactory for use in the chemistry laboratory or in certain industries.

Filtration bed. (*Penna. Dept. of Health*)

Chlorination

Usually the final step of purification is adding chlorine to water. This is accomplished by bubbling chlorine gas through the filtered water. Chlorine is a poisonous gas so very little is used. Just enough is added to kill any remaining bacteria, but not enough to harm human beings.

In some communities a small amount of fluorine is added to the water supply to help fight tooth decay in children.

Tanks of chlorine at reservoir.
(*Vincent J. Lopez—Dept. of Water Resources*)

CHEMISTS ARE CHOOSY ABOUT WATER

You have observed the many ways in which chemicals can get into water. Water is usually carrying some amount of solutes in solution. In addition, chemicals are added for purification. A chemist working in the laboratory must eliminate as many unknowns as possible. If he works with impure water, he may have as many unknown chemicals in the water as in what he is testing. The chemicals in the water will appear in the results of his tests. Even worse, they may give the chemist incorrect information. This could cause trouble.

The chemist uses the purest water available to make solutions. Even then, it may not be pure enough. Distilled water is usually used in the chemistry laboratory, although in some cases deionized water is also used. When water is distilled the impurities are removed. With distilled water there is little chance of unknown chemicals naturally in the water or added to purify it becoming a factor in laboratory work. In some areas of the country, tap water is pure enough for use in your experiments.

Water is the most important substance found in the laboratory. You should understand the chemical and physical properties of this compound. What dissolves in water, and what is only slightly soluble in water will become very important to you in your laboratory work.

Notice in the table shown that industries have quality requirements for water too.

Chemist checking turbidity (stirred up sediment in water. (*Vincent J. Lopez—Dept. of Water Resources*)

WATER QUALITY REQUIREMENTS FOR SELECTED INDUSTRIES*

(amounts in milligrams per liter of water)

MATERIAL IN WATER	TEXTILES (SCOURING, BLEACHING AND DYING)	CANNED, DRIED AND FROZEN FRUITS AND VEGETABLES	SOFT-DRINKS BOTTLING
Silica (SiO_2)		50.	
Iron (Fe)	0.1	0.2	0.3
Manganese (Mn)	0.01	100.	
Copper (Cu)	0.01		
Bicarbonate (HCO_3)		250	500
Sulfate (SO_4)		250	500
Chloride (Cl)		1	
Fluoride (F)		10	
Nitrate (NO_3)		250	
Hardness (as $CaCO_3$)		250	85
Dissolved solids	100	5	10

*Data obtained from Water Resources Division, U.S. Geological Survey

PROCESSING WATER FOR THE LABORATORY

Distillation is a way to make water soft. This process takes place in two steps. First, the water is evaporated by boiling. Second, the steam or vapor cools to the liquid phase. Distillation works because most impurities in water are solids and they do not vaporize. If the impurities can become gases, then distillation may produce pure water, if the impurities do not condense.

Fractional Distillation

Fractional distillation is one way of producing pure water by separating substances which volatilize at different temperatures. The more volatile substances will escape at a lower temperature than that at which water changes to steam. The low boiling fraction of the distillate may have special uses. Distillation can be continued until the substances in the original solution are completely separated. Fractional distillation is used in the oil industry to separate gasoline and motor oil from crude oil.

Deionization

The mineral particles in water solutions are charged with very small amounts of electricity. These particles are called IONS. Ions may interfere with an experiment the chemist wants to do. One way to remove this type of impurity is to pass the water solution through a deionizer column. The particles in the solution remain in the column and are replaced by particles from the column.

QUICK QUESTIONS?

1. Based upon your observations in Experiment 5.4, what kind of water do you think you should use in the chemistry laboratory?
2. How would you list a sample of water to find out if it is or isn't distilled water?

Seawater is flash distilled (quickly boiled) into steam in reduced pressure chambers.

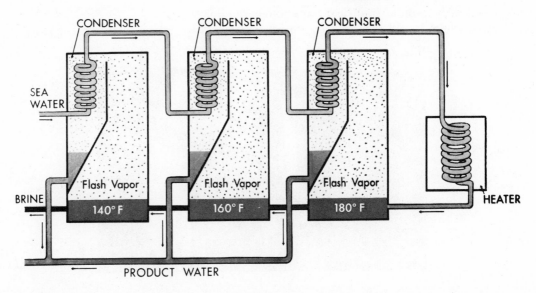

ANALYSIS AT SEA

The ocean chemist is a new kind of scientist. He can live at sea for many months at a time and carry out his investigations in a laboratory that rolls and pitches. Even under the most ideal conditions the accurate analysis of samples from the sea is difficult.

Once an analysis is made at sea, it is difficult to re-check a sample. The ship is on the move and to find the exact spot again is just about impossible. The chemist must be careful to do his work thoroughly and have enough samples on hand because the ship may be miles away from the original scene if he gets poor results from his tests.

Think of testing a few gallons of water and then applying the results to billions of gallons of water. Sometimes this happens in a given area of the sea where the depth of the ocean is five miles or more.

What are some of the problems that the ocean chemist tries to answer? He makes many tests to find out about the chemical nature of the sea. They are aimed at determining the amounts and kinds of salts found in the seawater, the amount of dissolved oxygen, and the amounts and kinds of chemicals which are the nutrients for the small plants (phytoplankton).

Should this mean anything to you? Well, the small plants may die of pollution. There may be a lack of oxygen or certain chemicals may be needed to keep the big fish alive. These fish in turn are food needed for millions of people.

Seawater is being studied as a source of many chemicals needed in the development of man's technology. The waters of the ocean may also be needed in the future as a source of fresh water for irrigation. Such developments depend on a great deal more understanding of what seawater is, and how we can protect and purify it.

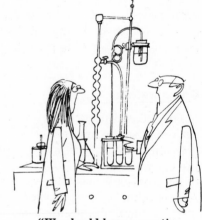

"We should have a reaction in about 36 hours . . . Call me when it happens."

(*Industrial Research, April, 1972*)

Sea chemist. (*Woods Hole Oceanographic Institution*)

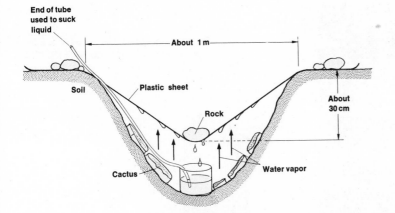

End of tube
used to suck
liquid

About 1 m

Soil

Plastic sheet

Rock

About
30 cm

Cactus

Water vapor

Survivor still. (*USDA*)

SURVIVOR STILL

Did you ever wonder how you would survive in the desert without water? Recently a way to use soil and plants as a source of water was developed. Civilian and military groups use it to obtain water wherever water is scarce or polluted.

There is plenty of water in the soil and in plant life. The basic idea is to use the sun to evaporate water from the soil or a plant, and condense it to water.

The materials needed to build the still are simple: 2 to 4 liter container, a clear plastic film about 2 meters by 2 meters, plastic tubing about 1.5 meters long and 0.5 millimeters in diameter, and a rock.

Dig a hole where sunlight hits throughout the day. Arrange the materials as diagrammed. Loam soil will yield 1.5 to 2 liters per day. If the soil is very dry, choose some fleshy plant like a cactus and place it in the still as shown. Barrel, saguaro, and prickly-pear cacti yield about 1.5 to 2 liters per day for about five days. When the yield decreases, fresh cactus can be used. One still is not sufficient for continued survival under extreme conditions. Two stills would probably meet the requirements.

The plastic film absorbs very little of the sun's energy. The soil or the plants do absorb this energy and therefore are at higher temperatures. The air inside the still becomes saturated with water vapor. As the water vapor hits the plastic, it condenses. If a film such as polyvinyl fluoride is used, tiny drops of water form and run to the bottom of the cone formed by the rock. Then, the water drops into the container.

During the night everything cools. Yet, the soil is warmer than the plastic. As much as $\frac{1}{3}$ the day's yield is formed at night.

Fertile valley of the Nile. (*Shostal*)

Alexandrian water clock. The tube (A) is filled with water. It flows out into the bowl (B). The flow is regulated to take an hour. (*Bettmann Archive*)

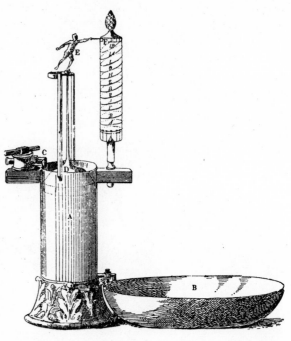

The Biography of Water

Water is born of hydrogen and oxygen. The reaction is the same today as it was the first time it happened millions of years ago. The compound is found everywhere on earth. Space scientists are interested in finding it in space because it is necessary to support life as we know it.

Water has always been important to mankind. Early civilizations were built along great rivers. The communities often flourished or died depending on the water supply. When a river changed its course, it could destroy a civilization by flooding, or the new river bed might be too far distant for the kind of irrigation known at the time. The Egyptians used the water of the Nile to irrigate their fields. They realized the need for regulating the flow of water. Today one of the

great dams of the world is across the Nile.

All through history, life on earth has been interwoven with water. Bitter wars have been fought over water rights. Fossil fish found high in the mountains show that once the area was flooded. Several times ice covered a large percentage of the earth. The glaciers have receded toward the poles leaving lakes and worn hills behind.

Man has made use of the properties of water. Because it is so common, people use water as a standard. They compare the density of liquids and solids to its density. This comparison of densities is known as specific gravity.

Water is also used to give the relationship of mass to volume in the metric system.

1 gram of water at 4°C occupies 1 ml or 1 cc.

Water is used to define a unit of heat, a calorie. One gram of water raised in temperature from 15°C to 16°C requires one calorie of heat.

From the golden days of Greece until about two hundred years ago, water was considered an element. In 1781, an English scientist, Henry Cavendish, ignited a mixture of hydrogen and oxygen. It reacted to form water. He found that water is eight parts by mass oxygen and one part by mass hydrogen.

Considering the old age of water, the chemical study of it, is in its infancy. Today chemists are discovering a lot about water, and there is still a lot to be discovered about it.

The Super Filters

When filter paper is used in the laboratory, the process of filtering is not hard to understand. With a microscope you can see the opening between the fibers of the filter paper. Big particles just don't pass through the small holes of the filter paper. Only very small particles can.

Within your body there are also filtering systems. Each cell has a thin outer layer which is called the cell membrane. It may act as a filtering system. Just like the filter paper the cell membrane is covered with holes or pores. Through these holes, food and oxygen enter the cell to support its life functions. The cell membrane also allows certain molecules of waste, like carbon dioxide, to pass out of the cell.

Scientists are studying the nature of the molecules which pass through the membranes, and those that do not. By investigating the nature of the molecules, the cell membrane and its operation, the strength of the membranes, how materials enter the cell and leave it can be determined.

Currently, man-made membranes are being developed for the purification of water. Certain plastics have been discovered which act like cell membranes. The man-made material contains minute pores in its thin, membrane-like structure. Why make such plastics? If the holes in the plastics can be made so that they are smaller than salt particles, they can be used as filters to purify water. These filters are being considered for use in industry. For instance, pure water is needed in electronics. Another important use, perhaps a vital one, will be the purification of sea water. At present, filtering systems exist using plastic membranes to filter seawater. If such systems become less expensive, we will then be able to draw drinking water and water for irrigation from the sea. Deserts will bloom with crops. These crops will be needed to feed the ever increasing population of the world.

Another use of plastic filters is the artificial kidney. The kidney machine, like the body's real kidney, provides a filtering mechanism for removing impurities from the blood. The machine, as well as the kidney, uses a complicated dialysis process, but it is basically a filtering process.

QUICK QUESTION?

In what ways is water used as a standard?

Plastic "spools" upon which tubular membranes will be coiled. Polluted water is then forced under various pressures through the membranes to be purified. (*Photo from Philco-Ford*)

Chapter 5

ACTION POINTS

Water dissolves and forms solutions with many different kinds of materials.
SOLUTIONS are uniform mixtures. They can be separated by physical means. They do not settle. They are clear.
CHEMICAL REACTIONS usually take place faster in solutions.
DOUBLE-EXCHANGE REACTIONS take place between two compounds to form two new compounds. One product may be a gas; one product may be of low solubility. Substances of **LOW SOLUBILITY** formed in a chemical reaction which separate from solutions as solids are called **PRECIPITATES.**
The **WATER CYCLE** is the evaporation of water by the sun; the cooling of the vapor to fall as rain.
HENRY'S LAW describes the behavior of gases in solution.
HARD WATER contains compounds that may obscure laboratory results.
Water is purified by **SEDIMENTATION, FILTRATION, AERATION, LIME-SODA TREATMENT,** and **CHLORINATION.**
Water is purified for the laboratory by **DISTILLATION** and/or **DEIONIZATION.** The **PROPERTIES** of water have made water useful to mankind through the ages.

Making Solutions

COFFEE, TEA, OR LEMONADE?

Many things that people drink are solutions. Some people like their solutions strong, some weak. People may like their solutions sour, others may like them sweet. It all depends on the individual. Some people are pretty fussy about the solutions they drink. Take coffee, for example: some people add an exact amount of coffee grounds (the solute) to an exact amount of water (the solvent). These coffee experts perk the coffee for an exact amount of time. How can they tell when the solution of coffee is made "just right?" Some people can tell by taste, and there are those who know just by the aroma that they have made a pot of coffee "just right."

At times more care is required in making the mixtures called solutions. A housewife may need a very strong soap solution to wash dirty clothes or a very weak solution to wash a delicate bit of fabric. But a doctor or nurse must be sure that they have a carefully prepared salt solution (saline solution) before using the solution to replace the blood of an injured person. To perform well, some engines require an exact mixture of oil and gasoline as a solution of fuel.

You use solutions every day in one way or another. It is important that you know the best ways to make solutions. They may even be critical to your life.

(Photo by Zubli)

"Be careful with that straw! It's the only one we've got!"

(Photo by Zubli)

Remember the Particles in Matter?

You did some laboratory experiments to demonstrate that matter was made up of very tiny particles. Remember the home lab in which you put some food dye in water? The dye spread throughout the glass (or diffused) until the water became evenly colored. The particles of dye diffused because they were in motion. It will help you to understand solutions if you remember that all solutes and solvents are made up of particles. And that all particles in matter are in motion. It is especially important to realize that, in solutions in a liquid phase, these molecules are moving freely.

Think of cars parked outside a parking lot of a sports stadium as solute particles. When the game ends you can see the cars stream out from the parking lot. The cars diffuse into the solvent which is the rest of the traffic in the city. At first, the solute particles (cars) are concentrated near the stadium. As the traffic clears, or diffuses, into the city, the distribution of the original parked cars becomes, more or less, even.

If you put a sugar cube into a glass of water you will observe activity similar to the diffusing cars. At first the molecules of sugar stream out from the sugar cube and are concentrated near their source. As the cube dissolves, however, and the solution stands for a time the sugar molecules will spread throughout the solution. You can test this by tasting different parts of a sugar solution. Make the solution as described above.

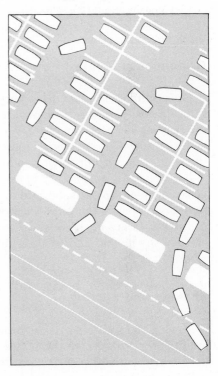

Cars leaving parking lot.

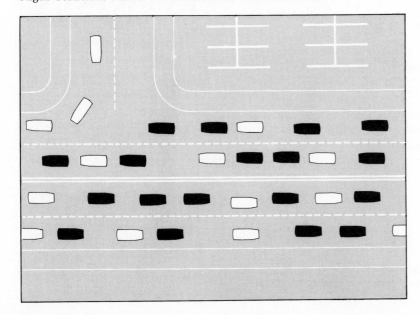

Cars from parking lot diffused into rest of city traffic.

THE DISSOLVING RACE: THE TEMPO OF SOLUTION

In music tempo refers to the speed of the beat—fast or slow. Tempo means time. Some solutes have a fast tempo of solution. Put the speedy solute into water and it goes right into solution. Some solutes have a slow tempo. They may need your help to speed up the solution process. There are three ways that you can help solid solutes go into solution in a liquid.

1. break the solute into smaller pieces
2. shake or stir the solute and solvent together
3. apply heat to the solution

In Experiment 6.1, *A Chemical Dissolving Race,* try the different ways to speed up dissolving.

Grinding the Solute

Let's compare the cars in the parking lot to the solute particles again. If more gates are provided in the parking lot, the cars can get out faster. Many gates help the flow of traffic better than one large gate. It is the same way with dissolving solute particles.

If you have a solid solute to dissolve, you should grind or break up the solid into small pieces. The smaller the pieces the more surface area. More particles of the solute are in contact with the solvent. The chemist uses the mortar and pestle to break up the solid solutes.

Shaking and Stirring

Moving the solute particles throughout the solvent is another way to dissolve the solute rapidly. What happens when you add sugar to iced tea? You stir it. The movement of the solute through the solvent causes it to dissolve more readily. The solute is more exposed to the solvent over a shorter period of time than if it wasn't stirred. Shaking a solution does the same thing.

Pharmacist using mortar and pestle. *(Bettmann Archive)*

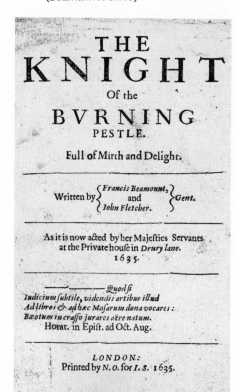

THE
KNIGHT
Of the
BVRNING
PESTLE.

Full of Mirth and Delight.

Written by { *Francis Beamount,* and *Iohn Fletcher.* } *Gent.*

As it is now acted by her Majesties Servants at the Private house in *Drury lane.*
1635.

——— *Quod si*
Iudicium subtile, videndis artibus illud
Ad libros & ad hæc Musarum dona vocares :
Bœotum in crasso jurares aëre natum.
Horat. in Epist. ad Oct. Aug.

LONDON:
Printed by *N. O.* for *I. S.* 1635.

Playbill from KNIGHT OF THE BURNING PESTLE. *(Berg Collection New York Public Library)*

Heat and Solution

Heat applied to the particles of a solute and solvent makes them move faster. With very little stirring, sugar will go into solution much faster in hot tea than in cold tea. The heat gives the solute particles extra energy needed to break away from the solid. Then the solute particles come in contact more often with the solvent particles and dissolving takes place faster.

MOLECULAR POWER IN SOLUTION

Molecules That Stick Together

Solids keep their shape because there are forces between molecules that hold the solid together. In some cases these forces are very strong. For instance, a piece of iron cannot be dissolved in water. It just doesn't work. Why? The bonding forces that hold iron and some other such hard substances together are not overcome by the water. A salt crystal placed in water, however, seems to do a disappearing act. Why? The forces that hold salt together are affected by the water environment. It requires energy to break apart the bonds that hold the particles together. Not everything about the energy involved in dissolving substances is understood by chemists. The following points are known:

Student heating test tube over burner. (*Mimi Forsyth, Monkmeyer*)

> it takes energy to break up a solid mass (changing a solid to the liquid solution phase).
> it takes energy for the separation of the solute particles so that the solvent particles can move among them.
> a release of energy occurs when the solute particles are attracted to the solvent particles.

A SOLID DISSOLVES IN A LIQUID

The solubility of a solid is the number of grams of the solid that will dissolve in 100 grams of water at a given temperature. Let's take a careful look at the above statement.

First, solids dissolve differently from each other.

Second, the amount of the solid that can be dissolved can be affected by the temperature.

Third, the standard amount of water used to measure solubility is 100 grams of water.

For example, the solid compound, potassium nitrate (KNO_3), belongs to a family of compounds called salts. Different amounts of it will dissolve in 100 grams of water at different temperatures.

If the temperature is 0°C up to 13.3 grams of KNO_3 will dissolve.
If the temperature is 60°C up to 110 grams of KNO_3 will dissolve.
If the temperature is 100°C up to 246 grams of KNO_3 will dissolve.

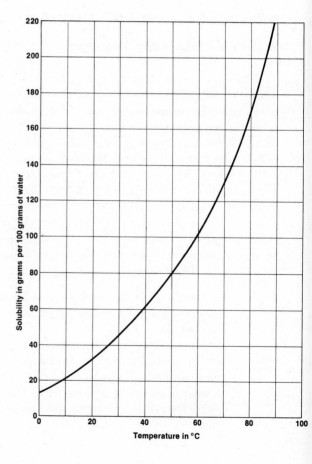

POTASSIUM NITRATE SOLUBILITY CHART

TEMPERATURE IN DEGREES CELSIUS	SOLUBILITY OF KNO_3 IN GRAMS PER 100 GRAMS OF H_2O
0	13.3
10	20.9
20	31.6
30	45.8
40	63.9
50	80.0
60	103
70	130
80	169
90	222
100	246

In order to obtain this information about solubility quickly, graphs have been set up. Along the bottom of the graph the temperature in Celsius is marked in regular intervals. The number of grams is marked along the side of the graph. Information for each substance is plotted and a line is drawn through the points. Note the Data Table and graph for potassium nitrate. Data for other solids are graphed on the chart of solubility curves on this page. See if you can determine the solid solute which is least soluble at 20°C. Determine the one which is most soluble at 20°C.

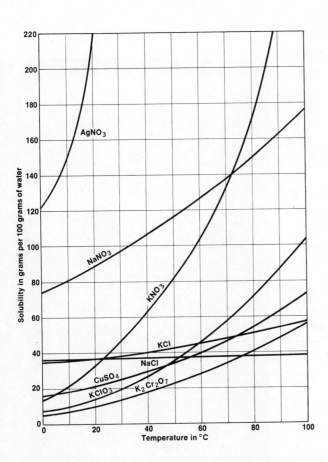

QUICK QUESTIONS?

1. In what ways do solutions depend upon particles?
2. Explain how heating, stirring, and grinding are important in cooking.
3. If you were given 100 grams of solid calcium carbonate to dissolve in 200 grams of water, how would you speed up your task?
4. Of the substances on the solubility graph, which is most soluble at 0°C? Which salt has about 54 grams dissolved at 80°C? Which is the least soluble at 60°C?
5. If you were given a solid, which gives off heat when it dissolves, would you heat it or stir it to make it dissolve faster?

SOLUBILITY AND SOLUTIONS

A Gas Dissolves in a Liquid

Have you ever watched people loading and unloading from an elevator during the noon rush hour? The door opens and as many people get into the elevator as it will hold. When the door closes, the people are often crowded together. When the door opens on the street level, the people pop out with an almost explosive force.

Molecules of gas can be forced into a solution in much the same manner. Carbon dioxide gas is forced into solution with great pressure so that the solvent can hardly hold another bubble's worth. Then the cap is put on the bottle. The molecules of gas are under pressure and remain in solution. But what happens when the cap is released, especially after it has been shaken or heated? There is a rush for the exit! The carbon dioxide gas molecules form bubbles which leave the solution. *The bubbling action is called EFFERVESCENCE.*

When discussing the solubility of gases in liquids two factors which must be considered are pressure and temperature. Think of a bottle of soda. It has more zest when the cap is on and it is cold. Why? Because gases are more soluble in liquids under pressure and at a low temperature. What happens when you open a warm bottle of soda? The gas rushes out of solution.

Carbon dioxide is forced into water under pressure. It stays in solution as long as the cap is on. It escapes when the pressure is released, or when the temperature rises.

In the same manner gases are forced in and out of your blood. The blood carries dissolved oxygen to the cells of the body. Divers descend to great depths underwater where the pressure is greater than at sea level. Under greater pressure, more gas (nitrogen as well as oxygen) is dissolved in their bloodstream. Unless the diver returns to sea level gradually, he will experience what is known as the "bends." This condition is caused by the release of excess nitrogen dissolved in the blood as bubbles. More bubbles are released as the pressure is decreased. Damage may be mild or severe, depending upon the quantity of bubbles and where they form in the body.

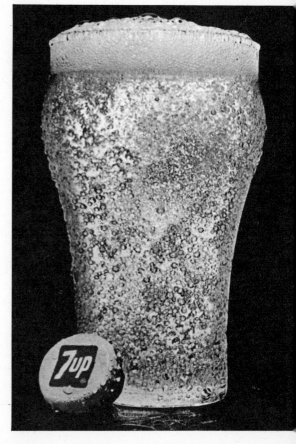

(Photo from the Seven-Up Co.)

Liquids Dissolve in Liquids

Liquids, too, may be solutes and dissolve in liquid solvents. Keep in mind that water is not the only liquid solvent. Carbon tetrachloride is an excellent solvent for fats and oils and is used to remove grease spots. Another example of a liquid solvent is gasoline. A fuel used in motor boats is oil dissolved in gasoline. The mixture provides both lubrication and fuel for the motor. Gasoline and oil are said to be MISCIBLE. *MISCIBLE means that the two liquids mix.*

Another example of miscible liquids is water and alcohol. They are miscible in all proportions. But, try to make a solution of oil and water. These liquids are IMMISCIBLE. *IMMISCIBLE liquids do not mix except slightly.* Oil floats on water because it is immiscible with and less dense than water.

NINE TYPES OF SOLUTIONS

SOLUTE	SOLVENT	EXAMPLE
Gas	Gas	air
Gas	Liquid	soda water
Gas	Solid	hydrogen in powdered platinum
Liquid	Gas	fog droplets in air
Liquid	Liquid	alcohol in water
Liquid	Solid	mercury in copper
Solid	Gas	soot in air
Solid	Liquid	seawater
Solid	Solid	gold in lead

QUICK QUESTION?

There are many different kinds of solutions in your environment. Give an example that is not in the Data Table for each of the following:

(a) the solute is a gas and the solvent a liquid
(b) the solute is a solid and the solvent a liquid
(c) the solute and the solvent are both gases
(d) the solute and the solvent are both liquids
(e) the solute is a liquid and the solvent is a gas

Alcohol and water are miscible. (*Mimi Forsyth, Monkmeyer*)

Oil and water are immiscible. (*Lynn Karlin*)

MAKING THE RIGHT SOLUTIONS

"So far the two researchers have successfully grown ordinary table beets in full-strength seawater, a solution containing 3.5% salt."

The above statement is a description of an experiment in which seawater was used for irrigation. The solution of seawater is described by the percentage of salts contained in the water. You can make a solution similar to seawater by dissolving 3.5 grams of table salt in enough water to make 100 grams of solution. Of course, seawater contains many different kinds of salts, but sodium chloride is the one present in the largest amount.

The mass of the solute in grams dissolved in 100 grams of solution indicates a concentration of solution. This method of expressing concentration is weight percent. Tincture of iodine is usually 2% iodine in ethanol.

Other kinds of directions are used to make solutions. For example, in canning peaches, the directions for making the syrup may call for 1 cup of corn syrup to $1\frac{1}{3}$ cups of water. Or, for extra thick syrup—1 cup of corn syrup to $\frac{1}{2}$ cup of water. This last solution is 67% concentration of corn syrup by volume. This method of expressing concentration is volume percent. In later chapters you will learn other methods of expressing concentration.

Beets grown in salt water. (*UCSD Photo*)

Unsaturated Solutions

When solutions are being made, the solute can be added until a definite amount is reached. Until the limit is reached all the solute dissolves. The solution is UNSATURATED at that temperature.

When solute that has been added falls to the bottom of the container and stays there after stirring, the solution is SATURATED at that temperature.

Saturated Solutions

Have you ever been to a show where every seat in the house has been occupied? You could say that the theatre is SATURATED. There is no seat for another person in the audience. Compare this case to solutions. When all of a solute has been dissolved that will go into solution, then it is a SATURATED SOLUTION. If another pinch of salt is added to a saturated salt solution, it will fall to the bottom of the container. Although some of these particles may dissolve, some particles will crystallize from solution to take their place. *In a SATU-*

Saturated solution. Notice the solute in the bottom of the flask.

RATED SOLUTION the rate of dissolving equals the rate of crystallizing.

$$\text{solid} \rightleftharpoons \text{dissolved solid}$$

When you read the chart for the solubility of potassium nitrate note that at 10°C, 20.9 grams of the solute will go into solution. At that temperature no more potassium nitrate will go into solution. Drop the temperature of the solution to 0°C. Some of the potassium nitrate may drop out of solution. According to the solubility chart only 13.3 grams of potassium nitrate is soluble in 100 grams of water at 0°C. This difference of solubility of potassium nitrate:

> At 10°C   At 0°C
> 20.9 grams − 13.3 grams = 7.6 grams.

It is possible that 7.6 grams of potassium nitrate will be on the bottom of the container at 0°C. But, what if it isn't?

Suppose that you cool the solution so slowly and carefully that nothing falls out of solution. In that case you have a SUPERSATURATED SOLUTION. You do this in Experiment 6.4.

Supersaturated Solutions

A SUPERSATURATED SOLUTION contains more dissolved solute than normally can be put into solution at the given temperature. It is an unstable solution. If you introduce a particle of the solute, even one crystal, an immediate precipitation of the excess solute will take place. In some cases, sudden jarring or shaking will cause the extra solute to fall to the bottom of the container.

Equilibrium The "Ins" = The "Outs"

Suppose you try to get into the packed theatre again. If someone comes out, you can go in. For every person leaving the theatre, one person can enter. The population of the theatre is in equilibrium. The number that goes in = the number that leaves.

Solutions are comparable. If the solution is saturated, and there is an amount of the solute lying on the bottom of the solution's container, the solution is in equilibrium. Particles leave the solution and reform as the solid substance. Other particles in the solid leave to fill some open space in the solution. *SOLUTION EQUILIBRIUM occurs when the rate of dissolving equals the rate of crystallizing.*

Supersaturated stadium. (*Paul Rico from fpg*)

CRYSTALS

CRYSTALS are those solids which have a definite arrangement of particles. Substances that form crystals, form them of a definite shape. It is a property that is sometimes used to identify a substance. Some substances form cubes, some form long needles, some form shapes with many faces, or sides. Table salt and sugar form crystals.

Three of the ways you can form crystals are:

by cooling a saturated solution of a crystalline substance under running water.
by evaporating the liquid from the saturated solution.
by adding a small "seed" crystal to a supersaturated solution.

Iridium crystal. (*E. W. Mueller Pennsylvania State University*)

The form of the crystal we see, suggests that it is based on the basic building blocks that make up the crystal. Crystals are composed of different kinds of particles. Until X-rays were used on crystals, the arrangement of the particles in the crystal was only guessed. Studies of X-ray diffraction patterns have helped the chemist to understand the structure of many crystals.

In the extension to Experiment 6.4 you study the shape of various crystals. Each of the substances you use are similar to one of the crystals pictured.

Cubic crystal of halite. (*B. M. Shaub*)

Monoclinic crystal of gypsum. (*B. M. Shaub*)

Tetragonal crystal of Vesuvianite. (*B. M. Shaub*)

Hexagonal crystal of calcite. (*B. M. Shaub*)

Orthorhombic crystal of sulfur. (*B. M. Shaub*)

Triclinic crystal of copper sulfate (*B. M. Shaub*)

Some Crystals Are Hydrates

As some substances crystallize from solution, they take a definite amount of water into the crystal. For each repeated unit of the crystal there is an amount of water held chemically. *The water held chemically in a crystal is called WATER OF HYDRATION or WATER OF CRYSTALLIZATION.* The formula which represents such a crystal has a raised dot in it to represent the loose chemical combination. For example, copper sulfate crystals are represented by $CuSO_4 \cdot 5H_2O$. *Crystals which contain water of hydration are called HYDRATES.*

Some substances change color when all the water of hydration is driven off. For example, copper sulfate is blue with water. When water is driven off, it turns white.

Gypsum is a hydrate. The formula for it is $CaSO_4 \cdot 2H_2O$. When it is heated, part of the water is lost. The remaining substance is plaster of Paris. It is used to make casts for injured parts of the body. As the plaster of Paris sets, it takes the water back to form a rigid mass of crystals which can hold the broken limbs in place. There are many other uses for hydrates. You will learn more about them as you study chemistry.

Some substances such as calcium chloride are used in desiccators to dry the atmosphere. (*Lab Con Co*)

Henry Moore using Plaster of Paris to create a sculpture. (*Rapho Guillumette*)

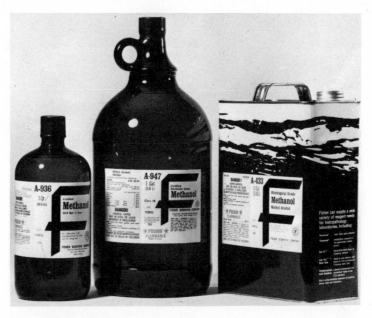

(Photos Courtesy of J. T. Baker Chemical Co. and Fisher Scientific Co.)

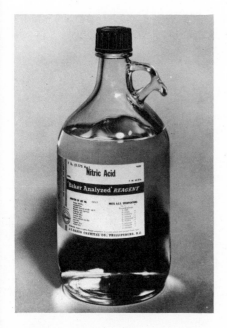

Purity of Chemicals

Just as the chemist requires pure water in the laboratory, he also requires chemicals of certain standards of purity. It takes both time and money to purify materials. As a result, the more nearly pure the chemical needed, the more expensive it is.

One of the methods of obtaining pure chemicals is by crystallization. As a substance crystallizes from solution, many of its impurities are left in the solution. If the crystal formed is repeatedly dissolved and recrystallized, a more nearly pure form of the crystal is obtained.

When you are in the laboratory, notice the labels on the bottles of chemicals. They will fall into a few categories:

(1) *USP* (United States Pharmacopoeia) or *N.F.* (National Formulary)—means that the chemical meets the standards used for medical purposes.

(2) *Technical or Practical* grade is used in laboratory work for many experiments. These chemicals are for ordinary work in the laboratory.

(3) *CP* (Chemically Pure) is a purer grade than technical.

(4) *Reagent* grade means that these chemicals are of maximum purity. Reagent grade chemicals meet the American Chemical Society's standards of high purity.

Study the labels. See if any have the ASSAY on them. *An ASSAY is the break down of the amounts of the substances, including the impurities in the chemical.* Even trace amounts of some elements are shown.

QUICK QUESTIONS?

1. Explain solution equilibrium, unsaturated solutions, and supersaturated solutions by using students and seats in a classroom.

2. How can you determine whether a solution is unsaturated, saturated, or supersaturated just by using a crystal of the substance dissolved and the unknown solution?

3. Using the idea of a crystal or a hydrate, how would you prove a substance is water?

4. Examine the labels of chemicals in the laboratory. List the chemicals according to standards of purity.

Chapter 6

ACTION POINTS

Solvents and solutes are made of particles which are in motion.

Three ways to speed dissolving are: **BREAKING UP THE SOLUTE; SHAKING, STIRRING, OR HEATING THE SOLUTION.**

Dissolving may take up energy or release energy.

The solubility of a solid is usually expressed in grams of solute dissolved in 100 grams of water at a given temperature.

EFFERVESCENCE is the release of gas bubbles from a liquid solution.

Liquids must be **MISCIBLE** to form solutions.

There are nine types of solutions.

Two of the methods of expressing concentrations of a solution are by weight percent and volume percent.

Solutions may be either **UNSATURATED, SATURATED,** or **SUPERSATURATED.**

SOLUTION EQUILIBRIUM occurs when the **RATE OF DISSOLVING** equals the **RATE OF CRYSTALLIZING.**

HYDRATES are crystals which contain **WATER OF HYDRATION** or **WATER OF CRYSTALLIZATION.**

STANDARDS of PURITY commonly used in the laboratory: *USP, Technical, CP,* and *Reagent.*

ACIDS · BASES SALTS

Unit 3

Contents

UNIT 3 ACIDS, BASES AND SALTS

Chapter 8 *READER TEXT* **Chapter 8** *LABORATORY MANUAL*

THE BITTER BASES AND THE SALTY SALTS

Acids: Compounds with "Zap"   7

The study of how man learns about things shows that grouping or classifying is one of his most important ways of knowing more. You have been grouping matter since you started the study of chemistry.

> You divided matter into solids, liquids, and gases.
> Then you learned that matter could be divided into elements, compounds, and mixtures.
> Later you read that elements could be divided into metals and nonmetals.
> Then you grouped matter in solution form into concentrated or dilute, saturated, unsaturated, or supersaturated.

In this unit another set of groups will help you to understand the chemical nature of things: ACIDS, BASES, SALTS.

You can look forward to plenty of action. There are many fizzes, color changes, and surprising results to observe in your laboratory experiences.

THESE FRUITS CONTAIN ACID.

Rhubarb. (*USDA*)

Fruit and branches of a muscadine grape. (*USDA*)

Valencia oranges. (*USDA*)

Delicious apples. (*USDA*)

THE ACID ACTION

What do you mean when you say, "Penelope has an acid tongue?" Use of the word *acid* to describe the nature of people means sour, biting, sharp, or tart in attitude. People with this kind of attitude are likely to be cutting and harsh.

In chemistry some substances are acid by nature. An acid is a type of compound. This type of compound does have characteristics which are sour, cutting, and harsh. The word itself comes from a Latin word that means "sharp." All acid substances are sharp and have a sour taste.

The common idea about acids is that they are destructive, fuming, and unpleasant liquids that can burn the skin severely. For a few of the highly corrosive acids this idea is true. Concentrated acid solutions will eat away skin tissue. These strong, corrosive, concentrated acids are DANGEROUS. Those who have experienced burns from an automobile battery acid know the "zap power" of an acid all too well.

Not all acids have such corrosive powers. There are acids that are mild and gentle in their actions. Citrus fruits owe their pleasant tang to the acids which they contain. Mild, dilute, acid solutions are sometimes used by doctors to wash out eyes. And, although hydrochloric acid can be strong and corrosive, your stomach contains a dilute solution of it to help digestion.

Although there are acid solutions which are corrosive and harmful, there are some acid solutions which are gentle and mild. We will learn which are which, and how to make good use of all of them.

"That Penelope!   She's always talking about people! She's so sarcastic . . . WHAT AN ACID TONGUE!"

QUICK QUESTION?

Give three properties of an acid.

Illustration from Aesop's fable about the "sour Grapes." (*The Bettmann Archive*)

Hannibal crossing the Alps. (*The Bett-mann Archive*)

An early distilling apparatus used to study acids.

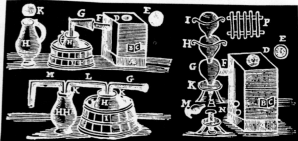

A History of Acid

Vinegar was probably the first acid recognized and used by man. It was produced by the action of air on the alcohol in wine. The ancient peoples surely knew that it's sour taste and odor was far different from the wine they enjoyed. It was also learned that wine could be kept from going sour by keeping it in a closed container.

The reaction or "zap power" of vinegar was also recognized. One Roman historian exaggerated this property when he claimed Hannibal dissolved rocks in the Alps with vinegar to make way for his elephants. Even for a strong acid this is a fantastic claim. Is vinegar a strong acid? Find out in the laboratory.

During the Middle Ages other acids were prepared. A mixture of two acids—hydrochloric and nitric—was used to dissolve gold.

This property caused the mixture to be called "aqua regia," meaning royal water. The alchemists could make gold disappear into aqua regia even if they were unable to make it reappear.

Although chemists knew about acids they did not know why acids acted as they did. One chemist reasoned that the particles that made up acids had sharp spikes. He claimed these spikes were the reason for its pinching feeling on the skin.

Lavoisier gave oxygen its name. He thought that oxygen was a necessary part of all acids. Oxygen means *acid former* (or in Greek: to make sour). About 1810 a group of chemists found that it was hydrogen, not oxygen that gave acids their characteristic properties.

In our study of acids we shall use the ideas of a Swedish chemist, Svante Arrhenius, who studied acids in water solutions.

Svante Arrhenius. (*Culver Pictures, Inc.*)

A CHEMICAL 'HOTFOOT' FOR METALS

Why should the word acid bring to mind something strong, powerful, and dangerous? Your experience in the laboratory with Experiment 7.1 *Metals and Acids* helps support this idea. Any liquid that "eats its way" into a metal is strong and powerful.

Acids react with most metals. Why is this? Acids contain hydrogen. Don't get the idea that all compounds with hydrogen in them are acids. There are many compounds that contain hydrogen that are not acids. Water (H_2O) contains hydrogen, and it is not an acid. Methane (CH_4), which is used for a cooking gas, contains hydrogen. It is not considered an acid.

What makes the hydrogen in acids different from the hydrogen in other compounds? It is the way the hydrogen is held in the acid. If a metal which reacts with an acid is placed in an acid, there is much action. The solution sizzles and foams up. There is no reaction when the same metal is placed in methane or water.

The sizzling and foaming are caused because a gas is formed. What is the substance found in all acids that is a gas when it is a free element? Hydrogen is the right answer. The next question: Why should hydrogen gas form when an acid is in contact with some kinds of metals? The hydrogen part of the acid is bound to the other parts of the acid in a certain way. When a metal comes in contact with an acid and reacts, the metal takes the place of the hydrogen part of the acid. When this replacement occurs, the hydrogen is pushed out of the compound that is an acid. When the hydrogen leaves as a gas, bubbles of a colorless gas are observed.

The metal joins with the part of the acid compound that remains after the departure of the hydrogen gas. The acid, having lost its hydrogen, is no longer an acid. The new compound that is formed is called a SALT.

This type of a chemical reaction is called a SINGLE REPLACEMENT reaction. *A SINGLE REPLACE-MENT reaction is one in which an element reacts with a compound to release a different element and form a new compound.* Single replacement reactions are not always metal with acid reactions.

A chemical sentence to illustrate a single replacement reaction is:

a new
element + compound ⟶ compound + replaced element
iron + copper sulfate ⟶ iron sulfate + copper

(The above is the reaction which took place in the iron nail Experiment 1.1.)

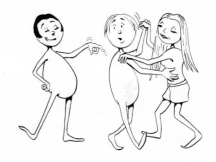

A single replacement on the dance floor.

QUICK QUESTIONS?

1. Which element do all acids contain?
2. What is a single replacement reaction? Represent one by the use of words.

COLOR CODING CHEMICALS (INDICATORS)

There are many kinds of indicators. Certain kinds of clouds and weather conditions, for example, may signal an on-coming storm. Your grades in school may indicate that you have worked hard or that there are problems which prevented you from working hard. The dials on the dashboard of a car may indicate the speed of the car, how much gasoline is in the tank, or the flow of oil through the motor. In each case, an indicator tells you about a condition. That is exactly what the indicators are used for in a chemical laboratory.

You can use many kinds of indicators to tell whether a solution contains an acid. Most indicators tell the acidic condition of a solution by color. There may even be a change in color. A color change seems perfectly natural when a compound is in contact with an acid. Each compound has its own color. If you change a compound, there is likely to be a change in its characteristics and this may include color.

A compound which reacts with acids to show a definite color change is an acid INDICATOR.

How does it work? Litmus, is a common acid indicator. It is a chemical derived from a plant. This chemical compound in its natural state has a bluish color. Put the chemical litmus into an acid, and it turns red. Just to make things convenient, paper is soaked in the litmus solution, and then the paper is dried. If litmus paper in its blue state is touched with an acid solution, the litmus turns a red color.

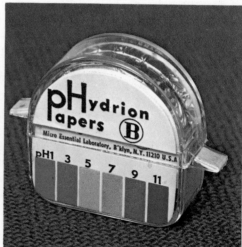

Indicator paper and pencils are useful to test the presence of an acid. (*Micro Essential Laboratory*)

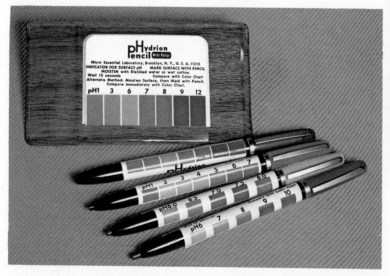

Home Lab

Many colors or pigments that are found in and around the home make good acid indicators. For example, food coloring, colored fruit juices, colors in flowers, and colored paper will serve as indicators. Cut out the colored parts of comic strips. Put a drop of vinegar onto the suspected color indicator. If it turns a different color, you have found an indicator.

Once you have found an indicator which seems to work, look around the house for things to test with your indicator. You may have some of the materials shown on page 3/**4**. There may be other household materials that give you results also.

Report to the class:

1. which indicators you found
2. which materials you tested
3. which of the materials contained acids.

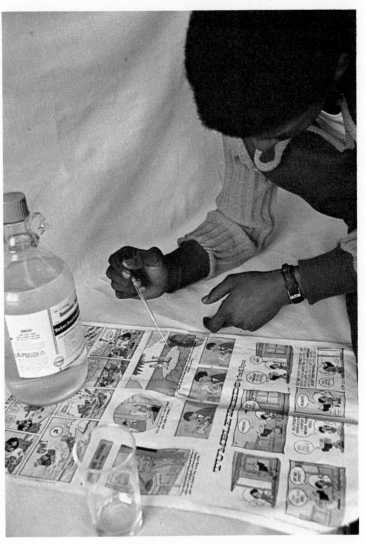

The student is adding a substance to the comic strips. Note the color change. Does vinegar have this effect on comic strips? (*Mimi Forsyth, Monkmeyer Press*)

QUICK QUESTIONS?

1. What is an indicator?
2. Name a chemical indicator.
3. Why is color an important factor in chemistry?
4. How would you demonstrate that a solution is acid?

THE STRONG AND THE WEAK

Acids can be classified as strong or weak according to how many hydrogen ions the acid provides in water solution. *An ION is an atom with an electric charge.* In this chapter we shall discuss hydrogen ions. We shall learn more about ions in Unit *4*.

The table of acids shown lists the strength of some common acids. You can observe the differences of strengths in chemical reactions. Note what happens in the test with different acids as they react with magnesium in Experiment 7.1.

One of the factors chemical reactions between acids and other substances depend on is the number of available hydrogen ions. You can predict a more vigorous reaction between zinc and hydrochloric acid than between zinc and acetic acid.

Testing for the concentration of hydrogen ions in a solution will tell how strongly acid the solution is.

Indicators tell us whether a substance is an acid or not. Now let's find out how strong or weak a solution of an acid is. Once more we can use indicators. Some indicators will turn different colors when in contact with various concentrations of free ions of hydrogen. There is a scale, called a pH range, which indicates the acidity or amount of free hydrogen ions. pH means "power" of free hydrogen ions.

The pH range is from 0–14. The value of 7 is the pH value for pure water. Between zero and seven are the readings for acid. The stronger the acid, the closer the reading is to zero.

A pH meter electronically indicates the strength of an acid. (*Fisher Scientific Co.*)

A GROUP OF THE WELL KNOWN ACIDS

CHEMICAL NAME	FORMULA	COMMON NAME OR SOURCE	SOLUBILITY	STRENGTH
Nitric	HNO_3	Aqua Fortis	Very soluble	Very strong
Hydrochloric	HCl	Muriatic	Very soluble	Very strong
Sulfuric	H_2SO_4	Oil of Vitriol	Very soluble	Very strong
Hydrofluoric	HF	Etching Acid	Moderate	Moderate
Phosphoric	H_3PO_4	Phosphoric Acid	Moderate	Weak
Acetic	$HC_2H_3O_2$	Vinegar	Soluble	Weak
Boric	H_3BO_3		Slight	Very weak
Citric	$H_3C_6H_5O_7$	Present in lemons	Slight	Very weak
Hydrosulfuric	H_2S	Hydrogen Sulfide	Soluble	Weak
Hydrocyanic	HCN	Prussic Acid	Soluble	Weak

Why should chemists use low numbers to represent more hydrogen ions? The system is based on mathematics. Water is used as the standard because it is neutral. Neutrality means that water has just as many hydrogen ions as hydroxide ions. When a water molecule breaks up, this is what happens:

water $\longrightarrow$ hydrogen ions + hydroxide ions
HOH $\longrightarrow$ H ions + OH ions

In order to obtain 1 gram of hydrogen ions, 10,000,000 liters of water is needed. That is a lot of water and a lot of zeros. (It's enough water to fill approximately 73 Olympic-sized swimming pools). Instead of writing the zeros, the chemist writes 10^7. The ^{7} here is an exponent. It stands for the number of zeros. Chemists assign pure water pH 7.

Since an acid has more hydrogen ions than water, less acid is needed to produce 1 gram of hydrogen ions. Suppose that 10,000 liters of hydrochloric acid solution produces 1 gram of hydrogen ion, then the hydrogen ions have a concentration of 1 g H ions per 1×10^4 liters of H_2O in acid solution or it has a pH of 4.

The pH scale from 7 through 14 represents substances called BASES. Bases have properties opposite of those of acids. We shall study about bases in Chapter 8.

SULFURIC ACID: THE INDEX TO INDUSTRIALIZATION

It has been said that the amount of sulfuric acid that a country uses could be a measure of the economy and the industrialization of that nation. You may use sulfuric acid more than any other acid in the laboratory. It is used in the textile industry, in making rayon, in refining gasoline from crude oil, in electroplating, in making corn syrup, in producing fertilizers, in the manufacture of explosives, and in making paper.

Sulfuric acid is most often made commercially by a method called the contact process. In it a CATALYST is used. *A CATALYST is a substance that changes the rate of chemical reaction without itself being used up.* In the contact process, air is forced over chambers in which sulfur is burned. The product from these chambers is sulfur dioxide (SO_2). In the next chamber, the sulfur dioxide combines with oxygen from the air in the presence of a catalyst forming sulfur trioxide. Next the sulfur trioxide is dissolved in concentrated sulfuric acid. Pyrosulfuric ($H_2S_2O_7$) is formed. The pyrosulfuric acid is then added to water to form sulfuric acid (H_2SO_4) of the desired concentration.

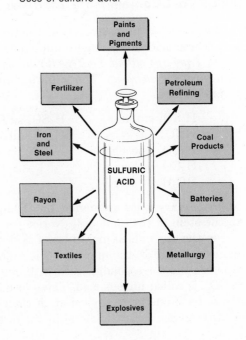
Uses of sulfuric acid.

NAMING THE ACIDS

The Two Big Groups

Acids can be divided into two large groups. The classification depends on the element carbon. If the element carbon is present in the acid molecule, then the acid is an organic acid. If the element carbon is not present, the acid is inorganic. Some chemists refer to the inorganic acids as mineral acids because they can be obtained from minerals. One exception is carbonic acid (H_2CO_3) which is considered an inorganic acid for many purposes.

Inorganic acids are generally more soluble in water than the organic acids. They are also, as a group, stronger than the organic acids. They free their hydrogen ions more readily than the organic acids.

Acids That Contain Two Elements

Hydrogen combined with a nonmetal element forms a BINARY acid. *BINARY means composed of two elements.* Hydrochloric acid (HCl) is a binary acid.

Binary acids are named by placing "hydro" before the stem of the nonmetal and "ic" after the stem, and by adding the word "acid." Thus HCl is called HYDRO-chlorIC acid. Another important binary acid is hydro-sulfuric (H_2S). A very difficult acid to handle is hydro-fluoric acid (HF). It is a moderately strong acid, but reacts with glass. Hydrofluoric acid is therefore stored in plastic or wax-coated containers.

Acids That Contain More Than Two Elements

Many acids contain hydrogen, a nonmetal, and oxygen. These acids are far more numerous than the binary acids. *They are called TERNARY acids because they contain three elements.* The following are examples of ternary acids:

H_2SO_4 sulfuric	H_2SO_3 sulfurous
HNO_3 nitric	HNO_2 nitrous
H_3PO_4 phosphoric	H_3PO_3 phosphorous
H_2CO_3 carbonic	
$HC_2H_3O_2$ acetic	

Many ternary acids are named by adding *ic* or *ous* to the stem of the nonmetal. Notice the difference between the *ous* named molecules of acid and the *ic* named acids. For example, HNO_3 is called nitric acid, whereas the corresponding acid with one less oxygen, HNO_2, is called nitrous acid. Those acids which end with the *ic* have one more oxygen atom than the *ous* named acids with the same nonmetal in the formula.

A Friendly Acid

If someone said, "Say how about a drink of carbonic acid?" would you accept the invitation? It sounds terrible, but that is exactly what you get in the soda-water type beverages. Carbon dioxide in soda water is a gas solute in the solvent water. When some of the carbon dioxide dissolves in water there is a reaction.

carbon dioxide + water ⟶ carbonic acid

This acid is very weak. As soon as you release the cap on a soda bottle, the dissolved carbon dioxide becomes less soluble and escapes. The carbon dioxide which reacted with the water goes through another reaction. It is a DECOMPOSITION REACTION. *A DECOMPOSITION REACTION is one in which a compound breaks up into simpler substances.*

carbonic acid ⟶ carbon dioxide + water

The bubbles from the carbon dioxide form in the water. This is the fizz. The carbonic acid that does not break up remains in the water to give the drink its tart or sharp taste.

PUTTING ACIDS TOGETHER

Making acids is big business. You might get the idea of how big, by watching a freight train pass in review. Notice that some tank cars are marked "CAUTION! CORROSIVE LIQUIDS." Most likely these cars contain acids on their way to a plastics factory, an oil refinery, or a hundred other different kinds of manufacturing industries.

How are acids made? There are three fundamental ways of making acids.

1. The simplest of all procedures is a direct union of the elements in the acid molecule. An example:

   hydrogen gas + chlorine gas $\longrightarrow$
   hydrogen chloride gas

   When hydrogen chloride gas is dissolved in water, the solution of hydrochloric acid is formed.

2. Another way is the one which led Lavoisier to misname oxygen. The procedure starts with the burning of sulfur in oxygen. The chemical sentence for this reaction is:

   sulfur + oxygen $\longrightarrow$ sulfur dioxide

   Sulfur dioxide is a gas. When it dissolves in water it forms sulfurous acid.

   sulfur dioxide + water $\longrightarrow$ sulfurous acid

3. Remember double replacement reactions? We first used them in Chapter 5 and then earlier in this chapter. In general, the use of sulfuric acid with a salt of the acid produces the new acid. Use of table salt with sulfuric acid produces hydrochloric acid.

   sulfuric acid + sodium chloride $\longrightarrow$
   sodium sulfate + hydrochloric acid.

Sulfur is burned.

Sulfur dioxide is collected in bottle.

Water is added to sulfur dioxide to form sulfurous acid.

(Photos by Mimi Forsyth, Monkmeyer Press)

QUICK QUESTIONS?

1. What is meant by a strong acid?
2. Name a strong acid. Name a weak acid.
3. Does a low pH or a high pH indicate an acid?
4. Does pH 4 indicate a stronger or weaker acid than pH 6?
5. What is an organic acid? Name an organic acid.
6. What elements are in hydrofluoric acid?
7. What is the name of $HBrO_3$? Br is the symbol for bromine.

WHERE DOES ALL THE ACID GO?

You are probably wearing something that was either made from an acid or was made from another product that was made from an acid. For example, if some of your clothes are made out of synthetics or acetates, the acid used in their manufacture was acetic acid ($HC_2H_3O_2$). Acetic acid is the same acid that is found in vinegar. Acetic acid is also used as a solvent for some organic compounds.

If the chair you are sitting on is metal, the chances are that one point in the manufacture of the metal it was cleaned by hydrochloric acid.

Sulfuric acid and nitric acid are used in the manufacture of fertilizers. Modern farming technologies depend more and more on the use of these fertilizers. The petroleum industry is a great user of sulfuric acid. Both nitric acid and sulfuric acids are also important to the production of fabrics and the manufacture of explosives.

QUICK QUESTIONS?

1. What acid is formed by the reaction of water with sulfur dioxide?
2. If wine is allowed to "go sour," what kind of acid is made?
3. What acid is made from table salt and sulfuric acid?
4. Name three products that you use which depend on acids for their manufacture.

Sulfuric acid is used in this refinery as a catalyst to produce high quality gasoline. (*Standard Oil Co., Ohio*)

Chapter 7

ACTION POINTS

ACIDS are compounds which have a sour taste and react with most metals.

ACIDS contain hydrogen.

SINGLE REPLACEMENT REACTIONS are the type of chemical reactions in which an element reacts with a compound to release a different element and form a new compound.

An **INDICATOR** changes color in acids and bases.

ORGANIC ACIDS contain carbon.

INORGANIC ACIDS do not contain carbon.

Acids which have two elements are called **BINARY.** The names of binary acids begin with **HYDRO** and end with **IC.**

Acids with three elements, one of which is oxygen, are called **TERNARY.** The names of ternary acids depend upon the amount of oxygen in the compound. Sulfuric acid can be made by the **CONTACT PROCESS.** The contact process uses a **CATALYST.** Acids are classified as **STRONG** or **WEAK** depending upon the number of hydrogen ions they provide in water solution. The **pH RANGE** is a method the chemist uses to express the number of hydrogen ions in water solution.

A DECOMPOSITION REACTION is one in which a compound breaks up into simpler substances.

Acids are used in many industries.

The Bitter Bases and the Salty Salts 8

THE IMPORTANCE OF OPPOSITES

For every up there is a down; for every front, a back; for every left, a right. For every force or push that we exert, an opposite force exists. Even when we walk and push against the earth, the earth pushes back against our feet.

In chemistry there are also opposites. In Chapter 7 you learned about acids. You learned how they react with metals and carbonates, and how they affect indicators. Many indicators that show the presence of an acid can also show the presence of a base.

Bases are a class of compounds that have characteristics which are opposite to those of acids. The two groups of chemicals, acids and bases, may be thought to balance one another. *We call the chemical interaction of acids and bases which produces SALT and water, NEUTRALIZATION.* We shall perform neutralization reactions and other procedures using bases in the laboratory. Many of these activities are important in everyday life. They will be discussed in this Chapter.

(Photos by Zubli)

HOW CAN YOU RECOGNIZE A BASE?

<u>From its formula</u>
You can tell an acid by the front end of its formula:
$\underline{H}Cl$ $\underline{H}_2SO_4$ $\underline{H}NO_3$
You can tell a base from the ending of its formula:
$Na\underline{OH}$ $Ca(\underline{OH})_2$ $Al(\underline{OH})_3$

<u>From its name</u>
You can tell a base from its name—it *usually* starts with a metal and ends with hydroxide:

> sodium hydroxide $NaOH$
> calcium hydroxide $Ca(OH)_2$
> aluminum hydroxide $Al(OH)_3$

What if you do not know the chemical's name or formula? You can tell if the substance is a base:

<u>From its physical properties</u>
Just as you can recognize other chemicals by their physical properties or characteristics—color, shape, taste, odor, sound, or feel, so too you can recognize bases. Bases can be recognized easily by how they feel or taste. CAUTION: BASES CAN CAUSE BURNS AND CAN BE POISONOUS. ONLY TASTE OR FEEL CHEMICALS WHEN DIRECTED BY YOUR TEACHER. In Experiment 8.1 *A Detective Assignment* you will determine how some bases feel. They taste bitter.

<u>From its chemical properties</u>
Indicators tell us about the pH of bases. Bases, like acids, change the color of indicators. However, the colors with bases are different from those with acids. The strength of bases, like the strength of acids, can be measured in terms of pH.

To a slight degree water molecules break into equal numbers of hydrogen and hydroxide ions.

> water $\longrightarrow$ hydrogen ions + hydroxide ions
> $H_2O \longrightarrow$ H ions + OH ions

(We will learn more about these ions in Chapter 10.)

When we add an acidic substance to water, the acid molecules react with water to form hydrogen ions. For example:
hydrogen chloride + water $\longrightarrow$
> hydrogen ions + chloride ions

Thus, in an acid solution we have more hydrogen ions than hydroxide ions.

When we add a basic substance to water, we increase the number of hydroxide ions. For example:
> sodium hydroxide $\longrightarrow$ sodium ions + hydroxide ions
> $NaOH \longrightarrow$ Na ions + OH ions

Do you see now why acids and bases are opposites? Your laboratory experiences will show you more about both acids and bases.

The teacher is testing ammonium hydroxide, NH_4OH, to see if it is slippery. It is one important base that does not have a metal in it. (*Mimi Forsyth, Monkmeyer*)

QUICK QUESTIONS?

1. What physical properties help you recognize a base?
2. How do the chemical properties of bases differ from those of acids?
3. What characteristic ion is found in solutions of bases?
4. Do indicators show the same color changes with bases as they do with acids? Give an example.

Lime is used to loosen hair from hides to produce leather. This scene is in Morocco. (*Barbara Gillam*)

Untreated olives are very bitter. They are treated with dilute solutions of sodium hydroxide to make them edible. (*California Canners and Growers*)

Biobriefs of Some V.I.B's (*very important bases*)

Sodium Hydroxide (NaOH)—Lye or Caustic Soda.

Sodium hydroxide is a white, crystalline substance that is sold in the form of flakes, pellets, or sticks. It takes water from the air and dissolves in it. It is sold for use in the home under the name of lye. It reacts with grease to form soap.

Great quantities of sodium hydroxide are used in industry. It is used in the canning industry to remove the peel from fruit. It is necessary to produce rayon.

A simple process is used to manufacture sodium hydroxide. It is a by-product when an electric current is passed through a solution of common table salt (NaCl). Hydrogen and chlorine gas are set free. The solution remaining contains sodium ions and hydroxide ions which are recovered as sodium hydroxide.

Ammonium Hydroxide (NH_4OH)—Household Ammonia Solution

Have you ever had a "whiff" of household ammonia? The sharp, jarring odor is from ammonia gas. When you dissolve ammonia gas in water, aqueous ammonia solution is formed. Sometimes, for convenience, the term *ammonium hydroxide* is used. The solution acts like a base. The ammonium part of the compound reacts as a unit. It is composed of the two elements: nitrogen and hydrogen. There is no metal in the ammonia solution. The chemical sentence for the chemical reaction between ammonia and water is:

ammonia gas + water $\longrightarrow$
ammonium ions + hydroxide ions

Large quantities of ammonia are used in household cleaning solutions as a disinfectant.

Calcium Hydroxide ($Ca(OH)_2$)—Slaked Lime

Calcium hydroxide is a white compound which is not very soluble in water. It is used commercially to remove hair from hides, in the preparation of whitewash, and mortar and plaster. Calcium hydroxide is formed by slaking, the reaction of water added to lime,

calcium oxide (lime) + water $\longrightarrow$
calcium hydroxide
$$CaO + H_2O \longrightarrow Ca(OH)_2$$

QUICK QUESTIONS?

1. What chemical formulas represent lye, slaked lime, and household ammonia solution?
2. Name two uses you make of chemical bases in your life.

Mark Twain's character, Tom Sawyer, used lime to whitewash a fence. (*The Bettmann Archive*)

Lime is used for lines on football fields. (*Dennis Brack, Black Star*)

Sodium hydroxide is used to make rayon. (*FMC Corp., American Viscose Division*)

Bases are used to make soaps. (*W. R. Grace & Co.*)

ACIDS MEET BASES: NEUTRALIZATION

How does neutralization work with acid and base opposites in chemistry? In Experiment 8.3 *Neutralization*, you see what happens when acids and bases are brought together. Much changing and interacting goes on. The solution in which you observe the acid-base reaction is no longer acidic nor basic. A change takes place. A neutral solution results if the correct amounts are put together.

This reaction happens because the opposites get together in water solution. Some of their parts combine. Remember it is the free hydrogen ions from the acids that are typical of acids. For our purposes, it is the hydroxide ions from bases that give the bases their properties.

A Case for Neutralization

The formulas for hydrochloric acid and sodium hydroxide show the parts that come together in neutralization.

HCl is the formula of the compound, hydrogen chloride. When hydrogen chloride gas dissolves in water, hydrogen ions are freed to form an acid solution.

In the base, sodium hydroxide (NaOH) there is a metallic ion for every hydroxide ion.

The hydrogen ion of the acid reacts with the hydroxide ion of the base to form water (HOH). This neutralizes both acid and base. Water is formed and a solution of SALT is left.

Sir Humphry Davy.
(*Brown Bros.*)

$$
\begin{array}{lcl}
\text{base} + \text{acid} & \longrightarrow & \text{water} + \text{salt} \\
\text{sodium hydroxide} + \text{hydrochloric acid} & \longrightarrow & \text{water} + \text{sodium chloride} \\
\text{NaOH} + \text{HCl} & \longrightarrow & \text{HOH} + \text{NaCl}
\end{array}
$$

Sir Humphry Davy, Chemist and Poet

Davy was born in Cornwall, Wales in the late eighteenth century. As a schoolboy he was mainly interested in poetry, but he also showed talent in making fireworks and fishing. He left school at the age of 15, but soon realized that he needed further training. He was apprenticed to a surgeon. At 19, he began his serious study of chemistry.

One of his first tasks was to investigate the effects of breathing certain gases. He breathed gases, both nonpoisonous and poisonous, and recorded his reactions. He almost killed himself by breathing some unknown gases. He discovered the intoxicating effects of nitrous oxide; also called "laughing gas." Not until after Davy's death did it come into use as an anesthetic for tooth extraction.

He discovered the metals sodium and potassium. In 1807 he passed an electric current through molten (melted) sodium hydroxide, (NaOH) preparing sodium (Na) for the first time. Using the same method with potassium hydroxide (KOH), he discovered potassium. He rose to the highest level of chemists, first as a lecturer and then as President of the Royal Society of London.

The End Point

How do you know when the point is reached where the amounts of acid and base form a neutral solution?

A way to detect the point at which there are chemically equal amounts of acid and base is called *TITRATION. TITRATION is the addition of measured amounts of a solution of known concentration to a measured volume of a solution of unknown concentration.* In an acid-base titration, an indicator changes color at about the point when neutralization takes place. *The point in the titration when the indicator changes color is called the END POINT.*

If one solution has known concentration, you can determine exactly how acidic or basic another solution is by titration.

You will do a titration with vinegar in Chapter 12. In Experiment 8.3 *Neutralization,* you neutralize a sodium hydroxide solution of unknown concentration with hydrochloric acid of known concentration. Phenolphthalein is an indicator used to find the end point. Phenolphthalein is colorless in an acid solution and a shade of red in a basic solution.

QUICK QUESTIONS?

1. What is neutralization?
2. What particles from acids and bases are active in neutralization.
3. What is always formed in neutralization?

The automatic titrator records the amounts of acid and base used and the end point. (*Beckman Instruments, Inc.*)

INDICATOR COLORS IN TITRATION

Indicator	Acid color	Transition color	Base color

WHY IS pH IMPORTANT?

Why is it important to know how acidic or basic a solution is? Many systems require a regulated pH. Hard water in swimming pools must be kept slightly acid to prevent clogging of the pipes with scale. Relatively small amounts of hydrochloric acid are added at regular intervals. The pH is checked carefully. The pH should be about 6.8–7.0. If the acidity is greater than this, the water is not safe for swimming.

In industries, many chemical reactions must be watched to keep the pH correct so that the desired results may be obtained. If the pH of a permanent hair waving solution were too high, hair would dissolve instead of curl! In the environment, there is a concern that certain industries will dump acid or basic liquids into nearby water. Such discharge may change the pH and threaten marine life. The pH value of solution is important to nature, to industry, and to human health.

QUICK QUESTIONS?

1. Why may the pH of a swimming pool be important?
2. What is the color range of universal indicator paper?
   (a) in acids
   (b) in bases

Analytical laboratory in which pH is tested. (*Monsanto*)

THE NATURE OF COMMON AND UNCOMMON SALTS

No doubt you heard the word *salt* long before you studied chemistry. When you said salt, you were probably thinking of only one compound, common table salt. There are thousands of different kinds of salts, and they differ widely in their properties.

Unlike acids and bases most salts do not contain similar parts such as the H ion or the OH ion. *A SALT is a compound which contains the nonmetal ion of an acid (other than hydrogen) and the metallic ion of a base.*

Salts of the Earth

Salts are the largest group of inorganic compounds. As the earth developed, many natural chemical reactions occurred. The elements that make up the crust of the earth came together to produce salts. Many of the soluble salts washed into streams and were swept into that vast reservoir of salts, the ocean. Sea water contains a mixture of salts. Eighty percent of the total is common salt, sodium chloride (NaCl). The remaining 20% is a little bit of everything inorganic you might find on earth. In the laboratory you evaporate some of the neutralized solution so only the common salt remains. Suppose that you could evaporate all of the water in the oceans so that only the salts are left. The amount of salt would be unimaginable—approximately six million cubic miles of salt.

This man is drilling for copper ore. Most copper ores are salts. (*The Anaconda Co.*)

PUTTING SALTS IN ORDER

There are so many salts that we need to arrange them in an order. An easy way to name them is to think of them as a product of a neutralization reaction between an acid and a base. The salt has two parts to its name. The first part comes from the name of the base. The second part may have a prefix + the non-metal root of the acid + the ending.

sodium hydroxide + hydrochloric acid $\longrightarrow$
sodium chloride + water

Salts formed from binary acids have "ide" for an ending.

	Acid		*Sodium Salt*
hydrochloric acid	HCl	chloride	NaCl

Notice the relationship of the names of the *ternary acids* to the salts they produce. Salts formed from acids other than binary acids have endings of *ate* or *ite*. Note how the acid name is related to the salt's name.

	Acid			*Sodium Salt*
per chlor *ic* acid	$HClO_4$	*per* chlor *ate*		$NaClO_4$
chlor *ic* acid	$HClO_3$	chlor *ate*		$NaClO_3$
chlor *ous* acid	$HClO_2$	chlor *ite*		$NaClO_2$
hypo chlor *ous* acid	$HClO$	*hypo* chlor *ite*		$NaClO$

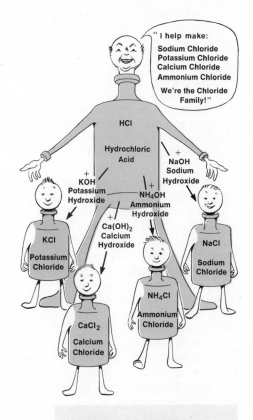

" I help make:
Sodium Chloride
Potassium Chloride
Calcium Chloride
Ammonium Chloride
We're the Chloride Family!"

HCl
Hydrochloric Acid

+ NaOH Sodium Hydroxide

+ KOH Potassium Hydroxide

+ NH$_4$OH Ammonium Hydroxide

+ Ca(OH)$_2$ Calcium Hydroxide

KCl Potassium Chloride

NaCl Sodium Chloride

CaCl$_2$ Calcium Chloride

NH$_4$Cl Ammonium Chloride

QUICK QUESTIONS?

1. Name the sodium salt for each of the following acids: hydrosulfuric acid; sulfurous acid; sulfuric acid; hypobromous acid, HBrO; and perbromic acid, $HBrO_4$.
2. Define the term *salt*.
3. Why doesn't it rain salt-water?

Home Lab

Put about a teaspoon of washing soda into a glass. Just cover the powder with water so that a saturated solution of sodium carbonate is formed.

Allow the glass containing the solution to stand for a day. Be sure to label the glass:

"DON'T DRINK—
CHEMICAL EXPERIMENT IN PROGRESS"

The next day observe the point of contact where the water meets the glass. You should see tiny crystals near the surface area of the solution.

What has happened? Can you devise another method by which you could have speeded up the formation of the crystals from the solution? Try your new experiment and report successes or failures to the class.

Biobriefs of Some V.I.S.'s, (very important salts) from three families

Nitrates

The nitrates are soluble salts of nitric acid. They are necessary for plant and animal life and are also important to the chemical industry. Nitrates are found in the soil, where they are produced by nitrogen-fixing bacteria. (See the NITROGEN CYCLE.)

Sodium nitrate ($NaNO_3$) called saltpeter is found in deposits in a hot dry section of Chile. It is thought that the deposits resulted from the decay of large amounts of vegetation when the area underwent a change in climate. Sodium nitrate is used in fertilizers, explosives, and in the production of potassium nitrate.

Ammonium nitrate (NH_4NO_3) is produced by mixing ammonia gas with nitric acid. It is a hazardous chemical which must be handled with care. It is explosive. The deaths of 400 people in Texas City in 1948 occurred when 3,000 tons of it exploded.

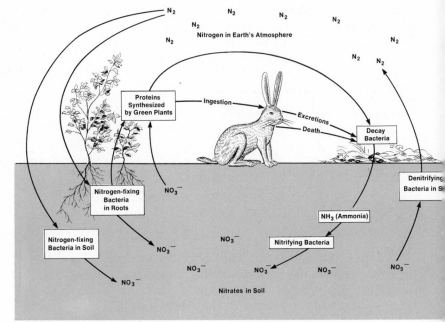

The nitrogen cycle.

Nitrates are used as explosives. (*Hercules Inc., Wilmington, Del. 19899*)

SULFATES

NAME	FORMULA	USE
Barium sulfate	$BaSO_4$	Manufacture of paints
Lead sulfate	$PbSO_4$	Manufacture of paints
Sodium sulfate	Na_2SO_4	Manufacture of paper, glass, pottery
Hydrated sodium sulfate (Glauber's salt)	$Na_2SO_4 \cdot 10\ H_2O$	Medicine
Hydrated copper sulfate	$Cu5O_4 \cdot 5\ H_2O$	Insecticide
Hydrated calcium sulfate (gypsum)	$CuSO_4 \cdot 2\ H_2O$	Filler for paper, making crayons, wallboard
Hydrated mag-nesium sulfate (Epsom salts)	$MgSO_4 \cdot 7\ H_2O$	Medicine

White Cliffs in Sussex, England. What do the cliffs and the shells have in common? (*Photo Researchers*)

Carbonates

Carbonates are salts which contain a metal and the carbonate particle. Most carbonates are soluble in water.

Acids decompose carbonates releasing carbon dioxide. This was done in Experiment 7.4, *The Bubblers*. Heat applied to carbonates or bicarbonates also causes carbon dioxide to be given off. In the following chemical sentence, the symbol over the arrow represents heat added.

calcium carbonate $\xrightarrow{\lambda}$
calcium oxide + carbon dioxide
$$CaCO_3 \xrightarrow{\lambda}$$
$$CaO\quad +\quad CO_2\uparrow$$

Excess carbon dioxide bubbled through a solution of carbonates forms the acid salts—bicarbonates. Bicarbonates of calcium and magnesium are more soluble than the carbonates and form "temporary hard water." If "temporary hard water" is heated, the carbonates are reformed causing the scale or deposits found inside teakettles or water pipes.

A variety of shells made of calcium carbonate. (*Carolina Biological Supply Co.*)

THE PREPARATION OF SALTS

Through experimentation in the laboratory you have discovered at least three ways of making salts. In Experiment 8.4 *Synthesis of a Salt* you observe neutralization and obtain the resulting salt by evaporating the water. Different combinations of acids and bases produce different salts. You might have poured a dilute solution of nitric acid and potassium hydroxide together. The salt which remains after the water is evaporated, is potassium nitrate (KNO_3).

nitric acid + potassium hydroxide $\longrightarrow$
$$\text{potassium nitrate + water}$$
$$HNO_3 + KOH \longrightarrow KNO_3 + H_2O$$

Salts may be formed when you add a metal to an acid.

zinc + hydrochloric acid $\longrightarrow$ zinc chloride + hydrogen↑
$$Zn + 2\,HCl \longrightarrow ZnCl_2 + H_2\uparrow$$

Many other combinations of acids and metals can be used as examples. Each case of a different acid and a different metal produces a different kind of salt.

In the laboratory when you combine different kinds of salt solutions, substances may react to form new salts. In Experiment 5.1 *Chemical Drop-Outs* you added salt solutions to each other. In some cases a precipitate formed which was only slightly soluble and fell to the bottom of the container.

silver nitrate + sodium chloride $\longrightarrow$
$$\text{sodium nitrate + silver chloride↓}$$
$$AgNO_3 + NaCl \longrightarrow NaNO_3 + AgCl\downarrow$$

Salts may also be prepared by the direct union of the elements. For example, sodium reacts explosively with chlorine to form sodium chloride.

sodium + chlorine $\longrightarrow$ sodium chloride
$$2\,Na + Cl_2 \longrightarrow 2\,NaCl$$

In Experiment 7.4, *The Bubblers,* you prepared a new salt from the action of an acid on a carbonate.

sodium carbonate + hydrochloric acid $\longrightarrow$
$$\text{sodium chloride + water + carbon dioxide↑}$$
$$Na_2CO_3 + 2HCl \longrightarrow 2NaCl + H_2O + CO_2\uparrow$$

Salts may be formed by:
1. reaction of an acid and a base—evaporate water to obtain salt.
2. single replacement reactions
3. double exchange reactions producing a solid
4. direct union of elements
5. an acid reacting with a carbonate

"OUR PLAN IS TO EXTRACT SULPHATES, BROMIDES, COPPER, SILVER, AND GOLD FROM SEA WATER. ALL WE'VE MANAGED TO GET SO FAR, HOWEVER, IS SALT."

DIFFERENT KINDS OF SALTS

In Chapter 5 we learned about salts called hydrates. These salts had water in the crystal called water of hydration. In this unit we study many kinds of salts.

Normal Salts

Most of the salts used in the laboratory are NORMAL SALTS. *A NORMAL SALT is one which does not contain either a hydrogen ion from the acid or a hydroxide ion from the base.* It usually contains a metal ion and a nonmetal ion.

Acid Salts

As you might expect, *ACID SALTS contain hydrogen from the acid.* One common acid salt found in the home is sodium hydrogen carbonate, $NaHCO_3$. It is commonly called sodium bicarbonate or baking soda.

Basic Salts

Some ores are BASIC SALTS. *A BASIC SALT is one in which a hydroxide ion (OH) is present.*

A valuable mineral mined for its copper content is malachite. Malachite is basic copper carbonate or $CuCO_3 \cdot Cu(OH)_2$.

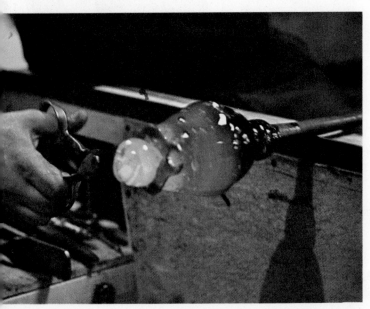

Salts are used in making glass. (*A. Bileci, Alfred University*)

Baking soda is an acid salt used in the kitchen. (*Zubli*)

Modern Research—
Salts for Air Conditioning

As an aid to cut the need for power for air conditioners, research is being done on salts. A special salt that freezes at 55°F has been developed that "stores cold" during the cool night and early morning hours. As the day warms, the salt melts. As it melts, it absorbs heat decreasing the load on the air conditioner. A house that requires a three-ton air conditioner could be cooled by a 1¼-ton unit running 24 hours on this cold-storage principle. The unit could consume at least 15 percent less power.

The Biography of Salt (Sodium Chloride)

Salt was used by man before recorded history. He probably first discovered it by the sea. The sun evaporated sea water caught in pools, and the white salt remained. He found many uses for salt besides flavoring for his food. It became an important item of trade. The road upon which the traders carried the salt to Rome in caravans was called the "Via Salaria." Our word "salary" comes from it. The Roman soldiers who guarded the caravans were paid in salt. From this practice we get the expression "he's not worth his salt."

Salt was found in underground deposits. Very deep mines were dug. Criminals were often sent to work in these mines because of the extremely poor working conditions. No one else wanted to work there.

The American salt industry was started along the East Coast in evaporation ponds. The beginnings of Saltville, Virginia were aided by the kidnapping of a Virginia woman by the Indians. As a captive she learned how to evaporate brine, a very concentrated solution of salt, to obtain salt. She brought back the technique to the colonists when she escaped.

Large deposits of salt were found in Europe. Many salt mines were developed in Germany. Because salt is necessary for the production of many chemicals, the availability of the salt was a factor in the establishment of Germany's great technology before and during the world wars. Near the end of World War II, the mines were used as shelters for equipment. The production of salt declined, and eventually the technical industries collapsed.

Today, the United States is both the largest producer and the largest consumer of salt.

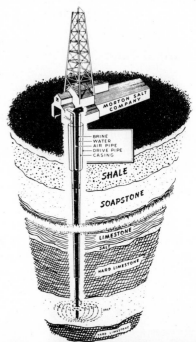

Diagram of a salt well. (*Morton Salt Co.*)

Painting of Roman aqueducts and Via Salaria by Zeus Diemer. (*The Bettman Archive*)

Salt mine at Grand Saline, Texas. (*Morton Salt Co.*)

Salt Around the House

As we all know common table salt, sodium chloride (NaCl) brings out the flavor in foods. It also has other uses around the house.

In a water solution it makes an effective gargle, or a cleanser of open wounds.
In the bath it has the same relaxing effect as a dip in the ocean.
Soak walnuts overnight in salt water. The nut meats will be easy to get out whole.
Butter can be kept firm without ice by wrapping it in a cloth wrung in salt water.
Add a pinch of salt to water in a vase to keep flowers fresh longer.
Throw salt on poison ivy and see what happens!

NANCY®

QUICK QUESTIONS?

1. Name three methods of preparing a salt. Give an example of each.
2. In Experiment 8.4 *Synthesis of a Salt*, you prepare calcium chloride. Is it possible to prepare sodium chloride using similar methods? If yes, write the chemical sentences for each method.
3. What are the differences among normal salts, acidic salts, and basic salts?
4. Some farmers rotate their crops every year or two. Why would they plant beans in a field a year after they had corn there?
5. Some salts decompose when heated. If you heated calcium carbonate, what gas would be given off? How would you test to find the identity of the gas? (See page **18** in the Laboratory Manual Unit *3*.)
6. What three methods do you know for obtaining sodium chloride?

Chapter 8

ACTION POINTS

BASES are chemical compounds with properties opposite to those of acids. They are useful around the house and industry.
BASES have a slippery feel and bitter taste.
BASES contain the hydroxide ion.
BASES cause the color of indicators to change.
NEUTRALIZATION is the reaction between an acid and a base which results in the formation of water and a salt in solution.
TITRATION is a procedure to determine the concentration of a solution. The indicator used turns a color at the **END POINT.**
Indicators change color at various pH's.
SALTS are a product of neutralization. They contain a metal ion and a nonmetal ion. They are named after the base and acid from which they are formed.
Three kinds of salts are: **NORMAL, ACIDIC,** and **BASIC.**
Three important families of salts are: **NITRATES, CARBONATES,** and **SULFATES.**
The **NITROGEN CYCLE** is helped by nitrogen-fixing bacteria on the root nodules of some plants. The bacteria take nitrogen out of the air and deposit soluble nitrates in the soil.
SODIUM CHLORIDE is prepared by the evaporation of natural salt water such as sea water, and by removal from salt wells and salt mines.

THE "WHY" OF CHEMICAL BEHAVIOR

Unit 4

Contents

UNIT 4   THE "WHY" OF CHEMICAL BEHAVIOR

Atomic Structure 9

ATOMIC STRUCTURE CLUES LEAD TO A BELIEF IN ATOMS

Mystery Boxes and Raisin Pudding

Everyone likes to get to the bottom of things. The easiest way to find out what's hidden within a mysteriously-wrapped gift box is to open it. Suppose you were given a box you could not open. Suppose the box were so small and so well-sealed that your fingers could not tear off the wrappings. You know there is something inside because your senses tell you so. Perhaps not even a microscope will magnify it enough so that you could really "see" it.

Ever since man has been presented with such a problem package, he has searched for ways to get inside it. This is true for the nature of matter. You have been unwrapping chemical packages in the experiments you have performed. You have found out a lot about nails and copper, acids and bases, cabbages and indicators and how they behave. These problems were easy to solve because the reactions were easy to see.

In Experiment 9.1 *Mystery Boxes,* you learn to describe what you really cannot see by using your other senses and a little imagination. Be careful to use the Scientific Method: to observe, test, make a guess, and test some more to confirm or disprove your guess. If your guess is wrong, don't be quick to accuse your senses of giving you wrong information. A prejudiced attitude (I've-already-made-up-my-mind attitude) can help form the wrong conclusion.

Our idea of the nature of things is based on facts and our imagination. By using these facts, we can unwrap the secrets of nature. Sometimes we can observe reactions directly. Sometimes we must use an indirect method to describe what we cannot actually see, such as we do in Experiment 9.1.

Atoms

Man has used indirect methods to describe nature since ancient times. The idea of the existence of the atom came from the Greeks. Atom comes from the Greek word *atomos* meaning indivisable or cannot be cut. In 460 B.C., Democritus (Deh-MAH-krit-us) was the first to describe all matter to be made up of atoms. His followers were called Atomists. They believed all matter

(*Joseph Bonadonna*)—Porter-Blum

Home Lab

Trace the four pieces of this puzzle on heavy paper. Cut them out and try to fit them together. They should make a perfect capital T. There will be no jagged edges.

This is how a scientist must think. He has all the pieces of his scientific puzzle (data). Fitting them together to get the correct picture takes imagination. Try it. You'll like it.

could be broken down into tiny particles. In an element, each of the particles is called an atom. Each atom of the same element is alike. *An ATOM is the smallest particle of the element that can react with another substance.* Not everyone agreed with Democritus about atoms. There was not enough experimental evidence to support his ideas. Another Greek, Aristotle (AIR-is-tah-tle), offered the theory that matter could not be broken down into tiny particles. This idea was believed for nearly 2,000 years.

Today scientist's believe in the existence of atoms. Why? No one has ever seen one. The atom is something like the mystery box. We have evidence that atoms exist. The Law of Conservation of Mass and the Law of Definite Composition give evidence of the existence of atoms.

Democritus
(*Bettmann Archive*)

Aristotle
(*Bettmann Archive*)

The Law of Conservation of Mass

About 200 years ago, the French scientist, Antoine Lavoisier (AN-twan La-VWA-see-ay), discovered that in a chemical change:

$$\text{mass of reactants} = \text{mass of products}$$

The Law of Definite Composition

In the late 1700's, Joseph Proust (PROWST), another French scientist found that:

1. The *elements* in a given compound are always the same.
2. The amounts of each element in a given mass of a compound are always the same.

Proust's law says that a compound always contains the same elements. It always contains the same proportion of elements by mass.

Hydrogen gas and oxygen gas unite to form water. If we were only to mix the gases, we could make a mixture of them in any proportion. But, each time the compound, water, is formed, the ratio of masses of hydrogen to oxygen must be 1 to 8. You can be sure that every sample of water has this ratio of hydrogen to oxygen.

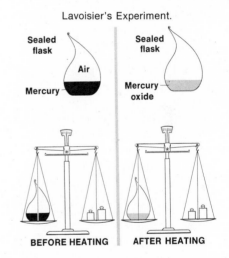

Lavoisier's Experiment.

BEFORE HEATING   AFTER HEATING

Proust's Experiment.

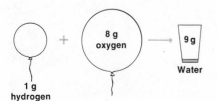

1 g hydrogen   8 g oxygen   9 g Water

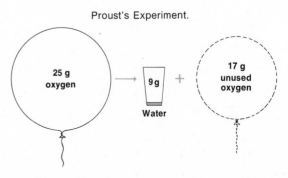

1 g hydrogen   25 g oxygen   9 g Water   17 g unused oxygen

Dalton's Atomic Theory

Observation + Imagination = New Theory

What must be the structure of matter if it behaves according to the laws Lavoisier and Proust discovered? In 1803, John Dalton, an English chemist, answered this question.

Dalton was familiar with the works of Lavoisier and Proust. He used their data and his own imagination to come up with the most revolutionary theory of modern times, the Atomic Theory. Without Dalton's Atomic Theory, our lives might be very different. The chemistry that gives us plastics, rubber, fertilizers, medicines, synthetic fibers, and atomic energy, might not have been discovered.

1. All matter is made up of basic particles called atoms. They cannot be divided nor can they be destroyed.
2. Atoms of the same element have the same average mass and the same chemical properties.
3. Atoms of different elements have different average masses and different chemical properties.
4. Atoms of different elements may combine in definite amounts to form compounds.

John Dalton (*Brown Brothers*)

Let's see how Dalton applied his theory to account for the Law of Conservation of Mass.

He reasoned:

Since atoms cannot be destroyed, then matter, made up of atoms, cannot be destroyed in a chemical change.

How did Dalton explain the Law of Definite Composition using his Atomic Theory?

When compounds are formed from atoms, they are always made of the same elements combined in the same way. The correct amounts (or mass) of each element is used.

The Law of Simple Multiple Proportions
Dalton Predicts a New Law

Dalton discovered that carbon can combine with oxygen to form carbon monoxide, (a poisonous, colorless gas.)

He also found that carbon combines with oxygen to form carbon dioxide, a non-poisonous, colorless gas given off by all animals and plants as a waste.

With a given mass of carbon it takes twice as much oxygen to form carbon dioxide (CO_2) as it does to form carbon monoxide.

Careful observation can lead to new discoveries. (*Fischer Scientific Co.*)

This relationship has been shown in other compounds. Another example is

Water   Hydrogen Peroxide (used for bleaching)

$$H_2O \text{ and } H_2O_2$$

With a given mass of hydrogen it takes twice as much oxygen to form hydrogen peroxide as it does to form water.

Notice that there is as much hydrogen in hydrogen peroxide as in water.

One of the important parts of a new theory is that it can predict a new situation. Dalton's Atomic Theory did predict new combinations of the same elements in part of his theory.

Our belief in atoms fits in with experimental facts. The work of scientists from many different countries supports the theory.

New discoveries help explain the unknown. (*Celanese Corp.*)

MODERN SYMBOLS

C—1 atom of carbon
O—1 atom of oxygen
O_2—2 atoms of oxygen

Carbon Monoxide
CO—1 atom of carbon and 1 atom of oxygen

Carbon Dioxide
CO_2—1 atom of carbon and 2 atoms of oxygen

Dalton's table of elements. (*Bettmann Archive*)

ELEMENTS

	w.t		w.t
Hydrogen	1	Strontian	46
Azote	5	Barytes	.68
Carbon	54	Iron	50
Oxygen	7	Zinc	56
Phosphorus	9	Copper	56
Sulphur	13	Lead	90
Magnesia	20	Silver	190
Lime	24	Gold	190
Soda	28	Platina	190
Potash	42	Mercury	167

Preview

Now we are about to pry open another mystery box. What's inside the atom? We also find that Democritus and Dalton did not imagine the atom to have parts.

But one scientist compared the atom to a "raisin pudding." The pudding consists of a volume of positive electricity in which enough raisins (negative electricity) were embedded to neutralize their charges. You study the nature of electricity and the electric charge in Demonstration: *Electric Forces.*

Of course, the "Raisin Pudding" theory of the atom is not really accurate. After you observe Demonstration: *Electric Forces,* read on. The pudding thickens!

ELECTRICAL FORCES—THE WORLD OF THE ATOM IS NEUTRAL

The most direct method of finding out what's inside a raisin pudding is simply to plunge a finger into it. In a way, this is what scientists did to find out what is inside the atom.

In Demonstration: *Electric Forces,* we learn that a positive charge has exactly the opposite effect of a negative charge. We designate this opposite effect by two symbols, + and −. Let's see how these opposite charges make the atom neutral.

The Heart of the Atom—You'll Get a Charge Out of the Nucleus

PROTONS

If you could put your finger on the center of the atom, you would find an *extremely tiny, dense center called a NUCLEUS that is electrically charged.* The charge is caused by the presence of positively charged particles called PROTONS (+).

Protons are tiny, but *heavy particles,* compared to the entire atom. PROTONS are *so small* that we must invent a new kind of unit to express their mass. We call this an *atomic mass unit* (1 amu). For every one proton found in the nucleus, the mass of the atom increases one amu. We will learn more about the mass of an atom in Chapter 11.

The number of protons in the nucleus of an atom is called ATOMIC NUMBER.

NEUTRONS

Neutrons are also found in the nucleus, but neutrons have no charge (0). A neutron has the same mass as a proton, 1 amu.

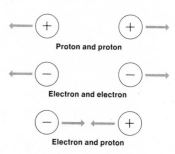

Proton and proton

Electron and electron

Electron and proton

QUESTIONS TO THINK ABOUT:

1. What indirect method would you use to detect the presence of sugar molecules in water?
2. If the necessary amount of hydrogen is chemically combined with the right amount of chlorine, forming hydrogen chloride with no elements left over, which law is illustrated?
3. Suppose you were to break up 10 g of water into the elements of hydrogen and oxygen. Would the combined mass of the hydrogen and oxygen equal 10 g? Why?
4. If another student told you, "I don't believe in atoms," how would you convince him that they do exist?

Hydrogen	Helium	Lithium	Beryllium
Atomic number = 1	Atomic number = 2	Atomic number = 3	Atomic number = 4

Ordinary hydrogen has no neutrons (○)

  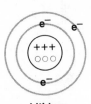 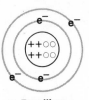

Hydrogen	Helium	Lithium	Beryllium
Number of electrons = 1	Number of electrons = 2	Number of electrons = 3	Number of electrons = 4

The Atmosphere about the Nucleus is Charged

ELECTRONS

For every proton in the nucleus of an atom, there is a *negatively charged electron* (e^-) *filling the space about the nucleus.* For every (+) charge of a proton in the nucleus, there is a (−) charge on an electron, which is busily filling the space around the dense center. The opposite charges cancel each other out to make every atom electrically neutral.

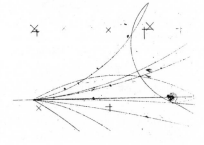

Nuclear particle tracks can be observed in a Bubble Chamber. (*National Accelerator Laboratory*)

Let's join forces to remain neutral!!

THE ATOM—SUMMARY

PARTICLE	SYMBOL	ELECTRICAL CHARGE	WHERE IT IS FOUND	amu MASS	SPECIAL PROPERTIES
electron	e^-	−1	filling the space about the nucleus	0	Light negative charge
proton	+	+1	in the nucleus	1.0	massive positive charge
neutron	0	0	in the nucleus	1.0	massive no charge

ELECTRON FLOW ON A WIRE

The circuit is open or broken, the electron flow is stopped.

The circuit is closed, the electrons flow to the proton source.

Behavior of Electrons

What is an electric current? On a wire, the electrons on the surface of the metal flow toward the strong positive charge. Opposite charges attract one another.

In a drycell, electrons from a metal flow through an external conductor toward the strong positive charge. This produces an electric current.

Electrons travel in straight lines.

Electrons can be bent away from a straight line with a magnet.

Electrons can bounce off metal plates.

The pictures on your TV screen are produced by electrons. The flow of electrons is controlled. The electron beam is scattered, producing dark and light spots on the screen

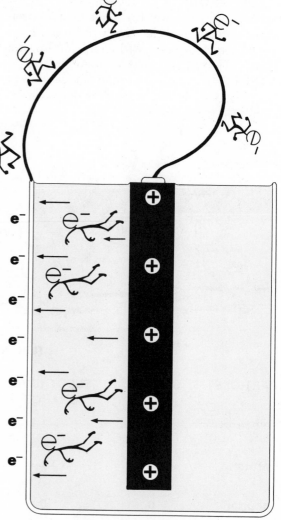

ELECTRON FLOW IN A DRY CELL

Answer to T-puzzle

What Makes One Element Different from Another?

Each element can be identified by the number of protons in its nucleus! Take the element hydrogen (atomic number 1), and sodium (atomic number 11). There are just 10 protons difference between them. But what a difference!

Hydrogen is a colorless, tasteless, odorless gas.

Sodium is a solid metal, soft and silvery white.

Hydrogen will burn, sometimes explosively. When it burns, hydrogen combines with oxygen in the air to form water droplets.

Sodium combines with oxygen in the air to form a gray, solid compound called sodium oxide. It looks like tarnished silver. Sodium will react violently with water, giving off tiny sparks. It will even react with water vapor in the air. For this reason, sodium is stored under kerosene to keep it dry.

What a difference a few protons make!

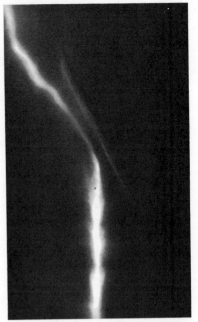

An electron beam can be deflected with a magnet. (*Physics International*)

Preview

ZEROING IN ON ORDER IN NATURE

You are about to arrange the elements in a way that makes good chemical sense. This will sharpen the picture of the atom. The number of protons in the nucleus will play a big part.

QUESTIONS TO THINK ABOUT

1. If there are 10 protons in the nucleus of an atom, what is its atomic number?
2. If there are 17 electrons in a neutral atom, how many protons would you expect to find in the nucleus?
3. Look up the difference between static and current electricity. Discuss them in class.

We must be able to take a closer view of the nature of matter, in order to understand its structure. (*American Optical Corp.*)

THE PERIODIC TABLE OF THE ELEMENTS

Most people like to arrange their belongings in an orderly way—pencils with their school supplies, and screwdrivers with their tools.

Dalton and other scientists had laid the groundwork for a systematic arrangement of the elements. Work was done on the "relative atomic masses" of atoms. From these masses some kind of order among the elements became apparent to some scientists. A Russian University professor, Dmitri Mendeleyev (Deh-ME-tri Men-deh-LAY-if), organized the elements into a table according to atomic masses. This table is called the Periodic Table of the Elements. You will learn more about atomic masses in Chapter 11.

What does the word periodic mean? You are familiar with the order in which night follows day, the way the seasons of the year occur, and the regular rhythms of the tides. These kinds of repeating, dependable events are called PERIODIC. They will occur over and over again in time.

Mendeleyev's Periodic Table showed that when the elements are arranged in order of increasing atomic mass, they form a pattern. Properties of the elements were found to be periodic. Elements with similar properties were placed in families. Families of elements are in vertical columns in the Periodic Table.

All the alkali metals discovered earlier by Humphry Davy began to line up in families on Mendeleyev's Table.

Nearly a third of the elements had not yet been discovered. Where there were holes in the orderly arrangement, Mendeleyev left blank spaces for the unknown elements. Fifteen years later, the metal germanium was discovered. It fit into the place predicted for it—just below silicon in the carbon family (column).

Mendeleyev's Periodic Table of the Elements was almost a masterpiece. But there were a few elements that were placed in the wrong families when arranged by increasing atomic mass.

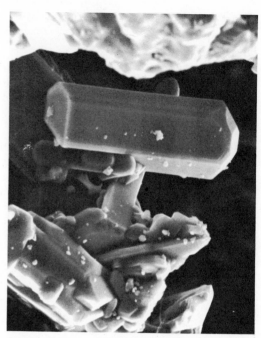

Apollo 14—Moon Rock Crystals. (*NASA*)

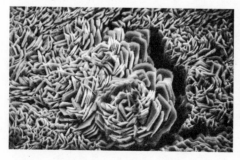

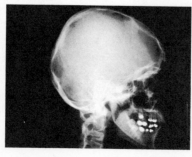

(Left) Electron photomicrograph of Zinc Crystals, (Middle) X-ray of a human skull, (Top) Electron photomicrograph of a crystal of MgF_2. (*Polaroid Corp.*)

X Rays Identify Some Misplaced Elements

n Brothers)

Henry Moseley, a brilliant, young English scientist, worked with x rays to determine the atomic numbers (number of protons in the nucleus of the atom).

Moseley placed a variety of metal elements as targets in the path of streaming electrons. Each element produced x rays with energies different from each other element.

He found that as the energy of the x ray of an element increases, the charge of the nucleus gets larger.

The elements were arranged in the correct order of their increasing atomic numbers.

This information placed argon (Ar) and potassium (K) in their proper families. The misplaced elements iodine (I) and tellurium (Te) of Mendeleyev's Table were placed in their proper column, or family, also.

X RAYS

X rays travel like waves in the ocean

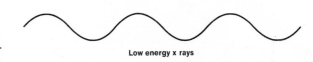

X rays have energy like light

Low energy x rays

High energy x rays

X rays are produced when high speed electrons strike a metal target

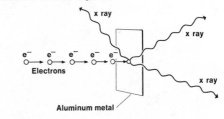

x ray
x ray
Electrons
x ray
Aluminum metal

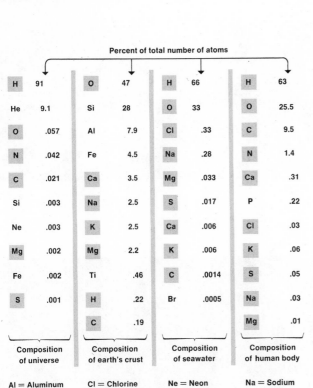

Percent of total number of atoms

Composition of universe		Composition of earth's crust		Composition of seawater		Composition of human body	
H	91	O	47	H	66	H	63
He	9.1	Si	28	O	33	O	25.5
O	.057	Al	7.9	Cl	.33	C	9.5
N	.042	Fe	4.5	Na	.28	N	1.4
C	.021	Ca	3.5	Mg	.033	Ca	.31
Si	.003	Na	2.5	S	.017	P	.22
Ne	.003	K	2.5	Ca	.006	Cl	.03
Mg	.002	Mg	2.2	K	.006	K	.06
Fe	.002	Ti	.46	C	.0014	S	.05
S	.001	H	.22	Br	.0005	Na	.03
		C	.19			Mg	.01

Al = Aluminum
B = Boron
Br = Bromine
Ca = Calcium
C = Carbon

Cl = Chlorine
He = Helium
H = Hydrogen
Fe = Iron
Mg = Magnesium

Ne = Neon
N = Nitrogen
O = Oxygen
K = Potassium
Si = Silicon

Na = Sodium
S = Sulfur
Ti = Titanium

To Sum Up

The Periodic Table of the Elements we use today is based on Moseley's findings. The elements are arranged in order of increasing atomic number (protons in the nucleus).

THE PERIODIC TABLE

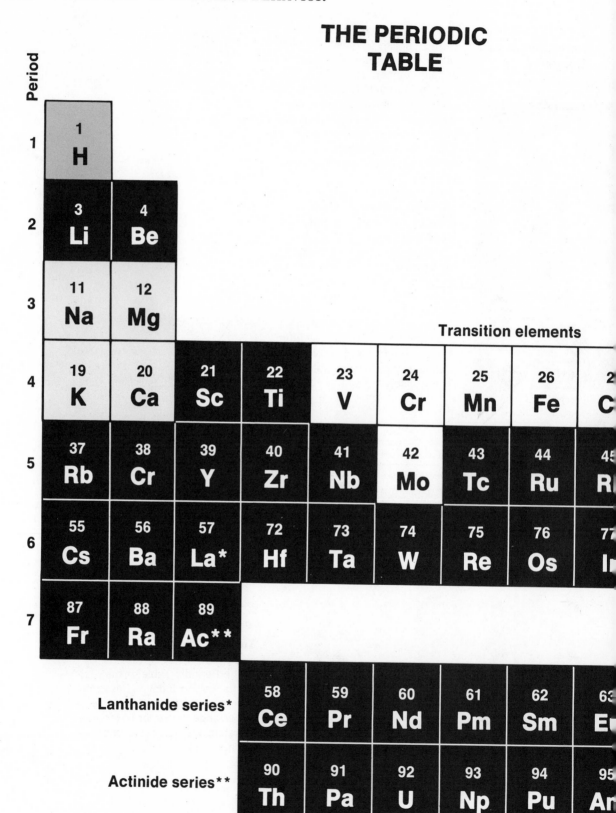

The four most abundant elements that are found in living organisms (hydrogen, oxygen, carbon and nitrogen) are indicated in the dark color. The seven next most common elements are shown in a lighter color. The 13 elements that are shown in the lightest color are needed only as tracer elements. (This table shows atomic numbers only. See inside back cover for complete table.)

						1 H	2 He
		5 B	6 C	7 N	8 O	9 F	10 Ne
		13 Al	14 Si	15 P	16 S	17 Cl	18 Ar
29 Cu	30 Zn	31 Ga	32 Ge	33 As	34 Se	35 Br	36 Kr
47 Ag	48 Cd	49 In	50 Sn	51 Sb	52 Te	53 I	54 Xe
79 Au	80 Hg	81 Tl	82 Pb	83 Bi	84 Po	85 At	86 Rn

65 Tb	66 Dy	67 Ho	68 Er	69 Tm	70 Yb	71 Lu
97 Bk	98 Cf	99 Es	100 Fm	101 Md	102 No	103 Lw

THE BOHR MODEL OF THE ATOM

In 1913 Niels Bohr, a young Danish physicist, presented a model of the atom. It is sometimes called the Solar System Model. It looks like our solar system on a small scale. If the nucleus represents the sun, then the electrons follow a pathway around the nucleus like the planets orbit the sun.

Energy Levels

Bohr proposed that the *electrons existed outside the nucleus only in definite pathways* called ENERGY LEVELS.

He believed that:
1. If the electrons stay in their electronic energy levels, they do not gain or lose energy.
2. Electrons closest to the nucleus are in low energy levels. Electrons further away from the nucleus are in higher energy levels.
3. The charge in the nucleus exactly balances the charge on the electrons surrounding it.

We may think of these definite energy levels as rungs on a ladder. It takes more energy to climb to a higher rung than to stay closer to the ground. *Electrons in their proper energy level are said to be in their "ground state."*

Bohr concluded that electrons can "jump" to higher energy levels if the atom absorbs energy. Atoms gain energy if they are heated.

When the electron drops back to lower energy levels, it gives off energy—often in the form of light.

But the electron can only "jump" from one rung of the energy level ladder to another—not in between rungs.

ELECTRONS IN MOTION

How a Scientist Builds a Model

When an inventor gets a new idea, for example, a new car or airplane, he builds a model to show others how it works. Dress designers show their fashions on models to let others imagine how the clothes might look on them. In a similar manner, scientists have tried to show what their ideas of the atom may be. *An idea of what the atom is like is called a MODEL.* We know that protons and neutrons are found in the dense center of the atom called the nucleus. The problem is to find how the electrons surround the nucleus, and to present a model of it.

The painter's "energy level" increases as he climbs each rung of the ladder. (*Zubli*)

ATOMIC FASHION

Niels Bohr won the Nobel Prize in 1922 for his brilliant explanation. Bohr's model could explain and even predict many experimental results that other models could not—especially J. J. Thompson's Raisin Pudding model of the atom.

The Bohr atom is not the last word in atomic fashion. It is not entirely correct. However, it is a good start toward understanding how electrons move about the nucleus.

Today scientists use the Schrödinger (SHRAY-din-jer) Wave Atom as the basis of modern concepts of the structure of the atom.

The basic differences between the models are: In Bohr's Solar System Atom, electrons never come closer to the nucleus than their allowed energy level. This model sets a boundary or "skin" on the size of the atom. The distances from protons in the nucleus to the electrons are constant.

In Schrödinger's Wave Atom, the electrons move about the nucleus in energy levels, but not in fixed pathways. There are no boundaries on the atom. In order for electrons to behave in this way, they must be part particle and part wave. This is a new way to think about matter. Laboratory observations lead scientists to the part particle, part wave theory.

The Electron: A Wave-Particle A New Way to Think

In order for an electron to behave as in Schrödinger's model, it must be imagined as being a tiny mass, or particle, and a wave, having energy, both at the same time. This is a new way to think about matter. Laboratory observations lead us to this conclusion.

What Are Waves Like?

Ocean waves, x rays, visible light and electrons are examples of waves.

Waves have Length—a wave length is measured from crest to crest.

Waves have Frequency—frequency is measured by the number of waves that pass an observer in a given time.

For the waves above: The waves with long wave lengths have a frequency of 2.

The next set of waves has a frequency of 3.

The short wave lengths have a frequency of 6.

Waves have Energy—High energy waves have a short wave length.

High energy waves have a high frequency.

Waves are Periodic—The wave repeats a pattern over and over.

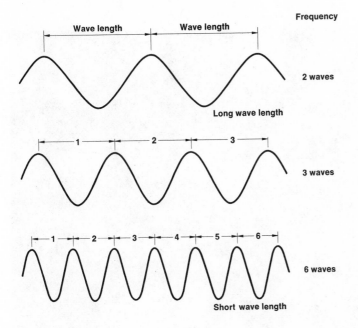

Wave length   Wave length   Frequency

2 waves

Long wave length

1   2   3

3 waves

1   2   3   4   5   6

6 waves

Short wave length

THE ATOM SHAPES UP

Arc Representations

We imagine the atom with a dense nucleus and electrons forming a sort of "charged cloud" around it. The chance of finding an electron closer to the nucleus is greater than finding it further away.

But, in order to represent the number of electrons allowed in any energy level, it is easier to use line pictures. We call these arcs.

The first energy level allows only 2 electrons.

Hydrogen   Helium

Arc Representation

The second energy level allows up to 8 electrons.

Lithium   Beryllium   Boron   Carbon   Nitrogen   Oxygen   Fluorine   Neon

The third energy level allows up to 8 electrons, also. You will represent these in the Exercise, Adding to the Periodic Table.

Metallic compounds give off different colors when energy in the form of light is released. (*Siegel, Photo Researchers*)

COLORED FLAMES

Electron "Energy Jumps"—Excited Electrons

What's the connection between the colors in a fireworks display on July 4 and the colored flames in Experiment 9.2? The colors are the result of electron "energy jumps" of metals.

The Bohr Solar System Atom and the Schrödinger Wave Atom models share the idea of electron "energy jumps." When energy is added to an atom, the electrons become "excited."

The electron wave gains more energy as it is heated. Higher energy of the wave means higher frequency of the wave.

But the jump to higher energy is only momentary. The added heat energy is not enough to keep the electrons at the higher frequency. They immediately lose energy and return to their normal wave length, or "ground state."

When an electron drops to a lower energy level, the frequency of the wave is lowered. The energy released is in the form of light waves. The colored flame you see is this light.

Sodium atom—electron excitation

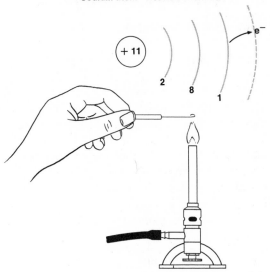

Energy in—electron energy "jump"

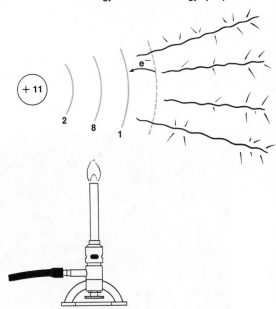

Energy release—Colored flame

The ball reaches its "ground state" when it hits the floor.

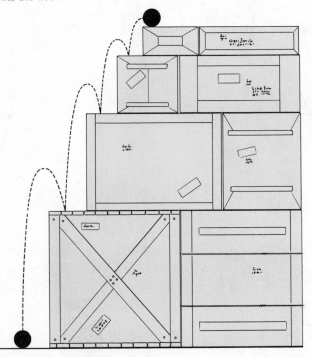

USING A SPECTROSCOPE

Fingerprints of Metals

The chemist uses a spectroscope to analyze unknown compounds when they are heated. Each metallic element leaves its "fingerprints" in the form of colored light, which can be photographed. The *bands of colored light* are called a *spectrum*. The line spectrum can be used to help the chemist identify "suspect" metals. By matching the spectrum of the unknown to a spectra for metals that are known, the chemist can decide which metals are present. You do this in Experiment 9.3, *Using A Spectroscope*.

We know the colors of some of the elements from the flame test:

Sodium—yellow-orange
Potassium—lavender
Strontium—red
Barium—yellow-green

Usually, more than one energy level is involved when electrons are "excited." Some electrons will have higher wave frequencies than others. Their energy levels are different. This accounts for the different bands of colored light seen through the spectroscope.

A laboratory spectroscope.

A continuous spectrum formed by white light passing through a prism. (*Eastman Kodak*)

FLAME TESTS FOR SOME METALS

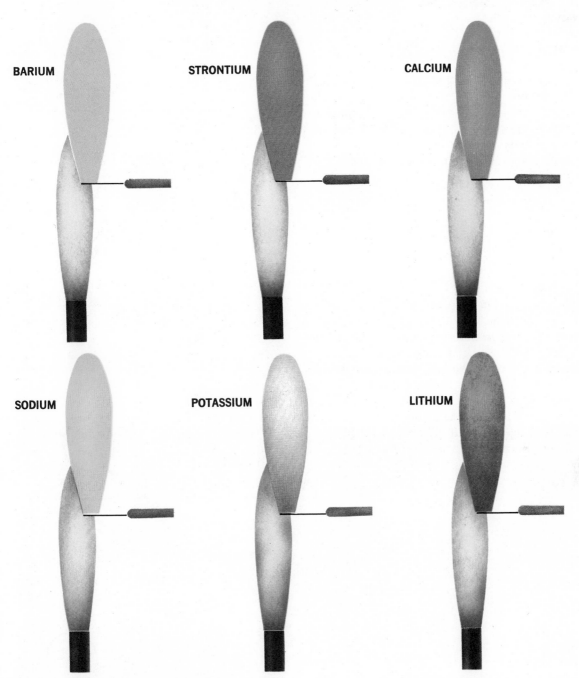

BARIUM

STRONTIUM

CALCIUM

SODIUM

POTASSIUM

LITHIUM

Masks of Many Different Colors

Sometimes one color covers another in a flame test.
Take lithium for example. Lithium gives a crimson-
colored flame. But crimson is made up of red, orange,
green, and blue. The spectroscope takes off the color
masks. It separates these colors into definite lines. Lithium's identity is known positively by these lines.

A TOOL FOR RESEARCH AND INDUSTRY

Infrared Spectroscopy

Infrared spectroscopy (spec-TRAHS-cup-e) is used when only small amounts of energy are needed to "excite" electrons. It is used to study the motion of molecules.

A molecule is the smallest portion of combined elements or compounds that can exist.

Molecules are able to move in several ways:

A molecule moves through space.
It may rotate round and round on its axis, like the earth.
A molecule may bend and stretch.

A Detective Story

A handkerchief has been left at the scene of the crime. The initials on it are I. A. G. It has small bits of matter on it. The material is scraped off and examined under the microscope. Some of it can be identified. Other samples are sent to the lab. A line spectrum is obtained. The metal found is lead. An infrared spectrum is made. The lead is found in a special paint used in building. The paint is traced to a construction company nearby that is using this paint. The handkerchief is found to belong to a worker whose initials are I. A. G. Spectroscopy helps put Mr. I. Am Guilty behind bars.

Moves through space . . .

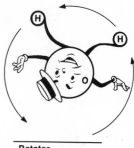

Rotates . . .

Bends . . .

Stretches

Chapter 9

ACTION POINTS:

An **ATOM** is the smallest particle of an element that can react with another substance.

The **LAW OF CONSERVATION OF MASS** states that in a chemical change, the mass of reactants = mass of products; that matter is not destroyed during a chemical change.

The **LAW OF DEFINITE COMPOSITION** states that a compound always contains the same kinds of elements in the same proportion by mass.

JOHN DALTON'S ATOMIC THEORY

1. All matter is made up of atoms. Atoms cannot be divided or destroyed.
2. Atoms of the same elements have the same mass and chemical properties.
3. Atoms of different elements may combine in definite amounts to form compounds.

The **LAW OF MULTIPLE PROPORTIONS** When two elements combine to form more than one compound, if the mass of one element remains constant, the ratio of masses of the second element is in small whole numbers in the series of compounds.

PROTONS are positively charged particles found in the nucleus of the atom.

NEUTRONS are uncharged particles, with approximately the same mass as the proton, found in the nucleus of the atom.

ELECTRONS are negatively charged particles surrounding the nucleus of the atom.

ATOMIC NUMBER is the number of protons in the nucleus of an atom of each element.

The **PERIODIC TABLE** is an orderly arrangement of the elements according to atomic number (number of protons in the nucleus.)

The **BOHR MODEL OF THE ATOM** pictures the electrons orbiting the nucleus in definite pathways called **ENERGY LEVELS.**

SCHRÖDINGER WAVE ATOM is a model of the atom based on modern findings. It pictures the electrons as moving about the nucleus in energy levels, but not in definite pathways.

The **WAVE PARTICLE** electron has the properties of solid particles and of waves.

The **GROUND-STATE** of an electron is the most probable distance from the nucleus that an electron is likely to be found.

EXCITED ELECTRONS are produced when energy is added to an element. This added energy causes the electron to "jump" to a higher energy level from its ground-state. The electron almost immediately returns to its ground-state giving off energy in the form of light.

A **SPECTRUM** is the band of colored light an element gives off after electron excitation.

A **SPECTROSCOPE** is an instrument used to examine the spectrum of each element.

Atom Hopping 10

GETTING IT ALL TOGETHER

Some people attract us. Our friends complete what we are. We see in them something we need. We, in turn, give of ourselves. Friendship is like that. Bonds are formed and it works both ways. There is magic in the chemistry of friendship.

The elements form a sort of chemical friendship. But it's not done by magic. There is giving, receiving, and sharing. The atoms share something from themselves to become complete. It isn't friendship, it's electrons. It's the only thing they have to give. That's what chemical bonding is all about.

It isn't ordinary electrons that get the elements together. They have to be "really way out in orbit."

Chemical bonds are formed between atoms using the highest energy level electrons. *The highest energy level is called the VALENCE ENERGY LEVEL. The electrons in the valence energy level are called VALENCE ELECTRONS.*

The chemical friendship of elements can be compared to human friendship. Elements are attracted more to some elements than to others. Atoms of some elements form very close relationships. These are elements that are not complete in themselves. There are, however, some elements that are complete in themselves. We need a closer look at these "chemical personalities."

THE COMPLETE CHARACTERS

Elements That Have It Made

Have you ever met a man who has everything? He'd almost have to be a king or at least a nobleman. You know the V.I.P.'s among the elements. You've met the Royal Family, the Noble Gases. They have everything. They've gone just about as far as they can go by completing the valence energy level.

The noble gases are complete in themselves. They hold the maximum number of electrons in their valence energy levels. There isn't room for any more.

All the other elements are trying to get there. By forming chemical bonds they are able to complete their valence energy levels. For an atom, that's everything.

Let's get the elements together.

Bonds of friendship. (*Gifford Wallace, Inc.*)

The Noble Gases

The noble gases are found in Group VIII (8) of the Periodic Table: helium, neon, argon, krypton, xenon, and radon. They all have complete valence energy levels. For this reason, they do not ordinarily form chemical bonds. However, some of these under very unusual conditions, have been found recently to form chemical bonds producing new compounds.

Xenon is the most reactive of the Noble Gases. It is a colorless, odorless gas. It forms chemical bonds with fluorine, which is also a gas. If the two gases are mixed in a nickel vessel, heated to 400°C and then cooled, colorless crystals are formed. The new compound is called xenon tetrafluoride, XeF_4. Tetra means "four." Four atoms of fluorine will chemically bond with one atom of xenon.

Xenon tetrafluoride and xenon oxide have been made at Argonne National Laboratory. Their formation stimulated great interest in the structure of these compounds and the theory of the chemical bond.

THE GROUP

Sharing is Pairing the Covalent Bond

Hydrogen is a "social" element. It likes company. It will share its one valence electron with another element. In return, its partner will share one of its own with hydrogen. This makes hydrogen complete. Its valence energy level is filled. Its partner also becomes more complete. They share a pair of electrons.

A *pair of shared electrons is called a* COVALENT BOND.

The compound water is formed by covalent bonds. How?

The hydrogen atom has one valence electron.

It needs one more electron to complete its valence energy level.

The oxygen atom has six valence electrons.

It needs two more electrons to complete its valence energy level.

Hydrogen and oxygen share a pair of electrons. A covalent bond is formed.

The valence energy level of oxygen is still incomplete. It needs one more electron to fill this level with eight electrons. Where will it get one to share? From another hydrogen atom.

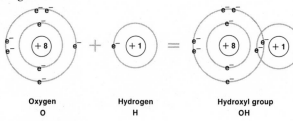

Oxygen   Hydrogen   Hydroxyl group
O   H   OH

Covalent bonding.

Balancing the Budget

The oxygen 2nd energy level is complete:
8 electrons: 6 of its own
             2 shared from 2 hydrogen atoms

Each hydrogen 1st energy level is complete:
2 electrons: 1 of its own
             1 shared from the oxygen atom

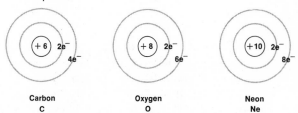

Structure of a water molecule.

Every proton has exactly one electron to balance the charge.

The new group formed is called a WATER MOLECULE.

A MOLECULE is the smallest part of an element or compound that has all the properties of the substance.

Short Review
Ideas We Need

1. In a neutral atom, the number of protons = number of electrons
2. The maximum number of valence electrons on the 1st energy level = 2
   The maximum number of valence electrons on the 2nd energy level = 8
   The maximum number of valence electrons on the 3rd energy level = 8
3. Arc representations of energy levels:

1st Energy Level Elements

Examples:

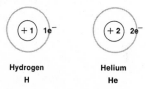

Hydrogen   Helium
H   He

2nd Energy Level Elements

Examples:

Carbon   Oxygen   Neon
C   O   Ne

QUICK QUESTIONS?

1. How many atoms of hydrogen are there in a water molecule?
2. How many atoms of oxygen are there in a water molecule?
3. What is the total number of atoms in H_2O?
4. How many covalent bonds are formed?

TWO IS COMPANY—
THREE'S A CROWD

Elements That Go Around in Two's—
the Diatomic Gases

Some elements are never found alone in nature. The need to fill the valence energy level is so great, that two atoms of the same element will team up together. A covalent bond is formed. They share a pair of electrons. They go around in two's.

All of the elements that exist in this way, two atoms in a molecule, have DIATOMIC MOLECULES.

The prefix "di" means "two."

Diatomic means "two atoms" in a molecule.

Five elements that are found in nature as diatomic molecules are gases. Hydrogen, oxygen and nitrogen are diatomic gases. The other diatomic molecules are found in Column VII (7) of the Periodic Table. The ones you will use frequently are: fluorine, chlorine, bromine, and iodine. Bromine is a liquid, iodine is a solid.

How does hydrogen form a diatomic molecule?

In the hydrogen molecule each hydrogen atom has the maximum number of electrons (2) on its valence energy level. They share a pair of electrons. A covalent bond is formed.

Look at page 36 at the Periodic Table. All the elements of Column VII (7) on the Periodic Table form diatomic molecules in the same way.

Each member of this family has seven valence electrons. Each needs one more electron to complete the valence energy level.

Formation of a diatomic molecule.

DIATOMIC MOLECULES

H_2 hydrogen molecule
N_2 nitrogen molecule
O_2 oxygen molecule
F_2 fluorine molecule
Cl_2 chlorine molecule
Br_2 bromine molecule
I_2 iodine molecule

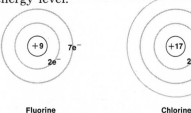

Fluorine
F

Chlorine
Cl

Here is how fluorine forms a diatomic molecule.

Now each fluorine atom has the maximum number of electrons (8) on its valence energy level. They share a pair of electrons. A covalent bond is formed.

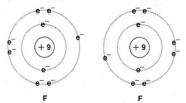

F

F

Two fluorine atoms before bonding

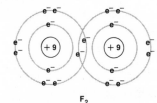

F_2

The fluorine molecule after bonding

SOMETHING FOR YOU TO DO

Draw the Bohr model of two chlorine atoms. Show the covalent bond to form a chlorine molecule, Cl_2.

The Double Covalent Bond

Oxygen is never found alone as a single atom in nature. Two atoms of oxygen form a diatomic molecule. Oxygen has six valence electrons. As you have seen, two electrons are needed to complete its valence energy level. When two oxygen atoms bond, *two* valence electrons from *each* atom are shared.

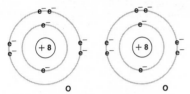

O   O

Two oxygen atoms before bonding

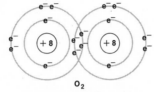

O_2

The oxygen molecule after bonding

Each oxygen atom has the maximum number of electrons (8) on its valence energy level, six of its own, two shared from the other oxygen atom. A DOUBLE COVALENT BOND is formed.

A DOUBLE COVALENT BOND *is formed when two pairs of electrons are shared between atoms.*

A covalent bond is very hard to break. A double covalent bond is even harder. It takes energy, usually heat. If we use a little "think" energy, we'll break this bond and form some others.

Carbon dioxide also has double covalent bonds. There is only one way an atom of carbon and two atoms of oxygen can get together to form carbon dioxide (CO_2). Watch this!

THE KEY QUESTIONS?

1. How many pairs of shared electrons are there in a double covalent bond?
2. How many double covalent bonds are found in CO_2?

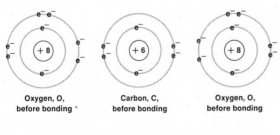

Oxygen, O,   Carbon, C,   Oxygen, O,
before bonding *   before bonding   before bonding

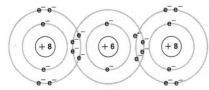

Carbon dioxide, CO_2,
after bonding

Add It Up

Each oxygen has 8 valence electrons—
    6 of its own
    2 shared from carbon
Carbon has 8 valence electrons—
    4 of its own
    2 shared from 1 oxygen atom
    2 shared from another oxygen atom

GUM DROPS AND TOOTH PICKS

Ball and Stick Models

There is an easy way to show models of the covalent bond. In Experiment 10.1 you use colored balls to represent atoms of different elements. Holes in the balls represent the number of electrons needed to complete the valence energy level. A stick connecting the holes represents an electron from each atom being shared to form the covalent bond.

Chemists use a shorthand to show this.

They write the symbol of the element (colored ball) and a dash to show the shared pair of electrons.

COVALENT MOLECULES

Ball and stick models	Structural formulas	Formulas
H H	H — H	H_2
F F	F — F	F_2
Cl Cl	Cl — Cl	Cl_2
O O	O = O	O_2
O C O	O = C = O	CO_2

MORE ABOUT THE COVALENT BOND

Nonpolar and Polar Molecules

Your nearest neighbor is more likely to share a laboratory burner in the lab with you than with someone across the room. It is not surprising then, that when chemical bonds are formed, electrons are shared by atoms with similar properties. These atoms are found close to each other on the Periodic Table. They are close neighbors on the far right of the table, the nonmetals.

Atoms of the same element, like the diatomic gases, form covalent bonds with each other. Hydrogen will also

Models of covalent molecules. (*Clara Aich and George Senty*)

Home Lab

Tinker toys make good ball and stick models. Different colored gumdrops with toothpicks will work just as well. Be sure to let only one color represent each element. To make the following models, you will have to know the number of valence electrons each element has.

1. Make arc representations for an atom of: (See 4/**18**)
   hydrogen
   carbon
   nitrogen
   oxygen
   sulfur
   chlorine
2. Decide whether single or double covalent bonds will be required to make the following molecules.
   HCl   hydrogen chloride
   NH_3 ammonia
   CO_2 carbon dioxide
   SO_2 sulfur dioxide
   CCl_4 carbon tetrachloride

team up to form covalent bonds with other elements. So will carbon. The question is: Will electrons in a covalent bond always be *equally* shared?

The structural formula for the water molecule is

When a mother makes up her baby's formula, she adds only certain quantities of each ingredient. A recipe used in cooking can also be called a formula. It tells you not only what goes into the dish, but also how much!

$$\overset{\text{O}}{\underset{\text{H}\qquad\text{H}}{\wedge}}$$

You know from H—O—H that there are one atom of oxygen and two atoms of hydrogen. But it tells you something more, how the atoms are arranged.

A building is often called a structure. If it is made of brick, you can see how the bricks are arranged to form a wall. Some structures are easy to break apart. Others have their building blocks so well placed that it takes heavy equipment to knock them down. The better the structure, the more energy it takes to tear it apart.

The hydrogen molecule is a very strong structure. It takes electric energy to break the covalent bonds.

A STRUCTURAL FORMULA shows:

1. The kinds of atoms in a molecule.
2. The number of each kind.
3. How the atoms are arranged.

Opposites Attract

We associate the word "polar" with bears that live at the North and South Poles. We call these regions "polar" because they are at opposite ends of the earth.

We use opposite poles in an electrical sense, too. Positive (+) and negative (−) electricity attract each other. They are opposite charges.

A region that is positively charged (+) is called a POSITIVE POLE

A region that is negatively charged (−) is called a NEGATIVE POLE

When the forces between both (+) and (−) charges balance each other equally, the region is called NONPOLAR.

A hydrogen molecule (H_2) is a nonpolar molecule. How do the forces of both (+) and (−) charges balance equally?

Hydrogen Table

a)

Each neutral atom of hydrogen has one proton and one electron.

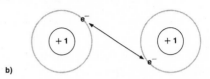
b)

The electrons from each atom repel.

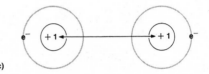
c)

The protons from each atom repel.

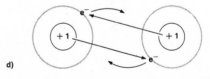
d)

But the proton of one atom attracts the electron of the second, and the proton of the second atom attracts the electron of the first.

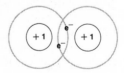
e)

Electrons forming the covalent bond are equally shared between the two hydrogen atoms.

More About Polar and Nonpolar Molecules

In a chemical bond, the electron-proton attraction helps complete the valence energy levels with the maximum number of electrons.

If the attraction is equal, a covalent bond is formed. The molecule is nonpolar.

CO_2, $O{=}C{=}O$ is another nonpolar molecule.

If the attraction is nearly equal, a covalent bond is formed, but, the molecule is polar like H_2O

$$O$$
$$H \qquad H$$

The forces between the same number of (+) and (−) charges are not quite equal.

In the diagram to the right the eight protons of the oxygen nucleus strongly attract the electron from each hydrogen atom.

This makes one end of the water molecule slightly negative (− −).

The opposite end is slightly positive (+ +). This is due to the protons of each hydrogen nucleus.

Eight protons in the oxygen nucleus have greater "pulling power" for electrons than one proton of each hydrogen nucleus.

In this tug-of-war, neither element actually wins. Covalent bonds hold, but it is not a case of "share-and-share-alike."

Water is a polar covalent molecule.

Carbon Likes Company—the Life of the Party

Carbon is an interesting element. The other elements find it attractive, too. It can form four covalent bonds. Hydrogen and oxygen are very important "social contacts" for carbon.

The carbon-hydrogen bond (C—H) is the starting point for all living matter, both plants and animals. Even the common cold virus can't get along without it.

Compounds containing only carbon and hydrogen are called HYDROCARBONS.

Here is how carbon forms four covalent bonds with four hydrogen atoms. The compound formed is called METHANE, CH_4.

Carbon Chains

Carbon can form single covalent bonds with other carbon atoms. Many carbon "chains" are possible. The members of these carbon chains are called the ALKANE SERIES.

Methane is the first member of this series. It contains one carbon atom.

The second member is ethane, also a colorless gas. Ethane contains two carbon atoms. They share a pair of electrons between them.

Each hydrogen shares a pair of electrons with carbon

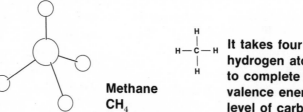

Methane CH_4

It takes four hydrogen atoms to complete the valence energy level of carbon.

TIME OUT

A Substitution

This is your big chance. The coach blows the whistle. Time is called. You go in the game for another player. Conditions are right. You can do the job. The coach's substitution was a good choice.

The chemist blows the whistle on the ethane molecule, C_2H_6. When conditions are right (in the reaction, the hydroxyl group (OH) is substituted for a hydrogen atom. The alcohol ethanol is formed, C_2H_5OH.

Making a substitution will produce a new product. (*Magnum Photos Inc.*)

Ethane

```
    H   H
    |   |
H —C — C —H
    |   |
    H   H
```

Hydroxyl group
```
—O —H
```

Ethanol
(ethyl alcohol)
```
    H   H
    |   |
H —C — C —H
    |   |
    H   O —H
```

Perfume, cologne, and after-shave lotion all contain ethanol because it makes a good solvent and it is VOLATILE (evaporates easily). Alcohol molecules carry the fragrance into the air to produce the pleasant scent.

This new compound can do the job.

Substitutions, replacing hydrogen atoms for the hydroxyl group, can be made on all the members of the alkane series. Alcohols are formed and they are all different. Most are poisons. All alcohols found in the lab are naturally poisonous. Some have been denatured (small amounts of poisonous material are added.)

Alcohols are denatured because alcoholic beverages are taxed, and that makes them expensive. Ethanol is denatured so it is not subject to this tax. Otherwise, it would be too expensive to buy for experimental work.

Chlorine can be a good substitute for hydrogen in the methane molecule. If 4 chlorine atoms replace the 4 hydrogen atoms, carbon tetrachloride is obtained. The Greek prefix "tetra" means four. Carbon tetrachloride is found in some dry cleaning solvents because it cuts grease and is volatile. It is a dangerous solvent to use, however, because the volatile vapors may injure the eyes, lungs, and liver.

The chemist has to know what he's doing when he makes substitution compounds, and he has to know how to handle them once they are formed.

```
    H
    |
H —C —H
    |
    H
```
Methane

```
    Cl
    |
Cl —C —Cl
    |
    Cl
```
Carbon Tetrachloride

A QUICK CHECK-UP

1. How many atoms are there in the ethane molecule?
2. How many carbon atoms?
3. How many hydrogen atoms?
4. Count the number of covalent bonds formed.

ATOM HOPPING

The Ionic Bond

You've heard the saying, "It's better to give than to receive."

Suppose a stranger asks to borrow a dime to make a phone call. She's from out of town and lives miles away. The dime helps her complete her travel plans and you're happy to do her a favor. You wouldn't expect to see the dime again. It could be repaid. But, it would take a little energy for both of you to arrange it.

Compare valence electrons to the dime. Giving and receiving valence electrons is another way to form chemical bonds. Giving electrons is just as good as receiving them. Each atom attains a completed valence energy level like the Noble Gas nearest it on the Periodic Table.

When one or more valence electrons are transferred from one atom to another, an IONIC BOND *is formed.*

On the Periodic Table, elements that are farthest apart "lend" or transfer valence electrons to form the ionic bond.

Metals are electron "givers." Nonmetals are electron "receivers."

In Experiment 10.2, you see how electrons "atom hop" to form ionic bonds.

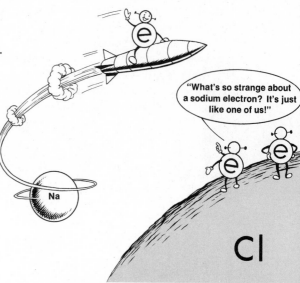

"What's so strange about a sodium electron? It's just like one of us!"

Sodium (Na) transfers its valence electron to chlorine (Cl) to form an ionic bond.

Visitors from Outer Space—Atoms to Ions

All electrons are alike. So, a visitor electron from the "outer space" of the valence energy level of a metal to a nonmetal would fit in.

Sodium is a soft, silvery poisonous metal.
A neutral atom has 11 protons and 11 electrons.
It is written Na^0 to show there is a balanced
  electric charge.

$$+11$$
$$-11$$
$$\overline{0}$$

Chlorine is a yellow-green, poisonous gas.
It is a nonmetal.
A neutral atom has 17 protons and 17 electrons.
It is written Cl^0 to show there is a balanced
  electric charge.

$$+17$$
$$-17$$
$$\overline{0}$$

The protons in the nucleus of Na^0 have a strong attraction for its valence electron.
The protons of Cl^0 *strongly* attract the valence electron of Na^0, too.
In this tug-of-war for electrons, chlorine wins.
The electron is transferred and an ionic bond is formed.
A metal and its valence electron are soon parted!

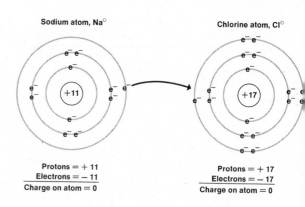

Sodium atom, Na^0

Protons = + 11
Electrons = − 11
Charge on atom = 0

Chlorine atom, Cl^0

Protons = + 17
Electrons = − 17
Charge on atom = 0

COUNT DOWN

Sodium has one *fewer* electron than the number
  of protons in the nucleus. $+11$
The sodium core is positively charged $(+1)$ -10
It is called a SODIUM ION, Na+ $\overline{+\ 1}$

Chlorine has one *more* electron than the number
  of protons in its nucleus. $+17$
Chlorine is negatively charged (-1) -18
It is called a chloride ion, Cl^- $\overline{-\ 1}$

An ION *is an atom or group of atoms that has lost or
gained valence electrons.*

The result of this ionic bond is the compound, sodium
chloride, table salt. These small, white crystals give food
a better flavor. They are easily dissolved in water. Sodium chloride is very different from the elements sodium
and chlorine. The ionic bond makes the difference.

Compounds made by ionic bonding form crystals, not
simple molecules. There are no molecules of sodium
chloride. The ionic bond is between Na+ and Cl⁻ ions
which attract each other. This attraction produces a
regular arrangement called a CRYSTAL LATTICE
made up of hundreds of these ions. The crystal structure is held together by the attraction between the +
and − charges.

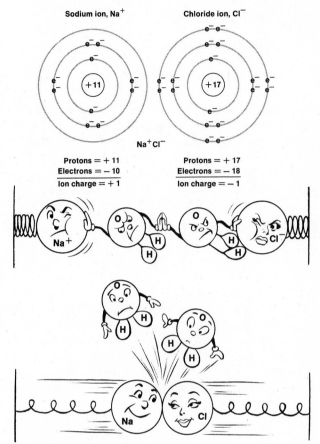

Sodium ion, Na⁺   Chloride ion, Cl⁻

Na⁺Cl⁻

Protons = + 11	Protons = + 17
Electrons = − 10	Electrons = − 18
Ion charge = + 1	Ion charge = − 1

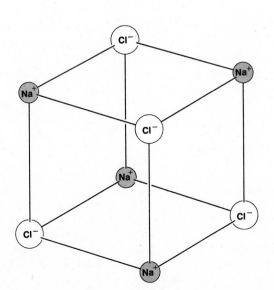

Home Lab

An Ion for an Ion Dissociation

Drop a few salt crystals into a Pyrex
dish or small pan of water. What happens? The salt dissolves. Water molecules "step in" to break up the crystal
lattice.

Recall that water is a polar molecule.
The oxygen end is slightly negatively
charged and the hydrogen end is positively charged.

Sodium and chloride ions Na⁺ and Cl⁻
are attracted to the opposite poles of the
water molecules and become separated.
The ions DISSOCIATE.

DISSOCIATION is *the separation of
ions in solution.*

There isn't much chance of the ions
getting together again unless the water is
evaporated. Heat the salt water solution
until it is nearly dry. White Na⁺Cl⁻ crystals reappear and the lattice structure is
restored.

THE PAY OFF

Ions to Atoms

Remember that dime you lent the stranger? It took quite a bit of energy to get it back to you. Here it is and thanks.

A large amount of energy also would have to be used to repay Na^+ its valence electron. Electric energy is used. The extra electron on the chloride ion, Cl^-, is returned to the sodium ion, Na^+. Both become neutral atoms again.

Electron Dot Formulas

In Experiment 10.2, Atom Hopping, you learn how to show the number of valence electrons an atom has on its highest energy level.

Write the symbol of the element. Place dots corresponding to the number of valence electrons around the symbol, one-by-one going from right to left (counter clockwise.) When there are more than four valence electrons, pair them in the same way.

Here are some examples of electron dot formulas showing the ionic bond.

The Core

Think of the atom like an apple. Cut off the outside and only the core is left.

Only valence electrons (the outer part of the apple) form ionic bonds.

The other electrons in the atom, together with the nucleus, are called the CORE.

Before Bonding

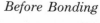

Na ⟶ Cl:

Sodium Atom   Chloride Atom
Na^0 Cl^0

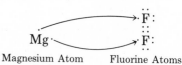

Mg· ⟶ :F:
          ⟶ :F:

Magnesium Atom   Fluorine Atoms
Mg^0 2 F^0

After Bonding

Na^+ :Cl:$^-$

Sodium ion   Chloride ion

Sodium chloride
Na^+Cl^-

:F:$^-$

Mg^{++} :F:$^-$

Magnesium Fluoride
$Mg^{++}F_2^=$

Ions Are Important to You

Your body depends on the presence of metal and nonmetal ions for good health. About $\frac{2}{3}$'s of the human body is water. Compounds with ionic bonds dissociate in water. The fluid of the bloodstream, called plasma, carries these ions to cells and where they are used. Every cell of the body is bathed in this fluid so ions can do their work for you.

Calcium ions, Ca^{++}, are present in these fluids in larger amounts than any other metal.

They form bones and teeth and are important for heart, muscle and nerve formation. Ca^{++} helps in blood clotting (coagulation) so that wounds heal.

Sodium ions, Na^+, are largely found in the fluids surrounding the cells. With chloride ions, Cl^-, they regulate the acid-base balance of the system. Too much or too little of either acid or base disturbs the pH at which the body functions best.

Potassium ions, K^+, are found principally in the fluids within the cells. There, they function very much like Na^+, to regulate the pH. Both Na^+ and K^+ are important for good muscle activity.

The role of the iron ion, Fe^{++}, is very important in the process of respiration. In respiration, oxygen is transported to all parts of the body. Without oxygen, the cells could not live. Fe^{++} is found in hemoglobin (heme-o-globe-in), a protein which gives red blood cells their color. Iron deficiency results in anemia and may cause intestinal diseases.

NUMBER PLEASE?

The Straight.and Narrow

Everyone at some time or other reads a road map or follows traffic signals. The road map in chemistry is the Periodic Table. The way to the "land of Compounds" is clearly marked. If we learn how to read the map we'll have no trouble in reaching our goal—formula writing.

There are four things we need to know:

1. The kinds of atoms that combine to form compounds.
2. The amount of each kind of atom in the compounds.
3. Metals form mostly ionic bonds with nonmetals.
4. Elements that are near each other on the right of the table form covalent bonds.

Now let's look for a few road signs to guide us. Look at the Roman Numeral over each family (column) of the Periodic Table.

The Straight and Narrow

Look at the Roman Numeral over each family (column) of the Periodic Table. This numeral tells us the number of valence electrons each member of the family has. For metals, this number is called the COMBINING NUMBER.

A Project

Certain foods contain the ions essential for good health.

1. Find out about the foods that are rich in Ca^{++}, Na^+, K^+, and Fe^{++}.
2. Ions of other elements are necessary for healthy human life. Try to find what these elements are and how they help the body.

Discuss what you find with your class.

Some foods are rich in ions. (*Courtesy of General Foods Corp.*)

THE PERIODIC TABLE

I																	Noble gases VIII
1 H	II	METALS										NON-METALS					2 He
											III	IV	V	VI	VII		
3 Li	4 Be											5 B	6 C	7 N	8 O	9 F	10 Ne
11 Na	12 Mg			Transition elements								13 Al	14 Si	15 P	16 S	17 Cl	18 Ar
19 K	20 Ca	21 Sc	22 Ti	23 V	24 Cr	25 Mn	26 Fe	27 Co	28 Ni	29 Cu	30 Zn	31 Ga	32 Ge	33 As	34 Se	35 Br	36 Kr
37 Rb	38 Cr	39 Y	40 Zr	41 Nb	42 Mo	43 Tc	44 Ru	45 Rh	46 Pd	47 Ag	48 Cd	49 In	50 Sn	51 Sb	52 Te	53 I	54 Xe
55 Cs	56 Ba	57 La	72 Hf	73 Ta	74 W	75 Re	76 Os	77 Ir	78 Pt	79 Au	80 Hg	81 Tl	82 Pb	83 Bi	84 Po	85 At	86 Rn
87 Fr	88 Ra	89 Ac															

Rare earth elements

58 Ce	59 Pr	60 Nd	61 Pm	62 Sm	63 Eu	64 Gd	65 Tb	66 Dy	67 Ho	68 Er	69 Tm	70 Yb	71 Lu
90 Th	91 Pa	92 U	93 Np	94 Pu	95 Am	96 Cm	97 Bk	98 Cf	99 Es	100 Fm	101 Md	102 No	103 Lw

For nonmetals, the combining number is obtained by subtracting the value of the Roman Numeral from 8 (number of electrons to complete the valence energy level.)

Example using column VII

$$VII = 7$$
$$8 - 7 = 1$$

Elements in column VII must gain 1 electron to become complete. If this is done, the atom would have a charge of -1. The combining number of elements in column VII is 1.

All the elements in Column I *lose* 1 valence electron to
  be complete.

The result is a charge of $+1$.

All the elements in Column VII must *gain* 1 valence
  electron to be complete.

The result is a charge of -1.

Column I metals have a combining number of 1.

Column VII nonmetals have a combining number of 1.

The elements of these two columns will form
  compounds using 1 atom of each kind. The
  compound has a balanced charge.

$$\begin{array}{r} +1 \\ -1 \\ \hline 0 \end{array}$$

IONS

I	VII
H^{+1}	F^{-1}
Li^{+1}	Cl^{-1}
Na^{+1}	Br^{-1}
K^{+1}	I^{-1}

Examples: H^+F^- Na^+Br^- H^+Cl^- Na^+Cl^-
Li^+Cl^- K^+I^- Li^+Br^- K^+Cl^-

CAUTION!

Write the symbol of the metal first.
Write the symbol of the nonmetal next.

The members of the family of elements in Column VII are called HALOGENS. Halogen comes from the Latin word meaning "salt former." All the compounds in the examples are salts. They are formed using a halogen.

All the elements in Column II must *lose* 2 valence electrons to be complete.
The result is a charge of +2.
All the elements in Column VI must *gain* 2 valence electrons to be complete.
The result is a charge of −2.

IONS

II	VI
Be^{+2}	O^{-2}
Mg^{+2}	S^{-2}
Ca^{+2}	Se^{-2}
Sr^{+2}	

1. What is the combining number of the elements in Column II?
2. What is the combining number of the elements in Column VI?

The elements of these two columns will form compounds using one atom of each kind.

Examples: BeO
MgO MgS
CaO CaS

We've come to an intersection in the road. We need to cross columns here before going on.
The combining number of metals in Column I is 1.
The combining number of nonmetals in Column VI is 2.
It takes two atoms of each metal to combine with one atom of each nonmetal to form a compound with balanced charge.

Examples: Na_2O
Li_2S
K_2O

	Combining Number		Number of Atoms	
Column I	+1	×	2	= +2
Column II	−2	×	1	= −2
				0 balanced charge

Now combine the metals of Column II (combining number 2)
with nonmetals of Column VII (combining number 1)
Column II $+2 \times 1 = +2$
Column VII $-1 \times 2 = -2$
0 balanced charge

Examples: BeF_2 $MgCl_2$ $CaCl_2$ $SrBr_2$

All the elements in Column III have a combining number of 3. Boron and aluminum are the most commonly used.

It takes 3 atoms of the elements in Column VII to form compounds with this group.

Examples: $AlCl_3$
BF_3

All the elements in Column IV have a combination number of 4.

It takes 4 atoms of the elements in Column VII (combining number 1) to form compounds with carbon.

In these compounds, the symbol for carbon is written first.

Examples: CF_4
CCl_4
CBr_4

How many atoms of hydrogen form covalent bonds with 1 carbon atom?

Remember, if carbon forms double covalent bonds with oxygen, carbon dioxide (CO_2) is made.

$:C:$ $\quad$ $\cdot\ddot{O}\cdot$ $\quad$ $:\ddot{O}::C::\ddot{O}:$

$O=C=O$ $\quad$ $\underset{|}{\overset{\cdot\cdot}{O}}-$ $\quad$ $O=C=O$

A Side Trip

In Column V, nitrogen and phosphorous interest us the most. Many different compounds are made with these elements.

They have two important combining numbers, 3 and 5. This is an exception to the rule.

Here is how nitrogen can have the combining number of +3 using electron dot formulas.

All the electrons are paired—3 covalent bonds

The nitrogen atom has a complete valence energy level—8 electrons

Each hydrogen atom has a complete valence energy level—2 electrons

$\cdot\ddot{N}\cdot$ $\qquad$ H
Nitrogen $\qquad$ Hydrogen

H
$H:\ddot{N}:H$ $\qquad$ NH_3
Ammonia

Transition Elements—Heavy Metals

Look at the Periodic Table. The TRANSITION ELEMENTS, that are also called "heavy" metals, are in the middle of the table.

The word "transition" comes from the Latin word *trans,* meaning *across.* These elements go across the Periodic Table but some of them are also able to change their combining number, the number of electrons given to a nonmetal.

These are the important elements to remember:

Iron(II) Fe^{+2}
Iron(III) Fe^{+3}

Examples: FeCl$_2$ Fe$_2$O$_3$
              Iron(II)Chloride   Iron(III)oxide
              Combining Number   Number of Atoms

	Combining Number		Number of Atoms		
Fe(II)	+2	×	1	=	+2
Cl	−1	×	2	=	−2
					0 balanced charge
Fe(III)	+3	×	2	=	+6
O	−2	×	3	=	−6
					0 balanced charge

Examples: CuCl   CuCl$_2$
              Copper(I)Chloride   Copper(II)Chloride   Copper   Cu^{+1} (Copper I)
                                                                Cu^{+2} (Copper II)

              Hg$_2$O   HgO
              Mercury(I)oxide   Mercury(II)oxide   Mercury Hg$_2^{+2}$ (Mercury I)
                                                                Hg^{+2} (Mercury II)

A PUZZLE

Just for fun, see how many formulas you can write using the chart below. Write the symbol of the metal first in each formula. Show the number of atoms needed by using small numbers just below the symbol.

We haven't mentioned Column VIII of the Periodic Table, the Noble Gases. Why *wouldn't* this make a good pathway to follow in forming chemical bonds?

COMBINING NUMBERS OF TRANSITION ELEMENTS

Chromium	Cr	+2, +3
Iron	Fe	+2, +3
Zinc	Zn	+2
Silver	Ag	+1
Copper	Cu	+1, +2
Mercury	Hg	+1, +2

	Cl	Br	F	O	S
K		KBr			K$_2$S
Na			NaF		
Ca		CaBr$_2$			
Mg				MgO	
Zn	ZnCl$_2$				
Iron(II)					FeS
Iron(III)				Fe$_2$O$_3$	
H			HF		
Ag		AgBr			
Hg(I)					Hg$_2$S
Hg(II)	HgCl$_2$				HgS

Now you are ready for Experiment 10.3, Number Please. Don't forget your map. Here is a sign for you while doing Exercises 10-1, Writing Dot Formulas, and 10-2, Writing Formulas.

WHAT'S ITS NATURE

Strength of Chemical Bonds

In Experiment 10.4, you are given a puzzle to solve. You are asked to sort out ionic compounds from covalent compounds after you perform a few simple tests.

Here are some pieces to the puzzle that will make everything fit into place. All the clues are here for you to get the whole picture.

First, we need to remember that:

1. All compounds are electrically neutral.
   The number of protons = number of electrons in a compound.
2. Covalent bonds = sharing a pair or pairs of electrons.
   Elements near each other on the Periodic Table form covalent bonds.
   Carbon and hydrogen always form covalent bonds.
3. The formula for a covalent compound represents a molecule.
4. Ionic bonds could be the result of electron transfer.
   Elements farthest away from each other on the Periodic Table form ionic bonds.
   Metals transfer electrons to nonmetals.
5. Ionic compounds form a crystal lattice structure of many groups represented by the formula and are not called molecules.
6. Ions become free of the crystal lattice when ionic compounds dissolve in water.

MELTING POINT

The Heat's On

Set an ice cube in the sun and watch it melt. The rigid, solid structure begins to spread out. The ice water molecules begin to flow as they melt.

With just a little heat energy from the sun, the molecules are forced apart. They are held less tightly together and separate to form a puddle of water.

Sometimes it takes more energy than the heat from the sun to force molecules apart as they melt. The temperature at which a compound changes from the solid to the liquid phase is called its melting point.

The melting point of a substance tells us a great deal about the kind of bonding within it. This is another example of the indirect method of forming valid conclusions about atoms we cannot see.

Get the picture? (Clara Aich and George Senty)

MELTING POINTS OF MOLECULAR SOLIDS

H_2	$-259°C$
Cl_2	$-103°C$
CO_2	$-56.6°C$
H_2O (ice)	$0°C$

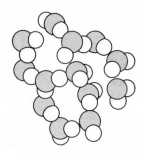

This piece of ice ....

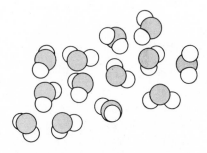

.... has melted to form a fluid

Ionic solids have very high melting points. It takes a higher temperature (over 100°C) than that needed to boil water to break up the strong electric attractions that hold the crystal lattice structure together. The stronger the attraction, the more energy it takes to melt a solid with ionic bonds.

When we succeed in melting an ionic solid, the melt remains electrically neutral. The melt can be compared to a rigid, orderly arrangement of a pile of rocks. It takes a lot of energy to move them. But once the landslide has been started, they all move along together.

Ionic solids have higher melting points than covalent solids.

Molecular solids, made by covalent bonds, have low melting points. It does not take much heat energy to disturb the molecules so that they "flow."

There are variations in the range of melting points for covalent compounds. Some covalent compounds are nonpolar, others are polar.

Nonpolar covalent compounds have extremely low melting points. Electrons forming the covalent bond are equally shared. The molecule has no polar ends because there are no electron tug-of-wars between elements. There are very small electric attractions to hold the molecule together. A little heat energy, even less than it takes to melt ice, is sufficient to separate a group of these molecules from each other.

Polar covalent molecules attract each other but very weakly. One end of the polar molecule is only partially charged +. The other end is partially charged −. These weak electric attractions between molecules can easily be broken up by a little heat energy.

Many covalent compounds are already in the liquid phase at room temperature (20°C). Some melting points are so low that the molecules remain as a fluid even in the freezer section of the refrigerator.

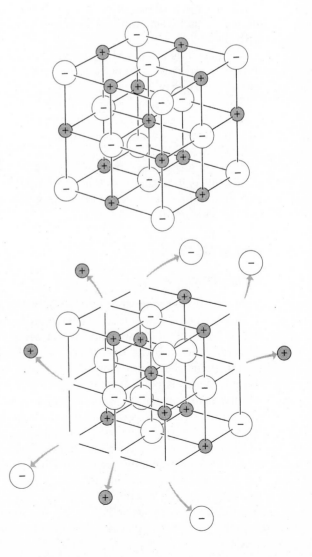

MELTING POINTS OF IONIC SOLIDS

CaF_2	1360°C
$BaCl_2$	962°C
$CaCl_2$	772°C
KBr	730°C
LiCl	613°C
LiI	446°C

ELECTRIC CONDUCTIVITY

Lights—Camera—Action

Ionic solids melt at very high temperatures. How do we know there are ionic bonds present? A very simple test will demonstrate the flow of electric charges. An apparatus like the one pictured has two metal conductors of electrical charges. They are attached to the light bulb with copper wires. The wires lead into a cord that can be plugged into a wall socket, a source of electric current. But the bulb will not light. The circuit is not complete.

If the conductors are dipped into a fluid that has + and − charges, electrons (the − charges) will flow through one conductor through the wires to complete the circuit. In the completed electric circuit the bulb lights.

When we dip these conductors into fluid ionic solids, melted at high temperature, the circuit is complete. The bulb lights.

If ionic solids are dissolved in water, this test will show the presence of ions by dissociation. The light bulb will glow brightly.

Nonpolar covalent compounds, solid or liquid, do not conduct this electric charge. The compound breaks up into molecules, not ions. There are no + and − charges on the molecules.

Polar covalent compounds will conduct the current only weakly. The slight + and − charge on the molecule due to unequal electron sharing will cause the light bulb to glow dimly.

SOLUBILITY

Gang—Busters

Have you ever wondered why some paint brushes are cleaned in paint thinner and others can be washed with water? Both paint thinner and water are good solvents. Both move in to break up "gangs" of molecules by dissolving them. But paint thinner is a nonpolar covalent solvent. Water is polar.

Some paints are made with oil, called an oil base. Oil is a nonpolar, covalent compound. Oil base paints can be cleaned from brushes with nonpolar paint thinner.

Other paints are made with a water base. Brushes used on water base paint can be washed in water. Both are polar covalent compounds.

Grease spots on clothing are cleaned with nonpolar solvents like Energene or K2-R. These solvents contain nonpolar carbon compounds that dissolve nonpolar grease.

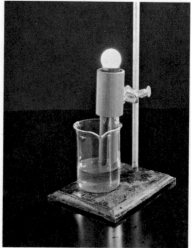

Ionic solutions conduct an electric charge.

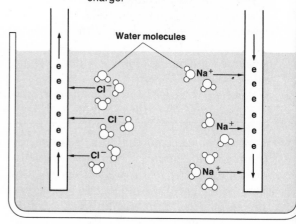

Water-base paints (polar compound) dissolve in water (polar solvent).

Water is a good cleaning agent for polar substances that readily dissolve in it.

It can therefore be said that "like dissolves like."

Nonpolar compounds dissolve in nonpolar solvents (like turpentine, carbon tetrachloride and benzene).

Polar compounds dissolve in polar solvents—like water and alcohol.

The solvent you use in Experiment 10.4, *What's Its Nature,* is water. Many ionic compounds dissolve readily in water. You have seen how polar water molecules surround the + and − ions. The + ions are attracted to the negative end of the water molecule. The − ions are attracted to the positive end.

Polar covalent molecules are attracted to the polar ends of water. Therefore, they are soluble.

Nonpolar covalent molecules do not dissolve in water at all. There is no electric charge on a nonpolar molecule, so the polar water can not break up these "gangs."

Chapter 10
ACTION POINTS

A **CHEMICAL BOND** is formed between atoms by an exchange of highest energy level electrons.

The highest energy level of an atom is called the **VALENCE ENERGY LEVEL.** The valence energy level electrons are called **VALENCE ELECTRONS.**

The **NOBLE GASES** are elements with a complete energy level of eight electrons.

A **COVALENT BOND** is formed by the sharing of a valence electron from each of two atoms.

DIATOMIC GASES are gaseous elements that are found as two atoms per molecule in nature.

A **DOUBLE COVALENT BOND** is formed when two pairs of electrons are shared between atoms.

A **STRUCTURAL FORMULA** shows not only the number and kinds of elements bonded together, but also how the atoms are arranged.

A **NONPOLAR MOLECULE** is one in which there is a nonpolar bond, or, if there is a polar bond the charges are balanced so that there is no polar region within the molecule.

A **POLAR MOLECULE** is one which has a polar bond. There are ends of the molecule which are more polar (more positive or more negative) than others.

HYDROCARBONS are compounds which contain the elements carbon and hydrogen.

A **SUBSTITUTION** results when an atom or atoms of one element are exchanged for another atom or group of atoms.

An **IONIC BOND** is formed when one or more valence electrons are transferred from one atom to another.

The **CORE** of the atom is the nucleus and all electrons except the valence (outer energy level) electrons.

An **ION** is an atom or group of atoms that has lost or gained one or more valence electrons.

DISSOCIATION is the separation of ions in solution.

ELECTRON DOT FORMULAS show the valence electrons available for bonding in an atom or group of atoms.

METALS are elements that give electrons to other elements.

NONMETALS are elements that receive electrons from other elements.

COMBINING NUMBER is the number of electrons that can be gained or lost on the valence energy level to make it complete with eight electrons.

TRANSITION ELEMENTS are the heavy metals on the Periodic Table that have more than one combining number.

The **MELTING POINT** of a solid substance is the temperature at which it melts. The tightly packed atoms or molecules begin to move about more freely in the liquid phase.

IONIC SOLIDS have very high melting points.

MOLECULAR SOLIDS (made by covalent bonds) have low melting points.

NONPOLAR COVALENT COMPOUNDS have low melting points.

ELECTRICAL CONDUCTIVITY: Ionic solids which dissociate in water conduct an electrical current

Polar covalent compounds weakly conduct an electrical current

Nonpolar covalent compounds do not conduct an electrical current

NONPOLAR COMPOUNDS dissolve in nonpolar solvents.

POLAR COMPOUNDS dissolve in polar solvents.

The Mass of the Atom 11

RELATIVE ATOMIC MASS

The actual mass of an atom was impossible to determine in John Dalton's time (1800). Since no balance could measure so tiny a particle, an indirect method had to be used. Your study of atomic mass is based on this method, RELATIVE ATOMIC MASS.

The measurement of the mass of an atom is based on the *LAW OF DEFINITE COMPOSITION: a compound always contains the same elements; the amount of each element in a given mass of a compound is always the same.*

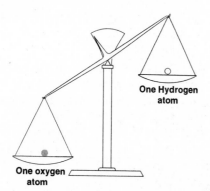

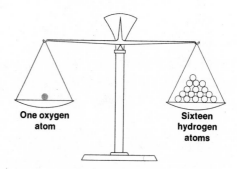

RELATIVE ATOMIC MASSES OXYGEN AND HYDROGEN

This is how it works. Water (H_2O) always contains two atoms of hydrogen and one atom of oxygen. If two grams of hydrogen are used, then it will take exactly 16 grams of oxygen to form water. In this case neither element is left over. Since there are two hydrogen atoms in a molecule of water and we start with two grams of it, then hydrogen must have an atomic mass of *one* relative to oxygen, 16. It wouldn't matter if we had used ounces, pounds, or tons. The relationship of one and 16 of hydrogen with oxygen would be the same. Assigning a relative atomic mass of one to hydrogen makes good sense. Hydrogen is the lightest of all the elements.

To make carbon monoxide (CO), it takes 12 grams of carbon to combine chemically with 16 grams of oxygen. We say that carbon has a relative atomic mass of 12.

The RELATIVE ATOMIC MASS of an element is a measure of the atomic mass of the element compared to the mass of the carbon-12 atom.

The structure of the atom determines the mass of an element required to bond with a given mass of another element. The secret of the mass of an atom lies in its nucleus.

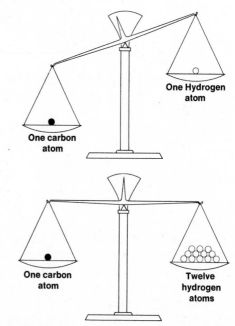

One carbon atom has twelve times the mass of 1 hydrogen atom

RELATIVE ATOMIC MASSES CARBON AND HYDROGEN

THE SECRET OF THE NUCLEUS

Atomic Mass Units

We can account for relative atomic masses by a closer inspection of the nucleus of atoms. Protons and neutrons are found in the nucleus. Both are heavy when compared to an electron. A neutron has the same mass as a proton, one atomic mass unit (1 amu).

The number of protons makes each element different from every other element. Adding or removing one proton makes a different element. Neutrons increase the mass of an element. The number of neutrons varies from element to element.

To find the atomic mass of an element, add the number of protons and the number of neutrons in the nucleus. Each element has its same relative atomic mass in atomic mass units.

ordinary hydrogen has no neutrons (n)

Hydrogen
Atomic number = 1
Atomic mass = 1

Helium
Atomic number = 2
Atomic mass = 4

Lithium
Atomic number = 3
Atomic mass = 6

Beryllium
Atomic number = 4
Atomic mass = 9

Atomic number and atomic mass of some of the lighter elements.

Carbon
Atomic number = 6
Atomic mass = 12

Oxygen
Atomic number = 8
Atomic mass = 16

Silver
Atomic number = 47
Atomic mass = 108

Gold
Atomic number = 79
Atomic mass = 197

Atomic number and atomic mass of some of the heavier elements.

AN EASY WAY TO WEIGH

Gram-Atomic Mass

Atomic masses are very useful to the chemist if they are measured out in gram units.

You have weighed all your chemicals in the lab using grams. So, if we weigh out the corresponding atomic mass in grams, each element retains its atomic mass relative to the atomic mass of every other element.

A GRAM-ATOM is the atomic mass of the element expressed in grams.

Examples:	Atomic mass unit	Gram-atomic mass
Hydrogen	1 amu	1 g
Carbon	12 amu	12 g
Oxygen	16 amu	16 g
Gold	197 amu	197 g

From these examples you can see that each element has its own relative atomic mass in gram-atom units.

A CHECK UP

1. A neutral atom of fluorine has 9 protons and 10 neutrons in the nucleus. What is its atomic mass?
2. What is the atomic mass of fluorine in grams?
3. A neutral chlorine atom has 17 protons and 18 neutrons in the nucleus. What is its atomic mass?
4. Find the gram-atomic mass of chlorine.

A GRAIN OF SAND

The Small Measure

To find out how much you weigh, you can use a bathroom scale, but it isn't sensitive enough to weigh an airmail letter. For the letter, you need the type scale used in the Post Office. In the same way, your laboratory balance isn't sensitive enough to measure the mass of one grain of sand. The balance is not sensitive enough to register such a small mass.

The Actual Mass of Atomic Particles

Modern laboratory methods have been used to find the *actual* masses of atomic particles. This kind of work was carried out in research laboratories with the help of special equipment and very precise measurements.

Your knowledge of scientific notation tells you that these masses are extremely small. They are not practical for our work in the lab, but they are interesting because they are important milestones in the development of chemistry.

Name	Actual mass in grams	Atomic mass unit (amu)
proton	1.67×10^{-24} g	1 amu
neutron	1.67×10^{-24} g	1 amu
electron	9.11×10^{-28} g	0.0005 amu

Looking at small particles.
(*Humko Products*)

In Experiment 11.1, you use an indirect method to find the mass of a single grain of sand. You don't need a computer to figure this out. All you have to know is the mass of your sample of sand and the number of grains in the sample. Simple division gives you the answer.

Mass of sample ÷ Number of particles
        = The mass of 1 particle of the sample

$$\textit{Example:}\quad \frac{5 \text{ grams of sand}}{5000 \text{ grains of sand}} = \frac{1 \text{ gram of sand}}{1000 \text{ grains of sand}}$$

$$= 0.001 \text{ gram per grain of sand}$$

Avogadro's Number

In 1811, Amadeo Avogadro (ah-meh-DAY-o ah-vo-GAH-dro), an Italian scientist, used this method to measure the mass of an atom. To do this, he had to know two things:

1. The gram-atomic mass of the element (atomic mass in grams)
2. The number of atoms in this mass

The first part is easy. To find the element's gram-atomic mass, add the number of protons and the number of neutrons in the nucleus of the atom. Measure out a sample of the element in this number of grams.

To find the number of atoms in this sample is a different story. But it has a happy ending.

Avogadro reasoned that elements bond with each other atom by atom. They combine in definite amounts by relative atomic mass. Then there must be the same number of atoms of each element in each gram-atomic mass.

Many scientists contributed toward finding that exact number of atoms in every gram-atomic mass of an element. They discovered that there were 602,300,000,000,-000,000,000,000 atoms! This number is almost too large to imagine. It is read as 602,300 quintillions. This number of molecules of liquid water (about 18 grams), would not even satisfy your thirst after playing in a basketball game.

Using scientific notation, the number of atoms can be written as 6.02×10^{23}, after rounding off. It is called the AVOGADRO NUMBER. Although Avogadro didn't find the number of atoms in a gram-atomic mass, it is named in his honor. He provided the reasoning that led to its discovery.

The Mass of an Atom

Now that we have all the information needed to find the mass of an atom, let's calculate the mass of a carbon atom.

1. The gram-atomic mass of carbon = 12 g
2. There are 6.02×10^{23} atoms in this sample (Avogadro's Number)

gram-atomic mass ÷ Number of atoms in the sample
    of sample   (Avogadro's Number) = mass of 1 atom of an element

$$\frac{12 \text{ grams of carbon}}{6.02 \times 10^{23} \text{ atoms of carbon}} = \text{mass of 1 carbon atom}$$

Complete this calculation in class with the help of your teacher.

Amadeo Avogadro (*Bettmann Archive*)

QUICK QUESTIONS?

1. On page *4/46* the actual mass of the parts of the atom are given in scientific notation. How much lighter is the electron compared to the proton and neutron?
2. What does Avogadro's number represent?

FINDING THE NUMBER OF MOLES IN A SAMPLE

A Mole Hunt

At this time of year, moles are in season. We have a free hunting license. Before we start our hunt, we have to know what we're looking for. How big is a mole? How much space does it occupy? Where shall we look? How many moles will we find? Are they friendly?

You won't have to worry on this expedition because moles are very tame, if you know how to handle them. We'll bring along an expert guide who made mole hunting a popular sport for chemists. Our guide is Amadeo Avogadro. Let him tell us about it.

Avogadro's Number—
A cast of quintillions
(Courtesy of Volkswagen of America, Inc.)

Same Volumes = Same Number of Molecules

The mole we're looking for doesn't burrow in the ground. It has no claws. A chemical mole isn't a furry little animal. It is far from being a garden nuisance.

The name "mole" is short for "molecule." But "mole" has a meaning all its own. This is how it all began.

I was the first to think that one molecule of oxygen must contain two atoms. I recognized that hydrogen also had two atoms in a molecule. I made this discovery after studying the work of the French scientist, Joseph Gay-Lussac (gay-loo-SACK). He found that when gases combine chemically with each other, a very simple relationship exists. This relationship compares the volumes of the *gaseous* reactants and *gaseous* products in the reaction. The volumes of each gas are related by small whole numbers.

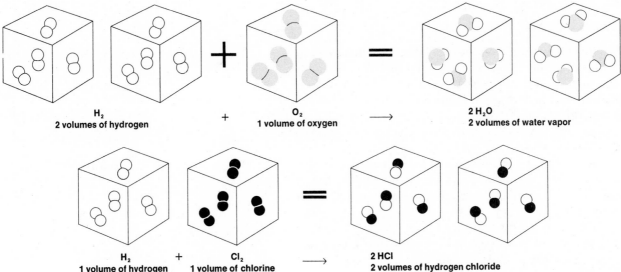

H₂
2 volumes of hydrogen
+
O₂
1 volume of oxygen
⟶
2 H₂O
2 volumes of water vapor

H₂
1 volume of hydrogen
+
Cl₂
1 volume of chlorine
⟶
2 HCl
2 volumes of hydrogen chloride

The volumes of gaseous reactants are related to the volume of their products by small whole numbers.

In order for these volumes to react in this way, I thought that these gases must be diatomic. No one had imagined this to be true before. The equations for the reactions would then read:

$$\underline{2}H_2 + \underline{}O_2 = \underline{2}H_2O$$
$$\underline{}H_2 + \underline{}Cl_2 = \underline{2}HCl$$

The amazing part of these conclusions is yet to come. I reasoned that if atom for atom, elements combine with each other to form compounds, then their gram-atomic masses must contain the same number of atoms. This number of atoms is called a mole of atoms. (Today this number is 6.02×10^{23} atoms.)

Why shouldn't the same be true of the gases with two atoms in a molecule? *The mass of the molecule measured in grams is called the GRAM-MOLECULAR MASS. The gram-molecular mass of elements or compounds must contain the same number of atoms or molecules (6.02×10^{23} molecules). This quantity is called a MOLE.*

From this relationship of volumes and number of molecules I concluded that:

Equal volumes of all gases contain the same number
   of molecules (provided the temperature and pressure
   of each are the same.)

Equal volumes of gases contain the same number of molecules at the same temperature and pressure.

**1 volume of
hydrogen**
=
**1 volume of
oxygen**
=
**1 volume of
nitrogen**
=
**1 volume of
chlorine**

What does equal volumes of gases containing equal numbers of molecules mean? If you had two boxes of equal size could you pack the same number of water-melons in one as you could grapes in the other? You know this would be ridiculous because watermelons and grapes aren't gases. They can't be compressed (pressed together) the same way molecules of a gas can. A gas takes the shape of its container. Gas molecules are in continuous motion. They exert pressure against the sides of their container. Pressure can be applied to the molecules, also. They can be packed together because there is so much space between them to begin with.

The work of many scientists reveals that a mole of molecules (6.02×10^{23} molecules) of a gas has a mass equal to its gram-molecular mass. It takes up 22.4 liters of space (at Standard Temperature and air Pressure, 0°C and 760 mm pressure.) We call this a MOLAR VOLUME. We will learn more about molar volume and standard conditions in Chapter 14.

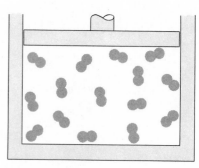
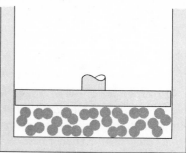

Gases can be compressed.

Don't Make a Mountain Out of a Molehill

Chemists have found the mole to be one of the most useful concepts in carrying out their experiments. It is easy to work with. It provides us with a tool for solving many industrial problems. It makes your work in the lab easy, too.

You have enough equipment to take along on your mole hunt in Experiment 11.2. Happy hunting!

The Molar Volume of a gas at Standard temperature and Pressure.

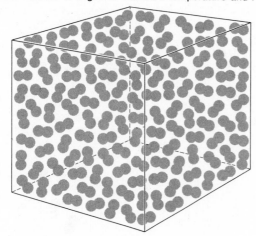

Oxygen gas at standard temperature and pressure
22.4 l = 6.02 x 10²³ molecules = 1 gram—molecular
mass = 1 mole

WHAT IS A MOLE?

1. A mole is the number of atoms in the relative atomic mass of any element when that mass is measured in grams.

   Carbon (C) has a gram-atomic mass of
   $$12 \text{g/mole or } (6.02 \times 10^{23} \text{ atoms}).$$

2. A mole is the number of molecules in the gram molecular mass of an element with diatomic molecules.

   Oxygen (O_2) has a
   gram-molecular mass of 2×16 g
   $$= 32 \text{ g/mole or } (6.02 \times 10^{23} \text{ molecules}).$$

3. A mole is the number of molecules in the gram molecular mass of a compound consisting of molecules.

   Carbon dioxide (CO_2) has a gram molecular mass of:

   atomic mass of carbon = 12
   atomic mass of oxygen = 16

No. of atoms		atomic mass	
1	$\times$	12	= 12 g/mole
2	$\times$	16	= 32 g/mole
			44 g/mole

   carbon dioxide (CO_2) = 44 g/mole
   or $(6.02 \times 10^{23} \text{ molecules})$

4. A mole is the number of formula units in the gram formula mass of a compound that does not consist of molecules.

   The formula mass of potassium nitrate (KNO_3) is:

   atomic mass of potassium = 39
   atomic mass of nitrogen = 14
   atomic mass of oxygen = 16
   or $(6.02 \times 10^{23} \text{ formula units})$

No. of atoms		atomic mass	
1	$\times$	39	= 39 g/mole
1	$\times$	14	= 14 g/mole
3	$\times$	16	= 48 g/mole
			101 g/mole

5. A molar volume of a gas at standard conditions (0°C and 760 mm pressure) is 22.4 liters.

   A molar volume of a gas contains the gram-molecular mass or $(6.02 \times 10^{23} \text{ molecules})$.

QUICK QUESTIONS?

1. In what ways may a mole mass exist?
2. What is a mole?
3. How does a gram molecular mass differ from a gram atomic mass?
4. How many molecules are in a molar volume of a gas?
5. Do solids and liquids have molar volumes like gases do? (Hint: the molar volume of water at 0°C and 760 mm pressure is about 18 ml.)
6. Is a mole like a dozen, a ton, a gallon, or a degree Centigrade? Explain your answer.

EGGS AND ATOMS

Isotopes of Hydrogen

Suppose we showed you a glass of water with ice cubes floating in it. There wouldn't be anything different about that. Then, suppose we drop another cube of ice into the glass, and it sinks to the bottom. Remove the cube and let it melt. It looks like water. It tastes like water. There is nothing hidden in it to make it sink. How can we account for this heavy cube of ice?

In Demonstration *Eggs and Atoms,* you discover that *ISOTOPES are atoms of the same element with the same number of protons, but a different number of neutrons.* Different numbers of neutrons in the nucleus cause the atoms to have different masses.

Ordinary hydrogen has 1 proton but no neutrons in the nucleus. The atoms have an atomic number of 1 and an atomic mass of 1. The second isotope has 1 neutron in the nucleus. It is called *deuterium* (dyoo TEER ee um). The letter D stands for this isotope. It has an atomic number of 1, but an atomic mass of 2. The third isotope of hydrogen is called *tritium* (TRIT ee um). Atoms of tritium have 2 neutrons in the nucleus. The atomic number is 1, but the atomic mass is 3.

Deuterium is found with naturally occurring hydrogen. About one out of every 6,500 atoms of hydrogen is deuterium. Deuterium reacts chemically with oxygen, like ordinary hydrogen, to form water. But this water is heavier than ordinary H_2O which weighs 18 g/mole. D_2O, deuterium oxide, weighs 20 g/mole. It is called "heavy water." Every glass of water you drink has a few molecules of D_2O in it. If we were to isolate enough deuterium oxide from the water found in nature, we could make an ice cube from it. A cube of this ice would sink in a glassful of ordinary water.

The isotopes of an element are often represented in another way to show their atomic mass. The three isotopes of hydrogen are also given the symbols H-1, H-2, and H-3.

All the elements have isotopes. Oxygen has three: O-16, O-17, and O-18. Carbon has two important isotopes, C-12 and C-14. The heavier isotopes of an element are rare in nature and they are difficult to separate. It is an expensive process. For this reason, one gram of a substance containing heavy oxygen, can cost up to $1000, depending upon how much of the isotope is present.

Isotopes of Hydrogen

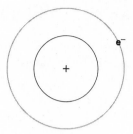

Hydrogen
Atomic number = 1
Atomic mass = 1

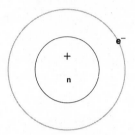

Deuterium
Atomic number = 1
Atomic mass = 2

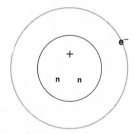

Tritium
Atomic number = 1
Atomic mass = 3

These chicks were hatched from similar-size eggs, although their weight may be different. (*Advertising Council*)

Average Atomic Mass

The atomic mass of an element must take into consideration all of its isotopes. Although the heavier isotopes are not as plentiful as are the ones with lower atomic mass, they are averaged into the total. This average is based on the per cent of each isotope found in a given sample. For example, O-16 is the most abundant isotope of oxygen that occurs in nature. About 99.76% of oxygen is O-16. Only 0.04% is O-17, and just 0.20% is O-18. Therefore, the average atomic mass of oxygen would be just a little over 16 amu when we consider the heavier isotopes.

You will see how these average atomic masses of the elements are placed on the Periodic Table in *Exercise: Completing the Periodic Table.*

RADIOACTIVITY

The Decay of the Nucleus

When a plant decays, the compounds that are contained in it break apart. Some of these split into small groups of elements. They serve to fertilize the soil by returning vital nutrients needed for future plant growth. Some of these decay products are gases which return directly into the air.

Little did Democritus and Dalton realize that the nucleus of an atom could also break up into parts. *We call the breaking of the nucleus of an atom into parts, RADIOACTIVE DECAY.*

Albert Einstein, in the early 1900's, had predicted that matter could change into energy by the famous equation: $E = mc^2$. The amount of energy released, E, is equal to the mass, m, of the material multiplied by the speed of light, raised to the second power, c^2. The speed of light is 186,000 mi/sec. This would mean that a tremendous amount of energy would be released if even a small amount of matter were converted to energy.

Some nuclei are STABLE. They do not break down. Others are radioactive. Radioactive nuclei decay into more stable particles by releasing energy. This process is often called FISSION. *FISSION is a term used to describe a nuclear reaction in which a heavy nucleus decays into two lighter nuclei.* Fission may occur spontaneously, without any outside help. It may also be induced artificially (made to occur) in a nuclear reactor.

QUICK QUESTIONS?

1. What do you think the term, radioactive isotope means?
2. The nucleus contains protons and neutrons. When the nucleus is broken down into simpler nuclei, what type of energy may be released?
3. What is the difference between fission and fusion?
4. What are the three kinds of radiation?
5. Compare spontaneous fission with induced fission.

Peaceful Use of the Atom

Radioactive Tracers

Carbon-14 has a very long half-life, 5,700 years. It is a radioactive isotope of carbon-12. All living things have carbon atoms in them. Plants and animals absorb some carbon-14 atoms from the atmosphere. When they die no new atoms are taken in. The carbon-14 atoms present begin to decay into carbon-12 atoms. After many thousands of years, fewer and fewer radioactive C-14 atoms will be present.

The radioactivity of a sample can be measured with a Geiger counter. By comparing the radioactivity of living samples with the unknown, the age of the unknown can be fairly accurately determined.

Dr. Willard Libby won the Noble Prize for this method of determining the age of animal fossils containing carbon. The process is called RADIOCARBON DATING. It is also used to study the biochemistry of living plants and animals.

THE ATOMIC BOMB

Induced Fission

If a slow moving neutron is shot into the nucleus of an uranium-235 atom, the atom breaks up into two or more parts. New kinds of atoms are formed. Some neutrons of the uranium nucleus may escape.

In a nuclear reactor, these escaping neutrons may bombard other uranium atoms, causing them to break up, too. This is called a CHAIN REACTION. Huge amounts of energy are released. In the nuclear reactor, D_2O, "heavy water," is pumped in to cool the area, to act as a shield against radiation, and to slow down the released neutron to continue the chain reaction.

This is the secret behind the atomic bomb. The millions of atoms which are split give rise to enormous amounts of energy. Dangerous radiation is released which may not disappear for many years. The following is one of the reactions that may occur.

$$_0^1n + _{92}^{235}U \longrightarrow _{56}^{138}Ba + _{36}^{95}Kr + _0^1n + _0^1n + _0^1n + Energy$$

Notice the conservation of atomic mass and atomic number. Add the atomic masses of the products and you obtain 238. The atomic numbers of the reactants add to the original 92.

The ancient alchemists had tried unsuccessfully to change one element into another preferably, gold). Their attempts at transmutation of the elements had failed, but it was accomplished by nature, itself.

Madame Curie (*Bettmann Archive*)

Madame Curie

Marie S. Curie is the only person who has won two Nobel Prizes in Science. She won the prize in Physics with her husband, Pierre, in 1903. In 1911 she won the prize for the isolation of the element, radium. She also discovered the element, Polonium, which she named in honor of her homeland, Poland.

The Discovery of Radium

Spontaneous Fission

In 1898, a chance discovery in a small laboratory near Paris opened the door to the Atomic Age. A Polish-born woman scientist, Marie Curie (CURE-ee) and her French husband, Pierre, discovered a new element. They found it by boiling down a ton of pitchblende, a mineral ore containing the element uranium. The new element appeared as a white crystal. It gave off a faint, blue light in the dark.

The Curies called this light RADIATION. They named their new element, radium, which means "shining element."

There were three kinds of radiation given off by radium. They're called ALPHA, BETA, and GAMMA rays, after the first three letters of the Greek alphabet.

An ALPHA particle is a helium nucleus. It has two protons and two neutrons giving it an atomic mass of 4, and an atomic number of 2. Its symbol is $_2^4He$.

A BETA particle is very much like an electron, but it comes from the nucleus! It is believed that it comes from the decomposition of a neutron, leaving behind a positive proton in the nucleus.

GAMMA rays are not particles. They are invisible waves like radio or television waves. They are very powerful and dangerous because they can penetrate into the human body to destroy cells.

The energy released in nuclear fission is due to the energy which holds the nucleus together called NUCLEAR BINDING ENERGY.

Radium eventually loses enough particles in the form of radiation to become lead.

Uranium also undergoes spontaneous fission. It can happen in several ways. For example, the radioactive isotope of uranium with an atomic mass of 238 (U-238) can decay into a thorium atom and an alpha particle with the release of nuclear binding energy.

$$_{92}^{238}U \longrightarrow _{90}^{234}Th + _2^4He + Energy$$

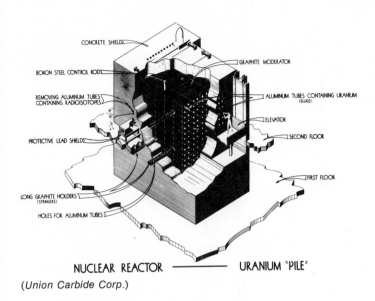

NUCLEAR REACTOR ——— URANIUM "PILE"

(*Union Carbide Corp.*)

The Big Build-Up Atomic Fusion

It is possible to produce a radioactive substance artificially in a nuclear reactor. These reactors are called PARTICLE ACCELERATORS. The element used as a "target" is bombarded with atomic "bullets," such as alpha particles, protons, or neutrons. This can be done in a CYCLOTRON, SYNCHROTRON, or in a LINEAR ACCELERATOR.

Nature, in outer space, provides its own "bullets" to produce radioactive elements. For example, Carbon-14 is a radioactive isotope of carbon. Neutrons from outer space can be "natural bullets." They collide with the nitrogen in the upper atmosphere changing some of it into C-14 and releasing a hydrogen atom.

$$^{14}_{7}\text{N} + ^{1}_{0}\text{n} \longrightarrow ^{14}_{6}\text{C} + ^{1}_{1}\text{H}$$

Half Life

The rate of radioactive decay is measured by an element's HALF LIFE. HALF LIFE of a radioactive element is the length of time required for one half of the atoms of the original sample to decay into simpler atoms.

For example, an isotope of iodine (I-131), is radioactive. It takes eight days for half of the atoms of a given sample to decay. After eight days, only one half of the mass of the original atoms remain radioactive. After 16 days, only one quarter of the atoms remain radioactive; after 24 days, one eighth of the atoms remain radioactive.

Each element has its own characteristic half life. A half life can range from a fraction of a second for polonium (P-214), to 4.5×10^9 years for uranium-238.

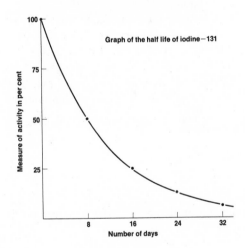

Graph of the half life of iodine—131

RADIATION FROM RADIUM

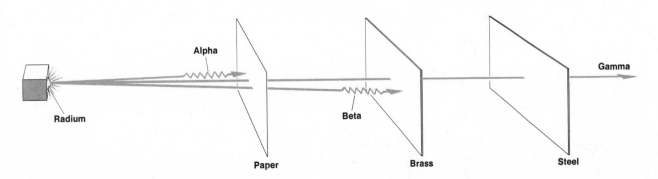

PERCENTAGE COMPOSITION

To Squeeze a Sugar Molecule

In Experiment 11.3, *Burnt Sugar,* you learn how to determine the percentage composition of water formed from a molecule of sugar. First "squeeze" all the water you can from sugar by heating it. Then you can calculate the per cent of water removed from the compound and the per cent of pure carbon remaining. The composition of table sugar, sucrose, is shown by the formula $C_{12}H_{22}O_{11}$. This bonding produces the sweet, white crystals that do not resemble black carbon or liquid H_2O.

Before you can perform Experiment 11.3, you may gain a better understanding of percentage composition from the Home Lab.

One Atom Makes the Difference

Let's compare the percentage of oxygen in carbon monoxide and carbon dioxide. Recall that these two compounds illustrate two familiar laws.

1. The Law of Definite Composition
   CO—always made of 1 atom of carbon and 1 atom of oxygen.
   CO_2—always made of 1 atom of carbon and 2 atoms of oxygen.
2. The Law of Multiple Proportions
   There are twice as many oxygen atoms in carbon dioxide as there are in carbon monoxide. The amount of carbon remains the same.

The per cent of oxygen in CO_2 is different from that in CO.

A mole of carbon monoxide:
$$C = 12 \text{ g}$$
$$O = 16 \text{ g}$$
$$\overline{CO = 28 \text{ g/mole}}$$

What fractional part of carbon monoxide is oxygen?

$$\frac{16 \text{ g oxygen}}{28 \text{ g/mole CO}} = \frac{4}{7} \qquad \text{Dividing:} \quad 7\overline{)4.0000}^{\,0.5714}$$

Percentage composition of oxygen in carbon monoxide is:
$$0.5714 \times 100 = \underline{57.14\%}$$

A mole of carbon dioxide:
$$C \qquad\quad = 12 \text{ g}$$
$$O_2 = 16 \times 2 = 32 \text{ g}$$
$$\overline{CO_2 \qquad\quad = 44 \text{ g/mole}}$$

What fractional part of carbon dioxide is oxygen?

$$\frac{32 \text{ g oxygen}}{44 \text{ g/mole CO}_2} = \frac{8}{11} \qquad \text{Dividing:} \quad 11\overline{)8.0000}^{\,0.7272}$$

Percentage composition of oxygen in carbon dioxide is:
$$0.7272 \times 100 = \underline{72.72\%}$$

Home Lab

Cut out 5 squares and 5 circles of nearly the same size from a piece of paper. They can all be the same color. Let the squares be atoms of the "element squarium," and the circles represent 5 atoms of the "element roundium."

Put all the "atoms" together in any arrangement you choose. The figure represents 100% of your new "compound," "squarium roundide."

Remove all the "atoms of roundium."

What per cent of your original compound is left?

What per cent of "roundium" was contained in your compound?

Cut out 5 triangles, about the same size as your other shapes. They represent 5 atoms of the element "triangulum."

Make the new compound "squarium triangulum roundide," by using all 15 "atoms."

Remove 5 "atoms of roundium."

What per cent of the total compound was "roundium?"

(Hint: The 15 shapes represent 100% of your compound. 5 of the 15 are round, $\frac{5}{15}$. What per cent of the total is this?)

What per cent of the compound is left?

Chapter 11

ACTION POINTS

The **RELATIVE ATOMIC MASS OF AN ELEMENT** is a measure of the atomic mass of the element as compared to the atomic mass of carbon-12.

The **ATOMIC MASS** of an element is found by adding the number of protons and neutrons in the nucleus of an atom of that element.

ATOMIC MASS UNITS (amu) is a unit invented to express the number of protons and neutrons in the nucleus of an atom.

A **GRAM ATOMIC MASS** is the atomic mass units of an atom expressed in grams.

A **GRAM MOLECULAR MASS** is the sum of the atomic mass units of a molecule expressed in grams.

AVOGADRO'S NUMBER is 6.02×10^{23} particles or items of any one kind. It is a count just like a dozen.

A **MOLE** of a substance may be 6.02×10^{23} atoms in one gram-atomic mass of an element, 6.02×10^{23} molecules in one gram-molecular mass of a compound, or 6.02×10^{23} formula units in the gram-formula mass of a compound that does not consist of molecules.

EQUAL VOLUMES OF ALL GASES under the same conditions of temperature and pressure, contain the same number of molecules.

A **MOLAR VOLUME** of a gas is the amount of space occupied by 6.02×10^{23} molecules of the gas. At standard conditions of temperature and pressure (0°C and 760 mm of mercury) this volume is 22.4 liters.

ISOTOPES are atoms of the same element that are chemically alike (same number of protons in the nucleus; same number of electrons) but differ in mass (the number of neutrons in the nucleus.)

AVERAGE ATOMIC MASS is calculated by measuring the percentage of each kind of isotope an element may have and then averaging these masses. The average atomic mass is listed on the Periodic Table for each element.

RADIOACTIVE DECAY is the tendency of an element to break apart spontaneously into a more stable arrangement of particles by releasing energy.

FISSION is a general term used for any nuclear reaction in which a heavy nucleus breaks up into two daughter nuclei. The sum of the masses of the two new nuclei roughly equals the mass of the original nucleus.

SPONTANEOUS FISSION of an atom takes place in an atom without any outside help.

INDUCED FISSION of an atom takes place artificially in a reactor by bombarding the nucleus with neutrons.

A **CHAIN REACTION** occurs in a nuclear reactor. Released neutrons from the induced fission continue to bombard other nuclei present.

RADIATION is the energy given off by radioactive elements.

NUCLEAR BINDING ENERGY is the energy which holds the nucleus of an atom together. A small part of this energy is released in nuclear fission.

HALF-LIFE is the amount of time required for a radioactive element to become half as radioactive as it was.

ATOMIC FUSION is the process in which two or more light nuclei combine to produce a single nucleus of heavier mass.

PARTICLE ACCELERATORS are nuclear reactors which produce radioactive isotopes of an element by atomic fusion. Examples of particle accelerators are: cyclotron, synchrotron and linear accelerator.

RADIOACTIVE TRACERS are radioactive isotopes used in research to follow the pathway of a particular element in a living or once living plant or animal.

PERCENTAGE COMPOSITION is the measure of the mass of a particular element in a compound.

Putting the Mole to Work 12

THE MOLE TAKES TO WATER

A "mole in water" can help the chemist just as much as "a mole on land." You have learned that a mole is a gram-atomic mass of an element. A mole is also the gram-molecular mass of the diatomic gases and of compounds. There are 6.02×10^{23} particles in a mole.

Every time you measure out the gram-atomic mass of an element or the gram-molecular mass of a compound you know just what you're getting. The relative atomic masses in grams tells you the number of atoms or molecules.

For this reason, if a mole of a compound is dissolved in distilled water, you will have a mole of molecules. A liter of solution (1000 ml) makes a convenient volume to use. You know exactly how many molecules there are in a liter of solution. We are not interested in counting these molecules. What does interest us is the fact that by taking fractions of the liter, we take fractions of the mole in solution.

A mole of a substance dissolved in 1 liter of solution is called a MOLAR SOLUTION.

You learn how to prepare a molar solution from a solid in Experiment 12.1. You also learn how to divide the molar solution and the mole to obtain any fractional part you need.

It is sometimes more convenient to do our work in chemistry by using solutions rather than solids. Molar solutions help the chemist "keep in the swim."

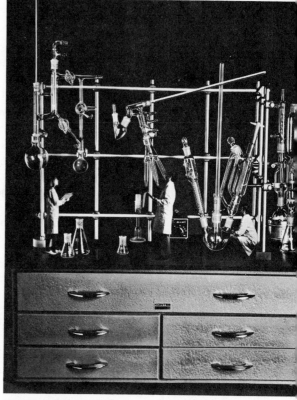

Work Small, Think Big. (*Kontes Corp.*)

DELVING FURTHER INTO pH

The Power of Hydrogen

In Experiment 12.2, *Delving Further Into pH,* you neutralize an acid with a base. The molar solutions of each are the same. Acids ionize in water to form H^+ ions. Hydrochloric acid, HCl, furnishes H^+ and Cl^- ions in solution.

Bases ionize in water to form OH^- ions (hydroxide ions.) Sodium hydroxide produces Na^+ ions and OH^- ions in solution.

If the solutions are both 0.1 Molar, you know that the number of ions in each must be the same. Drop by drop, the acid and base supply equal numbers of H^+

ions and OH⁻ ions to form water, HOH or H_2O. This process is called neutralization.

The base loses its basic properties and the acid its acid properties, as OH⁻ ions are bonded to H⁺ ions to form water.

An indicator is added to show a color change when neutralization occurs. One drop can cause this color change to be sharp and permanent. This is called the END-POINT. One extra drop of either acid or base can cause you to go over the end-point, and neutralization will have to be reestablished.

THE POWER OF 10

What do the numbers on the pH scale mean? Acids register a color range from 0 to just under 7. Bases show a color change from 7 to 14. A pH of 7 means the solution is neutral. A color chart is used to match up the color of the indicator you use with the pH of the solution. A pH of 7 is indicated on a color chart, or by a sharp change of color, when neutralization has occurred. You observed this in Unit III. Now are we going to be more exact?

The numbers on the scale are positive numbers. They come from a set of negative numbers. The negative numbers are powers of 10. They stand for the concentration of H⁺ ions in solution.

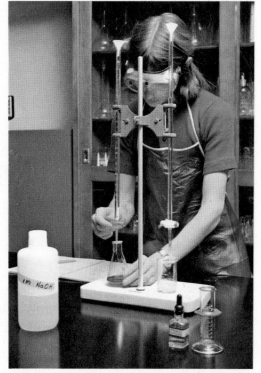

Finding the End-Point. (*Clara Aich and George Senty*)

pH Scale

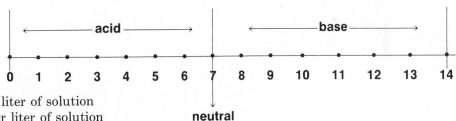

$10^0 = 1$ mole of H⁺ per liter of solution
$10^{-1} = 0.1$ mole of H⁺ per liter of solution
$10^{-2} = 0.01$ mole of H⁺ per liter of solution
$10^{-6} = 0.000001$ mole of H⁺ per liter of solution

By the time we reach 10^{-8}, we have a fraction of H⁺ ions so small, that the solution is more basic than acidic.

Notice the concentration of H⁺ ions gets smaller and smaller as the negative powers of 10 increase. It is easier to write positive numbers on the pH scale, but remember they stand for negative powers of 10. These numbers represent the fractional part of a mole of H⁺ ions in solution.

Pure distilled water has a pH of 7. The H⁺ ion concentration in water is 10^{-7}. The concentration of OH⁻ ions is also 10^{-7}. Water, H_2O, furnishes an equal number of H⁺ and OH⁻ ions, but this number is very small. Distilled water is perfectly neutral. It is the standard by which we measure the pH of other solutions.

THE CARE AND USE OF BURETS

The Uninvited

Clean dishes in your home are important to preserve good health. No one likes to drink from a glass that someone else has just used. We have enough to do to take care of our own germs. Besides, a trace of grapefruit juice would spoil the taste of your glass of milk.

We wouldn't want to water a treasured house plant from a pitcher that had just contained soapy water. Soap residue has never been known to be good for African violets.

Clean laboratory glassware is important, too. From your study of acids and bases, you saw what a fraction of a drop of extra acid can do to the end-point in a titration.

Ions in solution cling to glass, even after it has been rinsed. It wouldn't be uncommon to find millions of ions still hugging the sides of your graduated cylinder after it has been washed. For this to happen in a buret would be more than sad. Burets are used in the titration of an acid with a base. The end-point you thought you had reached would be due, in part, to the presence of uninvited ions. Your work would be spoiled.

The research chemist's work would be ruined, too, if he did not follow the procedures you learn in Experiment 12.3, *A Little Super-Super Dishwashing—How To Use Burets*. Even small quantities of unsuspected ions in hospital laboratory glassware could mean the difference between life or death to a patient.

A sterilizing unit for laboratory glassware. (*Forma Scientific*)

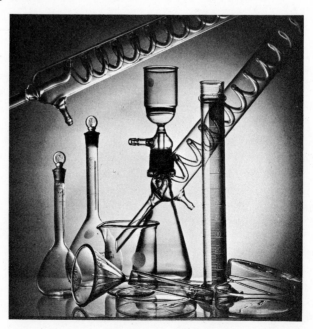

Laboratory glassware must be kept spotless. (*Corning Glass*)

HOW SOUR IS VINEGAR?

A Titration

In Experiment 12.4, you are asked to solve a problem much like that which the research chemist sees everyday. Using the tools of chemistry, complex puzzles can be simplified to help make our lives happier, healthier and more comfortable.

Many industrial problems are based on a knowledge of acid-base chemistry. Paper-making, sugar-refining, bacteriology and sanitary engineering depend on the processes you use in Experiment 12.4.

Vinegar is an acid. That's what makes it sour. You find out how much base of known molarity (concentration) must be used to neutralize a measured volume of vinegar. Drop by drop, the base is added to the vinegar until neutralization occurs. Knowing the volume of base it took for this to happen enables you to calculate how sour the vinegar is. You determine how much acid it contains. This process is called a titration. The acid found in vinegar is called *acetic (ah-SEE-tick) acid.*

Laboratory work can be done quickly and efficiently with electronic instruments. (*Fischer Scientific*)

A soil chemist can determine the acidity of the soil for proper plant growth. (*USDA*)

How Sour is Soil?

Acid-base chemistry is important to the farmer. The agricultural economy depends on it. The success of your lawn depends on it, too. Certain crops will not grow well if the soil is too acidic (sour). Testing the pH of soil is one way to find out if the land is suitable to plant tomatoes, wheat or corn. About four-fifths of the farm land in the central western part of the United States is too acidic to be agriculturally productive. The farmer "sweetens" the soil with fertilizers rich in basic content, ammonia, for example. He may add large amounts of basic lime (CaO), or Calcium hydroxide $(Ca(OH)_2)$. It is important to know how much of a base to add to adjust the pH. Acid-base chemistry plays an important role in good soil management. Chapter 21 is about agriculture.

pH in the Human Body

The balance of pH in different parts of the human body is critical to the proper maintenance of life processes. You have seen in Chapter 10 how important the metallic ions are to good health. These ions help to keep the pH of the bloodstream just slightly over 7, which is basic.

The pH of a portion of the digestive system, the stomach, is less than 7. The gastric juices of the stomach have a pH of 2, which is acidic. This is due to the presence of HCl, hydrochloric acid. Certain foods can be digested only in an acid medium. Another part of the digestive tract, the small intestine, must be basic for the digestive process to be completed. This is accomplished with the aid of bile which has been collected in the gall bladder or the liver.

The delicate balance of pH in a system is called EQUILIBRIUM. It is possible for the equilibrium or pH to be disturbed.

There are medicines that help restore it. Aspirin is made of acetyl salicylic acid. For some reason, still unknown, it relieves the pain of headaches. There are antacid (against acid) remedies for oversecretion of acids in the stomach. They are basic substances that neutralize the acid.

There are thousands of acid-base equilibrium systems in the human body. The study of acid-base chemistry is an important part of the training in the medical profession.

ANYTHING NEW UNDER THE SUN?

The words that fill the dictionary are made with just 26 letters of the alphabet. Short or long, these words must be formed by a correct arrangement of these letters to make sense to the reader. If we were to count the number of all possible words in all possible languages that could be written with these letters, we would have a tremendous task to perform.

Think what could be done with 104 letters of the alphabet. The "letters" of the chemical alphabet are the 104 elements. Combined with each other, with the proper arrangement and amounts, new "words," or compounds, are created. Most chemists can write the formulas of about 10,000 compounds. The research journals have reported more new compounds being made in the last 10 years than all those known up until that time. There is no reason to believe that the next 10 years will not produce the same results.

Moles of a few common substances.
(*Clara Aich and George Senty*)

Some of the compounds make life more comfortable. Others are life-saving. Some hold the secret of life itself.

As your knowledge of chemistry grows, you may decide that you want to share in the exciting activity of "chemical wordmaking." You may decide that science is the field for you. Whether you choose to be a research chemist, a research biologist, X-ray technician, doctor, nurse, inhalation therapist, or physical therapist, you want to be a good one. A knowledge of chemistry will start you on the road toward your goal. If someone should stop you along the way to ask, "Anything new under the sun?", why, you'd better believe it!

Without looking on the Periodic Table, see how many names of elements beginning with the letters in the word CHEMISTRY you can write.

Score

Over 40 —Expert
30-39   —Superior
20-29   —Excellent
10-19   —Good
Under 10—OK to peek

These students are performing a laboratory experiment which might lead to some new discovery. (*Project Physics*)

Chapter 12

ACTION POINTS

A **MOLAR SOLUTION** contains a mole of a substance dissolved in one liter of solution.

pH is the abbreviation for "hydrogen power" and is the measure of the strength of acids and bases. A pH from one to seven indicates the presence of an acid; a pH of seven indicates a neutral solution; a pH from seven to 14 indicates the presence of a base.

TITRATION is the process of either adding a base to an acid, or an acid to a base, drop by drop, until neutralization has occurred. From this we can calculate the unknown molarity of either the acid or base, if the molarity of one is already known.

The **END-POINT** in a titration is determined by an indicator. A color change will occur when neutralization has occurred.

EQUILIBRIUM is the delicate balance of pH in a system.

Chemical Reactions

Unit 5

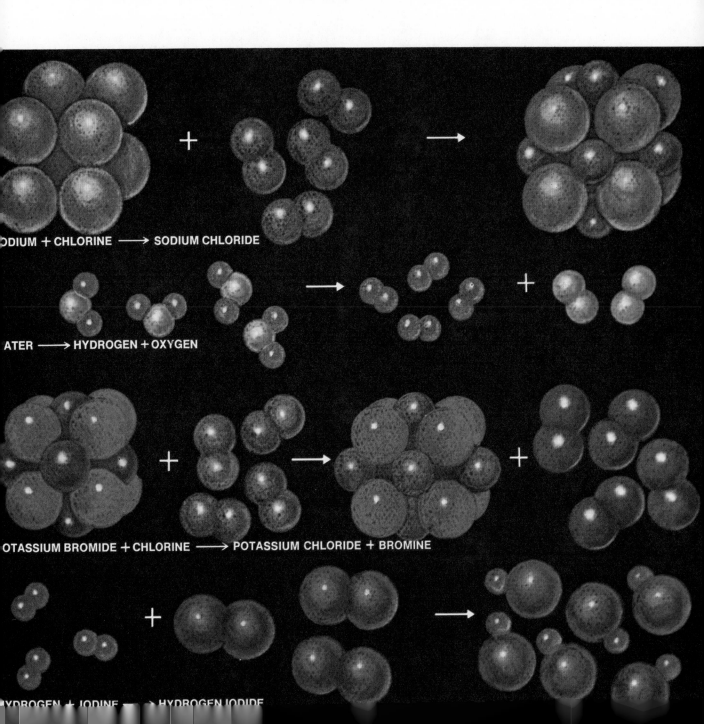

ODIUM + CHLORINE ⟶ SODIUM CHLORIDE

ATER ⟶ HYDROGEN + OXYGEN

OTASSIUM BROMIDE + CHLORINE ⟶ POTASSIUM CHLORIDE + BROMINE

YDROGEN + IODINE ⟶ HYDROGEN IODIDE

Contents

UNIT 5   CHEMICAL REACTIONS

Chapter 13   *READER TEXT*   **Chapter 13**   *LABORATORY MANUAL*

CHEMICAL REACTIONS

Chapter 14   *READER TEXT*   **Chapter 14**   *LABORATORY MANUAL*

CHEMICAL REACTIONS: PREDICTING AND USING THEM

Chemical Reactions 13

Where there is life there is chemistry. And where there is chemistry there are chemical reactions.

Some places have many chemical reactions going on. Other places have very few chemical reactions. For example, the gray, lifeless environment of the moon is very low in chemical activity. There is no air or water in which the chemicals react. Rocks on the moon lie in place for millions of years and are not changed much.

Take a trip to the seashore. A much different environment exists there. Billions of tiny organisms, some that you cannot see, are changing constantly. Many plants and animals are found in the pounding, oxygen-rich surf. Simple creatures make food for the more complex creatures, such as the fish.

In all of this activity there is a continuous range of chemical activity. You, too, have many chemical reactions going on within you. You might even say that you are many, big, complex, chemical reactions.

Even contact with things outside of your body depends on the activity of chemicals. For example, a moving car certainly depends on chemical reactions. Can you think of other examples?

In all chemical reactions, a change takes place. Changes that are going on right now inside you are caused mostly by chemical reactions. If you want to find the source of an interesting change, look for the chemical reaction. That's where the action is!

However, even in a chemical reaction, there is something that is conserved (saved).

Marine life in a tidal pool. (*Inez and George Hollis*)

This shot of the moon was taken by Apollo 10 from an altitude of 60 nautical miles. (*NASA*)

TOTAL CONSERVATION

What does conservation mean to you? Saving the environment? Not using our resources too rapidly? When talking about your surroundings, a good general policy might be: Use our resources wisely. It doesn't mean that we won't use something, or that our resources can't be used at all. Some day in the future it might mean the use of more of our resources over and over again. This is called recycling.

But to a chemist, conservation means more than recycling of our resources. When the chemist thinks about a chemical reaction, he knows that there can't be any loss of matter. Everything is conserved.

In a chemical reaction, the mass doesn't change. Even the number of atoms doesn't change. Yes, there may be a change in how the material looks. This change though, is usually caused by a rearrangement of atoms or molecules in the substance. Sometimes the change can be due to a phase change—matter going from solid to liquid, or liquid to gas, or something similar. The phase change is a physical change. In either case is there a loss or gain of matter? There is none. No old atoms are destroyed. No new atoms are created. This is true of all chemical reactions. This is also true of all physical changes.

"But what about fire?", you might say. "Isn't that a chemical reaction? There, the wood is gone and smoke pours into the air."

Yes, burning is a chemical reaction. The fuel is used up. But still, there is no loss of matter. However, as we discussed in Chapter 4, a chemical change results in a new substance being formed. The same atoms are still there but in different combination. They are disguised.

For example, an atom of carbon that was at one time in the fuel, is still around. While in the fuel, that carbon atom may have been attached to a couple of hydrogen atoms. After burning, that very same carbon atom may become hooked to a couple of oxygen atoms. Carbon dioxide, which is a gas, may form. The carbon atom is in a different disguise. Or maybe the carbon atom is resting peacefully in the ashes of the fire. But wherever it is, it's still a carbon atom—and the very same one that was there before the reaction.

Home Lab

Get an empty jug. Be sure it can hold at least a quart.

Cover the inside bottom of the jug with a layer of charcoal. Ashes or charcoal from burnt wood will do.

Next, cover the charcoal with a layer of sand. Make the sand layer about one inch thick.

Finally, place a layer of loose soil over the sand. Try to use clean soil. Make it about one inch thick.

Now, plant some grass, moss or ivy in the soil. You may do this by using two long slender sticks as tweezers.

Wet the soil well but do not make it real soggy. Just make it muddy.

Seal the top of the jug and then weigh it. Place the jug in indirect sunlight. Can anything get in or out of the jug? Sunlight does, of course, but do any chemicals enter or leave?

Will the jar and its contents change in weight as the plants grow?

What does energy have to do with this system?

Log fire. (*Photo Researchers: Frank J. Miller*)

GETTING READY FOR EQUATIONS

Equations are important in chemistry. Here is an example of an equation: Two plus two equals four. In working with equations, you must always treat the one side the same as the other side. For example:

$$2 + 2 = 4$$

Now add two to each side.

$$2 + 2 + 2 = 4 + 2$$

You still have an equation. Chemical equations must be handled in the same way. But in chemistry, you will use symbols and formulas rather than numbers.

Take a look at a simple chemical equation. You probably know that when one atom of chlorine combines with another atom of chlorine each shares an electron. Together they form a molecule of chlorine (Cl_2). This reaction can be written as

$$1\,Cl + 1\,Cl = 1\,Cl_2$$

This equation says that the mass of one chlorine atom plus the mass of another equals the mass of one chlorine molecule. To make it a chemical equation one more thing is done. Instead of an equal sign, an arrow is written. The arrow points toward whatever is produced. The chemical equation is

$$Cl + Cl \longrightarrow Cl_2$$

The Cl stands for one atom of chlorine. You don't have to write "one" in front of the symbol for chlorine. The symbol Cl_2 stands for a molecule of chlorine. The subscript "two" means that there are two atoms of chlorine in the molecule.

A complete and correct chemical equation must have the same number of atoms on one side as on the other. Count up the number of chlorine atoms on each side. How many are there?

OTHER MEANINGS IN THE CHEMICAL EQUATION

The plus sign ($+$) in a chemical equation means more than just addition. It means that the masses of the atoms or molecules can be added. The plus sign also means that the atoms or molecules are getting together. A reaction has taken place.

Every chemical equation stands for a chemical reaction. Of course, you just can't make up an equation. You have to be sure that the reaction it represents actually happens. Once you know that certain materials will react, then you can write an equation. Just remember, a chemical equation is a very clear and true statement.

Liquid bromine reacting with phosphorus. (From the CHEM Study film, *Bromine-Element From The Sea*)

BALANCING THE BUDGET OF CHEMICALS

Sodium and chlorine can join to form sodium chloride. You might think that the chemical equation for this change might be

$$Na + Cl \longrightarrow NaCl$$

The equation says that an atom of sodium and an atom of chlorine join. But chlorine atoms cannot exist by themselves. Chlorine atoms always comes in pairs, forming a molecule. This is written as Cl_2. So any chemical equation with chlorine has to have Cl_2 in it and not Cl.

$$Na + Cl_2 \longrightarrow NaCl$$

The above equation is not quite correct. There has to be the same number of atoms on one side as on the other. Since there are two chlorine atoms on the left, there must be two on the right. You could write

$$Na + Cl_2 \longrightarrow NaCl_2$$

Sodium chloride does not exist as $NaCl_2$ however. It is really NaCl. Another way to show two atoms of chlorine on the right would be to represent two units of NaCl.

$$Na + Cl_2 \longrightarrow 2\,NaCl$$

Now there are two chlorine atoms shown on each side. There is still something wrong. One atom of sodium is shown on the left, but two on the right. The easiest thing to do is to write

$$2\,Na + Cl_2 \longrightarrow 2\,NaCl$$

This is a balanced equation. Balanced means that the number of atoms of each kind on one side is equal to the number of atoms of each kind on the other.

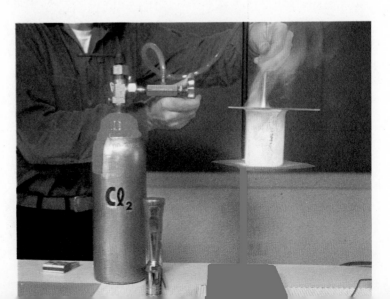

Chlorine gas reacting with sodium metal. (From the CHEM Study film, *Chemical Families*)

COMPOSING MOLECULES

The best coal is made mostly of carbon. It burns best when there is plenty of oxygen. The chemical equation describing the burning of coal is: $C + O_2 \longrightarrow CO_2$. Carbon dioxide ($CO_2$) is formed. This reaction is called direct union. This type of reaction is the combining of two substances to make a third substance.

Sometimes there is a shortage of oxygen when coal is burned. Then carbon dioxide is not formed. Instead, carbon monoxide, CO, is made. The chemical equation is $2C + O_2 \longrightarrow 2CO$. This is another example of a direct union reaction.

Many times you need to know how much material is needed for a chemical reaction or how much product is made. To find out, you can substitute the atomic mass for the symbol of each element needed. For example, suppose you wanted to know how much oxygen is needed in the reaction $C + O_2 \longrightarrow CO_2$.

Substitute the atomic mass numbers for each element: 12 g/mole for carbon and 16 g/mole for oxygen. But be careful. Those numbers stand for one mole of atoms. If you have two moles of atoms, as in O_2, then 32 g/mole must be used. The atomic mass equation would then be

$$C \quad + \quad O_2 \quad \longrightarrow \quad CO_2$$
$$12 \text{ g/mole} + 2(16 \text{ g/mole}) = (12 + 32) \text{ g/mole}$$

Different forms of coal. (*U.S. Bureau of Mines*)

Peat bog | Peat | Lignite
Bituminous—Bright Coal | Bituminous—Splint Coal | Bituminous—Cannel Coal
Anthracite | Coal areas of the United States | Coke

QUICK QUESTIONS?

1. What are two meanings for the word conservation?
2. Write an example of a mathematical equation and an example of a chemical equation. How are these two examples alike? How are they different?
3. A chlorine molecule is diatomic. It has two atoms of chlorine in it. Name some other diatomic molecules.
4. Balancing a chemical equation might be compared to balancing a household budget. How are a budget and equation alike? How are they different?
5. Balance the following equations.

   $Na + O_2 \longrightarrow Na_2O$

   (Remember: Start by balancing the number of oxygen atoms. You can show as many sodium atoms as you need.)

   $C + O_2 \longrightarrow CO$

   (Careful! CO is the product and not CO_2. Start by balancing the number of oxygen atoms.)

   $H_2 + S \longrightarrow H_2S$

6. Describe how Experiment 13.1 shows the Law of Conservation of Matter.

The equation tells you that 12 grams of carbon will need 32 grams of oxygen to make 44 grams of carbon dioxide.

The mass units don't have to be in grams. Kilograms, pounds, ounces, tons, or any other unit of mass may also be used.

Now try the same method for making carbon monoxide.

$$2\,C \quad + \quad O_2 \quad \longrightarrow \quad 2\,CO$$
$$2(12\ g/mole) + 2(16\ g/mole) = 56\ g/mole$$

The above equation says that to make 56 grams of carbon monoxide, you must have 24 grams of carbon and 32 grams of oxygen. It might have said that to make 56 tons of carbon monoxide, you must have 24 tons of carbon and 32 tons of oxygen.

Let's see what happens when a water molecule is taken apart. Taking apart a molecule is called decomposition. You can take apart a water molecule by putting an electric current through the water. If this is done, water decomposes to form hydrogen and oxygen. This reaction is shown by the equation:

$$2H_2O \longrightarrow 2\,H_2\uparrow + O_2\uparrow$$

The arrows pointing up mean that gas is formed. The above equation represents the decomposition of two water molecules. You can still use the atomic mass numbers in this equation.

$$36\ g/mole = 4\ g/mole + 32\ g/mole$$

This says that for every 36 grams of water that is decomposed, 4 grams of hydrogen is formed. What mass of oxygen forms? Using the mass relationships, 32 grams of oxygen is formed.

Decomposition reactions are also called analysis reactions. Here are two examples of such reactions.

Carbon dioxide bubbled into water makes carbonic acid: H_2CO_3. This is an example of a direct union reaction. But heating and shaking of the carbonic acid destroys it. What happens to the atoms? They return to form water and carbon dioxide. This decomposition of carbonic acid is described by

$$H_2CO_3 \longrightarrow CO_2\uparrow + H_2O \text{ (Is the equation balanced?)}$$

Here is another example. Heating of limestone decomposes it. The reaction is

$$CaCO_3 \text{ (limestone)} \xrightarrow{\;\Delta\;} CaO \text{ (quick lime)} + CO_2\uparrow$$

As you can see, limestone decomposes into carbon dioxide and calcium oxide (quick lime).

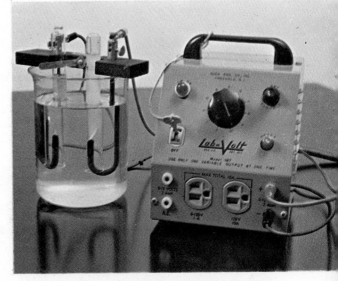

Electrolysis of water, hydrogen is forming in the left tube and oxygen is forming in the right tube. Notice the difference in the volumes of the gases formed. (*Clara Aich and George Senty*)

REPLACEMENT OF THE REPLACEABLES

In your laboratory work you found some of the replaceables. You also discovered something very important. Not all of the equations you can write actually represent a reaction that happens. The laboratory will be the judge.

In a single replacement reaction, an element reacts with one compound. The element takes the place of one of the elements in the compound. A new compound is formed. An element from the original compound is also formed. This is an example of chemical change by replacement. It is a single replacement reaction.

A dazzling example of a single replacement reaction is the replacement of hydrogen in water by sodium. This can be a dangerous reaction. Your teacher may demonstrate it for you. When a small piece of sodium is dropped into a container of water, a lot happens. There is much fizzing and bubbling. The sodium is actually bouncing around on the surface of the water. Even the temperature of the water increases. What's going on? Sodium is replacing the hydrogen in the water. A lot of energy is given off in this reaction. An explosion may even occur. Potassium reacts with water in the same way.

Potassium reacts with water explosively. (*B. M. Shaub and T. P. Schmitter*)

Students at work in a busy high school chemistry laboratory. (*Clara Aich and George Senty*)

The equation for the sodium reaction is:

$$2\,Na + 2\,H_2O \longrightarrow 2\,NaOH + H_2\uparrow$$

or,

$$2\,Na + 2\,HOH \longrightarrow 2\,NaOH + H_2\uparrow$$

You see the replacement clearly if you write the water formula as HOH. One of the hydrogen atoms is replaced by a sodium atom. This forms sodium hydroxide, NaOH. Did the hydrogen atom escape?

Other elements react with water to produce hydrogen. Only potassium, sodium, and lithium will make an explosive reaction. You can tell which elements replace hydrogen. Look at the Activity Series of the Elements in Chapter 14. All the elements above hydrogen on the list will replace it in compounds. Notice that the elements are metals. What class of hydrogen compounds react with the metals?

The hydrogen compounds are acids. For example:

$$Zn + 2\,HCl \longrightarrow ZnCl_2 + H_2\uparrow$$

This is a single replacement reaction. The equation says that zinc replaces hydrogen. In doing so, zinc chloride and hydrogen are formed. Zinc chloride is always $ZnCl_2$. Hydrogen is always diatomic. To balance the equation, two molecules of hydrochloric acid, HCl, must be represented.

You can see how the Activity Series works. The metals on the top replace hydrogen from water, some explosively. As you go down the list, the metals are less reactive. They will replace hydrogen from acids, but not from water. How do the metals react with compounds of metals? Do Experiment 13.3 *Batter Up!* to find out.

QUICK QUESTIONS?

1. Write the equation for the reaction of copper with sulfur.
2. Sugar ($C_6H_{12}O_6$) can decompose into alcohol (C_2H_5OH) and carbon dioxide (CO_2). Write a balanced equation for the reaction.
3. If 1000 grams of sugar decomposes, how many tons of alcohol can be made?
4. Write an example of a single replacement reaction.
5. How does Experiment 13.3 show single replacement reactions?
6. Balance the following equation for a reaction in hot water

$$Mg + H_2O \longrightarrow$$
$$Mg(OH)_2 + H_2\uparrow$$

DOUBLING THE REPLACEMENT

Do you remember about the chemical dropouts? You added one compound to another compound that was in solution. Out dropped a precipitate. That kind of chemical reaction should mean more to you now. Your knowledge of chemical equations will help you understand the reaction. You can predict how many grams of precipitate will be made.

For example, hydrogen sulfide reacts with copper chloride. This produces copper sulfide and hydrogen chloride. The equation is

$$H_2S + CuCl_2 \longrightarrow CuS + 2\,HCl$$

Using atomic mass numbers to study the reaction gives

$$H_2S \quad + \quad CuCl_2 \longrightarrow$$
$$(2 + 32)\ \text{g/mole} + (63.5 + 2(35.5))\ \text{g/mole} =$$
$$CuS \qquad + \quad 2\,HCl$$
$$(63.5 + 32)\ \text{g/mole} + 2(1 + 35.5)\ \text{g/mole}$$

Copper sulfide has a mass of 95.5 grams/mole. A mole of hydrogen sulfide has a mass of 34 grams. This means that for every 34 grams of hydrogen sulfide, 95.5 of copper sulfide will form. Or for every 1 gram of hydrogen sulfide, about 2.8 grams of sulfide is made.

The same thing can be done with the amounts of copper chloride and hydrochloric acid. Let's look at the equation in terms of moles.

$$H_2S + CuCl_2 \longrightarrow Cu + 2\,HCl$$

If the experimenter starts out with 48.25g of $CuCl_2$, he has a half mole of $CuCl_2$. He can expect to produce one mole of HCl or 36.5 grams. The use of mole is also useful in predicting final amounts.

The reaction just studied is an example of double replacement. Two compounds react and interchange members.

Double replacement reactions can get complicated. This happens when radicals are a part of the compounds.

A RADICAL is a group of atoms that acts as a unit that has a charge. Examples are: ammonium, NH_4^+; hydroxide, OH^-; sulfate, $SO_4^=$; nitrate, NO_3^-; and phosphate, PO_4^{-3}.

Just remember that radicals must be treated as a unit. Don't break them up in writing a chemical equation.

Here is an equation with two radicals. In this reaction, the radicals replace each other. The radicals are $(SO_4)^=$ and $(OH)^-$.

$$Al_2(SO_4)_3 + 3\,Ca(OH)_2 \longrightarrow 2\,Al(OH)_3 + 3\,CaSO_4$$

Copper is oxidized by nitric acid. The reaction is:

$$Cu + 4\,HNO_3 \longrightarrow$$
$$Cu(NO_3)_2 + 2\,NO_2 + 2\,H_2O$$

QUICK QUESTIONS?

1. Look at the equation describing the reaction between aluminum sulfate and calcium hydroxide. Give the following:
   (a) the total number of atoms of each element used
   (b) the total number of each kind of radical used

2. Complete the following equation.

$$NH_4OH + HNO_3 \longrightarrow$$

3. What is the difference between a double replacement reaction and a single replacement reaction?

OXIDATION-REDUCTION REACTIONS

Substances that gain electrons are reduced. Substances that lose electrons are oxidized. These statements might seem strange. How can matter gain something yet be reduced? Well, when an electron is gained, then the statement makes sense. For gaining an electron is like gaining a debt: both reduce the gainer.

Take a look at a simple reaction. Think about the movement of electrons. If magnesium is burned in air, there is a bright flash. After the burning, a filmy, white powder is left. This powder is magnesium oxide, MgO. The equation is $2\,Mg + O_2 \longrightarrow 2\,MgO$.

Besides the chemical change, what else changes? Well, before the burning, the magnesium atoms had no charge. This can be written as Mg^0. The zero means that there is zero charge or it is neutral.

In the actual burning, two magnesium atoms join with an oxygen molecule. This forms a compound containing one atom of magnesium for every atom of oxygen. During this reaction, the magnesium atom loses two electrons. It becomes a magnesium ion. This can be written as $Mg^0 - 2e^- = Mg^{+2}$, or,

$$Mg^0 \longrightarrow Mg^{+2} + 2e^-$$

This equation shows that each magnesium atom now has a charge of: $+2$. There was a loss of electrons. When this happens we say that oxidation has taken place. The magnesium was oxidized. *Loss of electrons is OXIDATION.*

What happens to the lost electrons? They are gained by an oxygen atom. This is written as

$$O^0 + 2e^- = O^-$$

or,

$$O_2{}^0 + 4e^- \longrightarrow 2O^{-2}$$

This equation shows that each oxygen atom now has a charge: -2. There was a gain of electrons. And, like gaining a debt, the oxygen was reduced. *Gain of electrons is REDUCTION.*

Since oxygen usually gains two electrons, we say that oxygen has an oxidation number of minus two. Magnesium usually gives up two electrons. Magnesium has an oxidation number of plus two.

Oxidation-reduction reactions provide energy in electrochemical cells. (a) Salt bridge is not in place. No voltage. (b) Salt bridge is in place to complete the circuit. Electron transfer causes voltage to show on voltmeter. (From the CHEM Study film, *Electrochemical Cells*)

ROUNDING UP THE CHAPTER

At the start of this chapter, you were told something very important: Atoms are neither created nor destroyed in a chemical reaction. This is a law of nature: the Law of Conservation of Matter.

This law states many things. One thing it says has to do with chemical equations. As many atoms of each kind must be shown on one side of the equation as on the other side. To balance an equation, you can't invent atoms. You can't change formulas either. There is one thing you can do. You can change the number in front of the formula.

So you learned to balance chemical equations, and to use the mole in a new way. You found out how to represent each atom with mole masses. You have used these masses in studying molar solutions. You will learn more about using moles in Chapter 14.

There are four kinds of chemical reactions:

Direct union or synthesis is a simple joining of two elements.

Decomposition is a pulling apart of compounds. An example of decomposition is the heating of mercuric oxide.

$$2\,HgO \longrightarrow 2\,Hg + O_2\uparrow$$

Lavoisier used that reaction to make oxygen.

You also studied single and double replacement reactions. These are common in chemistry. It is important that you learn how to balance all types of reactions.

Oxidation-reduction (Redox) equations are used to learn about the transfer of electrons. All chemical activity depends upon electron activity. The loss of electrons means that oxidation is taking place. The gain of electrons means that reduction is happening. There can be no reduction without oxidation. Electrons gained by one atom must come from another atom. The number of electrons gained must equal the number lost in a given reaction.

Lavoisier heated mercury (II) oxide to form oxygen. Oxygen is in the container at the right. (*The Bettmann Archive*)

QUICK QUESTIONS?

1. What do these symbols mean?

    $5e^-$; Cl^0; Fe^{+3}; I^-

2. There is no oxygen in this reaction

    $$2\,Na + Cl_2 \longrightarrow 2\,NaCl$$

    Yet oxidation is happening. Which element is being oxidized?

3. What are the oxidation numbers for the atoms in this reaction?

    $$4\,Na + O_2 \longrightarrow 2\,Na_2O$$

4. Even though an atom may be reduced (gain electrons), it is said to have an oxidation number. In the following equation what element is reduced? What is its oxidation number?

    $$Ca + Cl_2 \longrightarrow CaCl_2$$

Chapter 13

ACTION POINTS

A **CHEMICAL REACTION** always results in a new substance being formed.

MASS is **CONSERVED** in chemical reactions.

A **BALANCED CHEMICAL EQUATION** has the same number of atoms of each kind on both sides.

A **DIATOMIC MOLECULE** has two atoms in it.

The reaction of two substances to make a third is called a **DIRECT UNION** reaction.

MOLE MASSES can be used in a **BALANCED EQUATION** to find out how much is needed or made.

If a substance is taken apart in a chemical reaction to make two substances, then a **SIMPLE DECOMPOSITION REACTION** has occurred.

REPLACEMENT REACTIONS happen when substances change places in a chemical reaction.

CHEMICAL ACTIVITY is due to the loss, gain, or sharing of electrons.

OXIDATION occurs when an atom loses electrons.

REDUCTION occurs when an atom gains electrons.

Chemical Reactions: Predicting and Using Them

14

The Challenge

It was the beginning of another cold winter day as the young man left the breakfast table. He knew the weather would be cold. Maybe too cold for working in his homemade laboratory. A woodshed was not the best place to do chemistry experiments.

The year was 1886. The place was Oberlin, Ohio. Twenty-two-year-old Charles Martin Hall had just graduated from college. Among his courses in college, chemistry seemed to be special. To him, chemistry offered many challenges. There was so much

to know. And so much was unknown.

As he walked toward his wood-shed-laboratory, he remembered one of his chemistry classes. The professor had been telling his students about aluminum. That day Charles Hall had listened carefully as his professor was ending his talk.

"Gentlemen," the professor continued, "the properties of aluminum make it a very useful metal. It is light, strong and rustproof. It is also the most abundant metal in the earth's crust. But, there is one problem. It's too expensive

to take it from its ore. It just costs too much to separate the metal from the other elements. The largest piece of aluminum in the United States today is the cap of the Washington Monument. It weighs about six pounds."

The professor paused and looked toward his students. He then said, "Find a way to extract aluminum cheaply from its ore. If you can discover such a method, you will become famous. Not only would you do a great service for mankind, you would become a very rich person."

A representation of the woodshed in which Charles Martin Hall discovered an inexpensive method of producing aluminum. (*Alcoa*)

Original pellets of aluminum produced in Hall's experiments. (*Alcoa*)

That was quite a challenge. On that day, Charles Hall made a decision. He would work on the problem of extracting aluminum.

He entered the woodshed, rubbing his hands to get warm. He went to the small furnace he had built and started the fire. The furnace was not for his comfort, although it did give off a lot of heat. He had built the furnace to melt chemicals.

In the search for a cheap method of getting pure aluminum, chemists had used a process called ELECTROLYSIS. *ELECTROLYSIS is the passing of an electric current through a liquid or melted substance.* In many cases of electrolysis, pure substances are produced at the negative and positive terminals. Chemists thought that maybe aluminum could be obtained in that manner. First, the aluminum ore had to be melted or made liquid. That's when a furnace comes in handy.

Chemists before Charles Hall had melted an ore called cryolite. This had aluminum in it. They then passed an electric current through it. Nothing happened. Electrolysis did not seem to work for aluminum compounds.

It was then that Charles Hall had an idea. And today, February 23, 1886, he was going to try it out. After getting his furnace started, he placed some cryolite in it. While he was waiting for the cryolite to melt, he went through his reasoning again. Maybe the liquid cryolite would dissolve another ore containing aluminum called bauxite. If cryolite did dissolve the bauxite, then the bauxite would be broken up

into its separate elements. Aluminum would be free to move about. He would then have a liquid mixture of cryolite with aluminum particles in it. A current through the liquid mixture would then carry the aluminum particles to the negative plate. And then, perhaps, aluminum metal.

The cryolite had melted. Very carefully he added some powdered bauxite. It disappeared into the liquid cryolite. Did it dissolve? He would soon find out. He placed two carbon rods into the hot, liquid mixture and connected them to a battery. He let the current pass through the mixture for several hours. Then he let it cool.

If pure aluminum had been made, it should be found near the negative carbon rod. Carefully he probed into the cooled mixture. And there, in the bottom of his container, he found small pieces of pure aluminum. Charles Martin Hall had done what no one had done before. He made pure aluminum in a very inexpensive way. The aluminum industry was born.

Charles Hall used his knowledge of chemistry to *predict* what could happen. He predicted that aluminum oxide would separate into aluminum and oxygen. The equation is $2\ Al_2O_3 \longrightarrow 4\ Al + 3\ O_2\uparrow$. He knew that if this happened, aluminum could be recovered by electrolysis.

In this chapter, you will learn how to predict two things about chemical reactions:

You will learn to predict *what* substances are formed.

You will learn to predict *how much* is formed.

QUICK QUESTIONS?

1. Where did Charles Hall hear of the problem of getting aluminum?
2. Describe the electrolysis method.
3. What was the purpose of using cryolite?
4. Describe Charles Hall's prediction.

PREDICTING CHEMICAL REACTIONS

In order to be able to predict something correctly, all the factors concerning the event must be understood. For example, the ancient Babylonian priests were pretty good at predicting eclipses. Yet they really did not understand the movement of the sun and moon. But they did know that eclipses would occur on a predictable schedule. Their ancient records told them this. They knew how the sun and moon behaved.

But people had to understand more about the moon to land on it. The men who aimed for it did not have ancient records to use. They predicted a moon-hit because they understood certain laws of nature.

In your study of chemistry, you will learn to make predictions. The products of many chemical reactions can be predicted. For example, you probably know what will happen if you add copper to a silver nitrate solution. You did this in Experiment 13.3. Can you predict what will happen if you add copper to a lead nitrate solution? Will there be a reaction? If so, what will be produced?

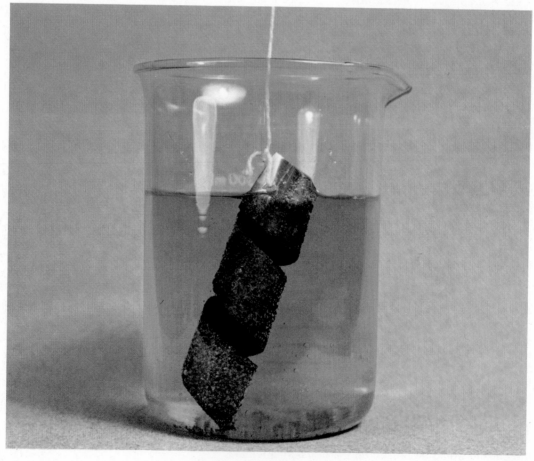

Aluminum replaced copper in this copper chloride solution. Aluminum is above copper in the activity series. (*Felix Cooper*)

ACTIVITY SERIES OF THE ELEMENTS

METALS	NONMETALS
Lithium	Fluorine
Potassium	Chlorine
Calcium	Bromine
Sodium	Iodine
Magnesium	
Aluminum	
Zinc	
Chromium	
Iron	
Nickel	
Tin	
Lead	
HYDROGEN	
Copper	
Mercury	
Silver	
Platinum	
Gold	

Chlorine replacing bromine from sea water. (From the CHEM Study film, *Bromine-Element From The Sea*)

You can predict what will happen. You may even be right, if you know something about the Activity Series of Elements.

For a long time, chemists kept records of chemical reactions. These records help us today to predict correctly certain reactions. The results of these records are stated briefly in the Activity Series. It tells us, for example, that nothing happens when copper is added to a lead nitrate solution. How does the Activity Series tell us that? Look at it for a moment. Locate copper, silver and lead in the Series.

The metals in this series are ranked on their reaction ability. The higher on the list, the more reactive the metal. An element that is higher up in the series will always replace a combined one that is lower when they react. Copper will not replace lead in a reaction. So, copper is ranked lower than lead. Will lead replace copper? According to the table, it will, and it does.

QUICK QUESTIONS?

1. Arrange the following elements in order of their activity. Place the most reactive at the top.

   H, Pb, Cu, Au, Ag, Al, Fe, Na

2. Try prediction reactions for the following. Check with your teacher to see how good your predictions are.
   (a) $Ag + NiSO_4$
   (b) $Al + CuSO_4$
   (c) $Ca + FeSO_4$

FAMILIES OF THE ELEMENTS

The Activity Series of the Elements is not the only tool that is used in predicting reactions. The Periodic Table is also of great help in making chemical predictions. Take a look at it.

The Periodic Table has been divided into Periods and Groups. The up and down columns are the Groups. The Group classification is what we will use in predicting reactions. Groups are also called families. There are eight numbered groups or families in the Periodic Table. There are also two special groups with names: the Transition Elements and the Rare Earth Elements.

Compounds of the elements set up according to the Periodic Table. Note that the compounds of the transition elements are mostly colored. (From the CHEM Study film, *Vanadium, A Transition Element*)

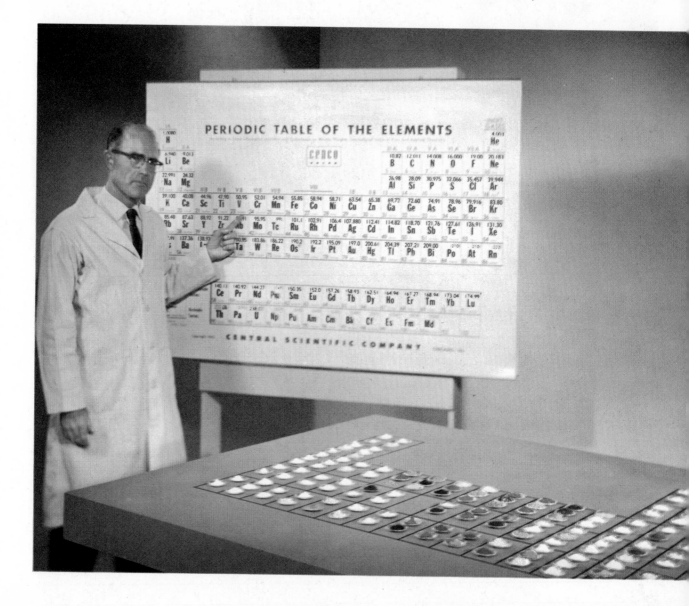

Look at the Group I elements, the Sodium Family. Some members of this family are lithium, sodium and potassium. These are common elements. Other members are rubidium, cesium and francium. A simple reaction with sodium taking part is:

$$2\,Na + 2\,H_2O \longrightarrow 2\,NaOH + H_2\uparrow$$

Now, if potassium is used instead of sodium, the same reaction happens. Instead of sodium hydroxide forming, potassium hydroxide is formed. The equation is:

$$2\,K + 2\,H_2O \longrightarrow 2\,KOH + H_2\uparrow$$

If lithium is now used, the same reaction occurs again. Lithium hydroxide is formed.

$$2\,Li + 2\,H_2O \longrightarrow 2\,LiOH + H_2\uparrow$$

What would you predict if cesium, rubidum or francium is used? You're right! The same reaction takes place. Why does this happen? How can it be explained?

Here is one good explanation. Chemical reactions depend on the number of electrons in the valence energy level. Sodium has one electron in its outer level. So do lithium, potassium, rubidium, cesium and francium. Because of this, the chemical properties of the Sodium Family are very much alike. Their same behavior can be expected for one reason. They all have one electron in their valence energy level.

Now look at Group II. This is the Calcium Family. They each have two electrons in their valence level. You would expect them to react in the same way. And they do. Let's look at an equation representing a reaction of a Group II element in a compound. For example, calcium oxide reacts with carbon dioxide to make calcium carbonate. The reaction is $CaO + CO_2 \longrightarrow CaCO_3$. Suppose magnesium oxide were used instead of calcium oxide. Predict what would happen. What would form?

The other families of the Periodic Chart show strong resemblances also. In Experiment 14.2, you will get a chance to study these family resemblances in the laboratory.

Family resemblances are very helpful in predicting reactions. You'll be using them often. From now on, you should be able to make some rather good predictions. But notice that, first of all, you really have to know something about chemical reactions. Sure, sometimes you might be guessing. But an educated guess works more often than dumb luck. The more you learn, the better you get at predicting. The unknown is really an exciting place to explore. But it's even more exciting if you have prediction power!

USING NUMBERS IN YOUR PREDICTIONS

Predicting *what* will react and *what* does actually form is one thing. Being able to predict *how much* to use or *how much* is made is another thing. You can learn to do it. Again a few rules are needed. You have a head start in mastering these 'how much' problems. For you know how to balance chemical equations. You know about moles and atomic masses. If you feel rusty on those ideas, you should review them. If you remember

(1) how to balance equations,
(2) the mole concept, and
(3) what atomic masses mean

then you are ready to use numbers in your predictions. Let's begin.

There are three kinds of 'how much' calculations.

1. When you know how much *mass* is reacting and you want to find out how much *mass* is made. Or vice-versa. This is called a *mass-mass* calculation.
2. When you know the *volume* of a gas reacting, and you want to find out *how much volume* of a gas is made. Or vice-versa. This is called a *volume-volume* calculation.
3. Finally, if you know how much *mass* is reacting, and you want to know the *volume* of a gas made. Or vice-versa. This is called a *mass-volume* calculation.

PREDICTIONS: MASS-MASS CALCULATIONS

Suppose you were studying the reaction of magnesium and oxygen in the laboratory. How many grams of MgO would be produced if you ignited a two-gram piece of magnesium ribbon? The equation for the reaction is

$$2 \, Mg + O_2 \longrightarrow 2 \, MgO$$

$$\text{moles of Mg} = 2 \text{ g} \times \frac{1 \text{ mole}}{12 \text{ g}}$$

$$= \frac{1}{6} \text{ mole Mg}$$

$$\text{moles of MgO} = \frac{1}{6} \text{ mole Mg} \times \frac{1 \text{ mole MgO}}{1 \text{ mole Mg}}$$

$$= \frac{1}{6} \text{ mole MgO}$$

$$\text{mole mass of MgO} = 1 \times 12 \text{ g/mole Mg} = 12$$
$$\underline{1 \times 16 \text{ g/mole O} \quad = 16}$$
$$28$$

$$= 28 \text{ g/mole MgO}$$

$$\text{mass of MgO} = \frac{1}{6} \text{ mole} \times \frac{28 \text{ g}}{1 \text{ mole}}$$

$$= 4.66 \text{ g of Mg produced}$$

Bauxite being mined. (*Kaiser Aluminum & Chemical Corp.*)

Predictions in Industry: Making Aluminum

Industry makes aluminum by using the same number relationships that you do. They begin with the ore bauxite. This is aluminum oxide with impurities. The impurities are usually silicon oxide and iron oxide. If the ore is of good quality, it contains about 50% alumina. Alumina is Al_2O_3, aluminum oxide. Alumina is separated from the impurities. Then the Hall Process is used to get the pure aluminum.

If the ore is of good quality, it takes about two kilograms to get one kilogram of alumina. If one kilogram of alumina is put through the Hall-Héroult Process, about ½ kilogram of aluminum is recovered. This mass is also predicted by the chemical equation.

$$2\ Al_2O_3 \longrightarrow 4\ Al + 3\ O_2$$

408 grams of alumina and 216 grams of aluminum. (*Clara Aich and George Senty*)

QUICK QUESTIONS?

1. Name the three kinds of chemical calculations using equations.
2. Look at the following equation.

   $$2\ Fe + 3\ S \longrightarrow Fe_2S_3$$

   If you used 40 grams of iron, how much sulfur would be needed to react with it?
3. Show how alumina (Al_2O_3) is about 50% aluminum.

THE RESTLESS MATTER: GAS

The next predictions of "how much" deal with gases. When, working with gases we shall use a relationship between volume and mass.

Gases are very important to us. We use them every day, from the oxygen we breathe to the gas we use for cooking. They have special characteristics.

What is so special about gases? It seems that volumes of gases change when the temperature or pressure changes. We are all familiar with temperature. What is pressure? *PRESSURE is force per unit area.* For instance, notice the difference in pressure on a high heel compared to a flat heel in a shoe.

The pressure which interests the chemist is atmospheric pressure. It is the same pressure the weatherman is talking about in the weather report. The atmospheric pressure is the force the air in the atmosphere exerts on the earth. It is measured by a BAROMETER. Very simply a barometer is a dish of mercury with a long, closed tube inverted in it. The pressure of the air on the mercury in the dish causes the mercury to stay up in the tube. The greater the pressure the higher the mercury rises. The chemist measures the height of the mercury in millimeters. The weatherman talks about inches of mercury. In working with gases we will use the term, mm of Hg (millimeters of mercury).

The fact that gas volumes change when temperature and pressure change presents a problem. If chemists do any experiments with gases, they have to note both the temperature and pressure. Suppose you do a gas experiment and report your results. If someone else does the same experiment, the results probably won't be the same as yours, unless he does it at the *same temperature* and *same pressure* as you did your experiment.

To make things a bit easier, chemists have chosen one special temperature and one special pressure to use when doing gas experiments. These are called *Standard Temperature and Pressure,* STP for short.

The *Standard Temperature* is *0°C.* This is the temperature of melting ice.

The *Standard Pressure* is *760 mm of mercury.* This is the height of a 760-mm column of mercury. It is pushed up that high by average air pressure at sea level.

At STP a mole of a gas occupies 22.4 liters. This volume is called the MOLAR VOLUME of a gas. All gas experiments can't be done at STP. But the results can be adjusted for that temperature and pressure by calculations.

So we know that a gas is a sensitive kind of matter. What else do we know about gases? Quite a bit!

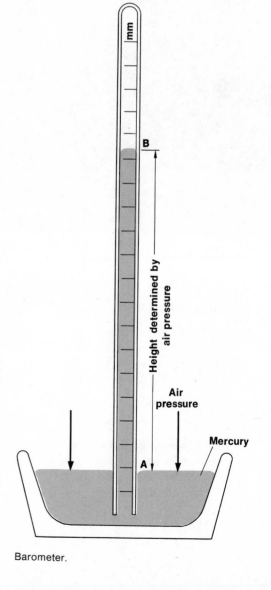

Barometer.

Why are temperature and pressure used in studying gases? In a volume of 1000 ml, there are easily ten thousand, billion, billion molecules of gas. Not only that, but these particles are moving very fast. At room temperature, air molecules move at about 1000 feet per second. That's fast! It is the speed of a rifle bullet as it leaves the gun. At a higher temperature they move even faster. Of course, these molecules are moving in all different directions.

A sample of gas has a very low density. Compared to molecules in solids or liquids, there is a lot of empty space between gas molecules. When pressure is put on a gas sample, the molecules crowd closer together.

Do gases themselves cause pressure and temperature? Gas pressure is caused by the gas molecules hitting the side of the container. You can imagine billions and billions of molecules moving about and bumping one another. Eventually, they meet the walls of their prison. The more gas molecules, the greater the pressure. Of course, if the container is made smaller, the pressure also increases. Then the molecules just collide more often with the wall.

The temperature of a gas is caused by the motion of the gas molecules. The faster they move, the higher the temperature. A bunch of slow-moving gas molecules has a lower temperature than if the same bunch were moving faster.

When we discuss gases, we must know about the pressure, temperature, and volume of the gas. The pressure, temperature, and volume of a gas are very closely related. Suppose we heat a container of gas. The temperature of the gas rises. And so does the pressure. Those molecules are moving faster and hitting the wall more often. Up goes the pressure, if the volume is kept constant. A French physicist named Charles studied this cause and effect.

Boyle studied the effects of pressure on gases.

QUICK QUESTIONS?

1. What is special about 22.4 liters?
2. What is meant by STP?
3. Describe the journey of a gas molecule inside a closed container filled with gas.
4. To what two things are gas volumes sensitive?
5. How is gas temperature caused?

MOLAR VOLUME

Now we know that pressure and temperature have effects on gas volume. All volumes of gases contain molecules. Remember the number of molecules in a mole of a substance——6.02×10^{23}. It is called Avogadro's number. Avogadro also left us his principle with which to work: *Equal volumes of gases under the same conditions of temperature and pressure contain the same number of molecules.*

The volume of gas at STP which contains the Avogadro number of particles is 22.4 liters. This is the MOLAR VOLUME of a gas. The molar volume of each gas has a different mass. By using these figures we shall be able to predict results of reactions of gases.

The molar volume of a gas at 0°C and 760 mm Hg pressure contains 6.02×10^{23} molecules. (*Clara Aich and George Senty*)

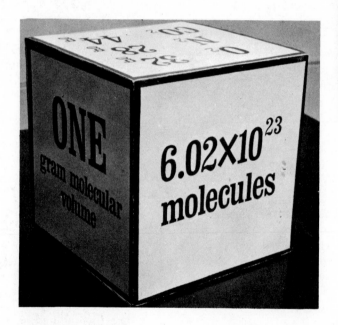

Home Lab

Find out the effect temperature has on a gas by using a balloon.

Blow up a regularly-shaped balloon. Tie the opening with a single knot. Make sure that no gas can escape. Use a tape-measure to measure its circumference if it's round, or its length if it is long. Put the balloon in a refrigerator for about an hour. Measure it again. Did it change in size?

Find out what happens to a balloon's size when it is held high over a hot plate.

Do not burst the balloon.

Assume that the pressure on the balloon is kept constant. What did you find out about the effect of temperature changes on the balloon?

Boyle and companion conducting experiments. (*The Bettmann Archive*)

Pressure and Volumes of Gases

Robert Boyle was an Irish physicist and chemist. He was the first to distinguish between an element and a compound. The nature of a chemical reaction was also studied and explained by him.

He is most famous for his study of gases. The law which describes the relationship of pressure to a volume of confined gas is named after him.

Boyle's Law: *When the pressure is doubled on a gas, its volume is halved, if the temperature is kept constant. If the pressure is halved, the volume doubles, if the temperature is kept constant.* Thus, as the pressure changes, the volume of a gas changes inversely if the temperature is kept constant. Of course these statements apply to a given amount of gas. None is allowed to escape.

In 1783 the Montgolfiers brothers filled a balloon with smoke from a straw fire. The balloon rose because hot air is less dense than cool air. In the same year Charles filled a balloon with hydrogen gas. Why did it rise? (*The Bettmann Archive*)

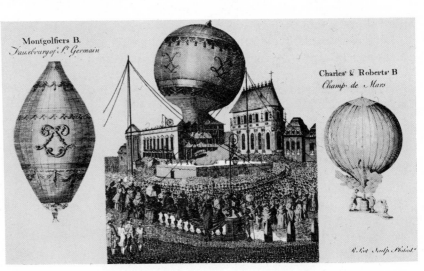

Temperature and Volumes of Gases

Jacques Charles, a French physicist, was interested in balloons. He was the first to fill them with hydrogen gas. In 1783 he went for a balloon ride up almost 2 miles using such a balloon. The air is a lot colder up there than it is on earth. Of course he became aware of the characteristics of gases. He noticed the effect of temperature change on volumes of gases and described it. The description is Charles' Law.

When the temperature of a confined volume of gas is changed, the volume of gas changes directly as the Kelvin temperature, if the pressure is kept constant.

He noticed that the volume of gas changed as the temperature rose from 0°C to 1°C by $\frac{1}{273}$ of what the volume was at 0°C. The use of the Kelvin temperature scale makes calculations easy.

$$0°K = -273°C$$

Its use allows all temperatures to be above 0°K.

PREDICTIONS: VOLUME-VOLUME CALCULATIONS

When working with gases, it is easier to use *volume* than mass in our calculations. The mole idea is still useful to us, however. What is the connection between gas volume and moles? Let's find out.

Helium is a monatomic gas. One mole of helium has a mass of about 4 grams. At STP its volume is 22.4 liters.

Oxygen gas is diatomic. Each molecule is made of two atoms. A mole of oxygen has a mass of about 32 grams. At STP it occupies 22.4 liters.

Suppose we take a mole of another gas. Let's use nitrogen. One mole of nitrogen has a mass of 28 grams. At STP how much volume would it occupy? It would occupy the same volume as one mole of helium or oxygen, 22.4 liters, because it has the same number of molecules.

If we collected one mole of any gas, we would find that each one takes up 22.4 liters of space at STP. It is the molar volume of a gas.

You might be puzzled by now. Why should all these different gases, with different masses, have the same volume? Remember, they all have one thing in common. They each are one mole. Of course, if we made them each $\frac{1}{2}$ mole, each volume would be one half of 22.4 liters, or 11.2 liters. Or, if we had two moles of each, the volume would then be 44.8 liters.

Let's use this information. One molar volume is 22.4 liters at STP. Let's try some volume-volume calculations.

Hydrogen gas and chlorine gas combine to form hydrogen chloride gas. The equation is

$$H_2 + Cl_2 \longrightarrow 2\,HCl$$

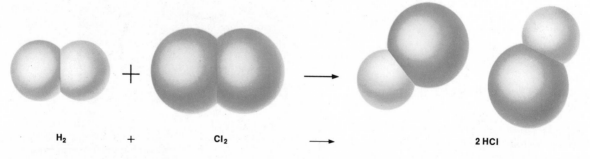

$$H_2 \qquad + \qquad Cl_2 \qquad \longrightarrow \qquad 2\,HCl$$

If 9 liters of hydrogen is used, how many liters of hydrogen chloride gas is made?

First, write the knowns and unknowns.

$$\overset{\text{9 liters}}{H_2} + Cl_2 \longrightarrow \overset{\text{? liters}}{2\,HCl}$$

Then, write the mole relationships.

$$\overset{\text{9 liters}}{\underset{\text{1 mole}}{H_2}} + Cl_2 \longrightarrow \overset{\text{? liters}}{\underset{\text{2 moles}}{2\,HCL}}$$

$$\text{Liters of HCl} = 9 \text{ liters of } H_2 \times \frac{2 \text{ moles HCl}}{1 \text{ mole } H_2}$$

$$= 18 \text{ liters of HCl}$$

Try one more. Suppose we have the following chemical reaction at STP.

$$2\,CO + O_2 \longrightarrow 2\,CO_2$$

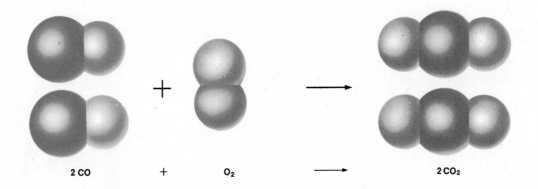

2 CO   + O_2 $\longrightarrow$ 2 CO_2

This says that two moles of carbon dioxide will react with one mole of oxygen to make two moles of carbon dioxide. Let's use five liters of oxygen. How many liters of carbon dioxide will be made?

$$2\,CO + \overset{\text{5 liters}}{\underset{\text{1 liters}}{O_2}} \longrightarrow \overset{\text{? liters}}{\underset{\text{2 liters}}{2\,CO_2}}$$

$$\text{Liters of } CO_2 = 5 \text{ liters } O_2 \times \frac{2 \text{ liters } CO_2}{1 \text{ liter } O_2}$$

$$= 10 \text{ liters } CO_2$$

QUICK QUESTIONS

1. Suppose you have one mole of each of ten different gases. How are they alike at STP?
2. Give an example of Boyle's Law at work.
3. Give an example of Charles' Law at work.

PREDICTIONS: MASS-VOLUME CALCULATIONS

Many times a gas will be given off during a reaction. In Charles Hall's famous experiment, oxygen was made. The equation is

$$2\,Al_2O_3 \longrightarrow 4\,Al + 3\,O_2\uparrow$$

Suppose he wanted to know how much oxygen would be made. All he would need to know is the mass of aluminum oxide, Al_2O_3, used. Let's say he used 408 grams of aluminum oxide. How many liters of oxygen would be made?

First, write the knowns and unknowns.

$$\overset{408\,g}{2\,Al_2O_3} \longrightarrow 4\,Al + \overset{?\,\text{liters}}{3\,O_2}\uparrow$$

Next, write the mole relationships below each substance.

$$\overset{408\,g}{\underset{2\,\text{moles}}{2\,Al_2O_3}} \longrightarrow 4\,Al + \overset{?\,\text{liters}}{\underset{3\,\text{moles}}{3\,O_2}}\uparrow$$

This tells us that two moles of aluminum oxide will produce three moles of oxygen. Now write the mass of two moles of aluminum oxide and the volume of three moles of oxygen.

$$\overset{408\,g}{\underset{2(102\,g)}{2\,Al_2O_3}} \longrightarrow 4\,Al + \overset{?\,\text{liters}}{\underset{3(22.4\,\text{liters/mole})}{3\,O_2}}\uparrow$$

This tells us that 204 grams of aluminum oxide (2×102 g) will make 67.2 liters (3×22.4 liters) of oxygen.

But we are using 408 grams of aluminum oxide. That's two times 204 grams, or 4 moles. So twice as much oxygen should be made. This gives us 2×67.2 liters = 134.4 liters of oxygen. Or,

$$\text{moles of } Al_2O_3 = 408 \text{ g} \times \frac{1 \text{ mole}}{102 \text{ g}}$$

$$= 4 \text{ moles } Al_2O_3$$

$$\text{moles of } O_2 = 4 \text{ moles } Al_2O_3 \times \frac{3 \text{ moles } O_2}{2 \text{ moles } Al_2O_3}$$

$$= 6 \text{ moles } O_2 \text{ prepared}$$

$$\text{liters of } O_2 = 6 \text{ moles } O_2 \times \frac{22.4 \text{ liters}}{1 \text{ mole}}$$

$$= 134.4 \text{ liters } O_2$$

Suppose hydrogen has to be generated in the laboratory. We need 100 liters of it at STP. How much zinc will be needed to generate it?

Does this lady have a MASS problem, or a VOLUME problem?

First, write the knowns and unknowns.

$$\underset{\text{1 mole}}{\overset{\text{? grams}}{Zn}} + 2\,HCl \longrightarrow ZnCl_2 + \underset{\text{1 mole}}{\overset{\text{100 liters}}{H_2}}$$

Next, write the mole mass or molar volume below each substance, as required.

$$\underset{\text{65.4 grams/mole}}{\overset{\text{? grams}}{Zn}} + 2\,HCl \longrightarrow ZnCl_2 + \underset{\text{22.4 liters/mole}}{\overset{\text{100 liters}}{H_2}}$$

$$\text{moles of } H_2 = 100 \text{ liters } H_2 \times \frac{1 \text{ mole}}{22.4 \text{ liters}}$$

$$= 4.46 \text{ moles of } H_2$$

$$\text{moles of } Zn = 4.46 \text{ moles } H_2 \times \frac{1 \text{ mole } Zn}{1 \text{ mole } H_2}$$

$$= 4.46 \text{ moles } Zn \text{ used}$$

$$\text{mass of } Zn = 4.46 \text{ moles } Zn \times \frac{65.4 \text{ g } Zn}{1 \text{ mole}}$$

$$= 292 \text{ g } Zn$$

The mass of zinc needed to produce 100 liters of H_2 at STP is 292 grams.

LOOKING BACK

Take a few moments to think about this chapter. What did you study?

You began with Charles Hall's challenge, an example of the power of prediction. Then you learned how to predict some chemical reactions: *what* will react, *what* will be made. You did this using family resemblance and the activity series of elements.

Next, you learned to predict *how much* was produced. These types of calculations were used to answer the question of how much. These are

(1) mass-mass calculations
(2) mass-volume calculations
(3) volume-volume calculations

You then read about the behavior of gases and how the use of STP is important. Two Laws, Charles' and Boyle's, described the relationship between the pressure, temperature and volume of a gas.

You will find all these ideas useful as you continue your study of chemistry.

QUICK QUESTION?

Hydrogen is formed from iron and hydrochloric acid. This is the equation for the reaction:

$$Fe + 2\,HCl \longrightarrow FeCl_2 + H_2\uparrow$$

How many liters of hydrogen will be formed at STP if 56 grams of iron reacts with an excess of acid?

Chapter 14

ACTION POINTS

PREDICTIONS are very useful in chemistry.

The **ACTIVITY SERIES OF ELEMENTS** is useful in making predictions.

FAMILIES of the Periodic Chart can be used in making predictions.

CHEMICAL BEHAVIOR depends on the **NUMBER OF ELECTRONS** in the valence energy level.

MASS and **VOLUME CALCULATIONS** can be made using the **MOLE CONCEPT.**

GASES are studied while knowing their **PRESSURES** and **TEMPERATURES.**

STANDARD TEMPERATURE is 0°C.

STANDARD PRESSURE is 760 mm Hg.

BOYLE'S LAW says that the volume of a gas is decreased if the pressure is increased, if the temperature is constant.

CHARLES' LAW says that the volume of a gas increases if the temperature increases, if the pressure is constant.

ONE MOLE of any gas at STP occupies a volume of 22.4 liters.

ORGANIC CHEMISTRY AND BIOCHEMISTRY

Unit 6

Contents

UNIT 6 ORGANIC CHEMISTRY AND BIOCHEMISTRY

Chapter 16   *READER TEXT*   **Chapter 16**   *LABORATORY MANUAL*

BIOCHEMISTRY

ORGANIC CHEMISTRY 15

CARBON: THE BACKBONE OF LIVING MATTER

There are thousands of different kinds of plants and animals. Some are too small to be seen without powerful microscopes. Yet, they all carry on with the business of life; taking in food, digesting it, giving off waste material, reproducing, and growing.

The kinds of molecules found in living organisms are varied, but they nearly always have one element in common—CARBON.

Football player running on synthetic turf, one of the many new products from organic chemistry.
(*3M Company Photo*)

HYDROCARBONS: THE BACKBONE OF ORGANIC CHEMISTRY

We are familiar with the ad: "Organically Grown Foods Sold Here." We connect the word "organic" with "back-to-nature, no pesticides used."

The terms "organic" and "inorganic" are used to distinguish between two different groups of compounds.

Originally, organic was used to describe only those compounds that came from living matter. It was believed that organic compounds could only be made by the mysterious life force of plants and animals.

Inorganic compounds had to come from nonliving substances like rocks and water. It was also believed that compounds synthesized (put together) in the lab must be inorganic, even though the substances from which they were made came from living things.

Today, the definition of organic compounds is not limited to those substances made by living organisms. *ORGANIC COMPOUNDS include all substances that contain carbon except oxides of carbon and carbonates.*

Caveman Chemistry

Scientists are curious about compounds found in or produced by plants and animals. Cavemen, too, were curious. They discovered that the black, thick, tarry liquid oozing from the ground would burn. They made torches dipped in pitch (tar) and lighted them.

Prehistoric man began to explore. He wandered over the land. Water separated one land from another. Boats were needed to continue the search for food and adventure. Man learned that pitch would seal his boats watertight.

Cavemen didn't understand that pitch was formed from the dead remains of ancient plants and animals. They didn't know it contained the element carbon. But early man did learn that this material containing carbon was useful.

By the beginning of the nineteenth century, scientists had isolated and identified many substances from plants and animals. During that time, the methods of chemical analysis were being developed. It was discovered that only a few of the many elements made up the compounds from living things.

For example, natural rubber contains only carbon and hydrogen. Sugars, alcohols, and acetic acid are made only of carbon, hydrogen, and oxygen. Urea (found in animal liquid waste) and morphine contain the elements carbon, hydrogen, oxygen and nitrogen.

This knowledge was the breakthrough that was needed for today's chemistry. The story of carbon compounds is so important to modern living that without it, we might still be using pitch just to mend our leaking boats.

They may be made by living organisms or prepared synthetically in the lab. Of these compounds, *all the compounds that contain only the elements hydrogen and carbon are called HYDROCARBONS.*

Look around you. Almost everything you see is made of an organic compound: your shoes and socks, shirts, dresses, athletic equipment and uniforms. Even this paper is organic.

Study the lists of organic compounds below. Everyday we use organic materials. We will discover which of these are hydrocarbons, or to which other group of organic compounds they belong.

SOME COMMON ORGANIC COMPOUNDS

Alkaloids and hormones
Antibiotics and vitamins
Dyes and pigments
Explosives (some)
Fertilizers (some)
Foods: fats, oils, sugars, proteins
Fuels: wood, paper, coal, oil, gasoline, petroleum
Man-made fibers: polyesters, nylon, Orlon

Insecticides
Wool, silk, cotton
Paints (parts)
Perfumes and flavors
Plastics
Refrigerants (some)
Rubber

The Organic Explosion

You have heard that "we live in a Nuclear Age." It is also true that we live in the "Organic Age." There has been an explosion in the number of organic materials. They have been isolated from living organisms and they have been prepared in the lab.

Over one million different organic compounds have been identified. Every year, thousands of new substances are being found in nature or made in the lab.

In 1880, the number was 12,000. In 1910, it was 150,000. In 1940, over 500,000. It is not uncommon for an organic chemist to prepare more than one thousand *new* organic compounds during his lifetime.

The Organic Revolution

In 1828, the German chemist Friedrich Wöhler solved a riddle. He was working in his laboratory with a chemical everyone thought was inorganic, although it contained both carbon and hydrogen. It was ammonium cyanate, NH_4—OCN.

From this compound, Wöhler made urea (you-REE-ah).

$$\begin{array}{c} NH_2 \\ | \\ C{=}O \\ | \\ NH_2 \end{array}$$

Everyone knew urea was an organic substance found in the urine or liquid waste of animals. But everyone did not know that it could be made without using a plant or an animal. They didn't know that it could be made from a compound quite different from urea.

Wöhler opened the door to a whole new way of thinking about chemistry. He helped change scientists' minds about organic compounds.

Now, many other chemists are trying organic synthesis. The organic revolution is on.

QUICK QUESTIONS

1. Which of these organic compounds are made by a plant or animal? Name the plant or animal.
   (a) wax
   (b) sugar
   (c) alcohol
   (d) acetic acid
   (e) urea
   (f) morphine
   (g) rubber
   (h) coal
2. What do we mean by organic compounds?
3. What is organic chemistry?

Diamonds Are a Girl's Best Friend

Carbon, the element has a few disguises. We know it as diamond: clear, brilliant, hard and beautiful.

We also know it as graphite: black, greasy and soft. Graphite is used to lubricate locks and ball bearings because it is so slippery. It is also used as the "lead" in pencils.

Coal is almost pure carbon. Hard coal (anthracite) burns with a hot, clean flame. Soot, charcoal, and coke are almost pure carbon, also.

How is it that carbon has so many different forms? Why can carbon form over one million different compounds?

You remember that a carbon atom has six protons in the nucleus and six electrons surrounding the nucleus. The four electrons on the second energy level are the bonding electrons.

The four bonds formed with one carbon atom are covalent bonds. One or more pairs of electrons can be shared with other elements. A carbon atom can form covalent bonds with another carbon atom and atoms of almost every other element.

We shall see that *carbon forms long chains with other carbon atoms.* Long chain hydrocarbons are called *ALIPHATIC* hydrocarbons.

Carbon can also form rings of hydrocarbons, called CYCLIC (as in cycle or circle) *hydrocarbons.* Some of these carbon rings have a very strong, but pleasant, odor. Aroma also means odor. For this reason, the cyclic hydrocarbons are sometimes called *AROMATIC HYDROCARBONS*.

While diamonds may be flashed on ringed fingers, the cyclic hydrocarbons can be worn proudly, too, in many different ways. Synthetic fabrics have been made from hydrocarbons.

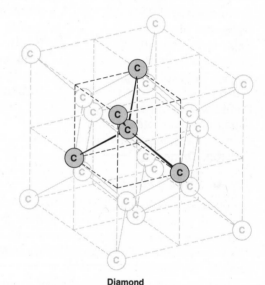

Diamond

Diamond structure.

Diamond in sandstone and a graphite pencil. (*The American Museum of Natural History*)

Graphite structure.

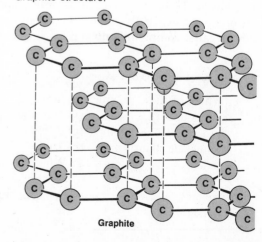

Graphite

FAMILIES OF HYDROCARBONS

Homologs

In Experiment 15.1, *The Homologs,* you discover that a *HOMOLOGOUS SERIES is a listing of organic compounds that are alike except that each successive member differs from the one before it by a small unit such as the* —CH_2 *group. The members of a homologous series are called HOMOLOGS.*

Carbon Chains

Carbon can form single covalent bonds with other carbon atoms. Many carbon "chains" of different lengths are possible. The compounds that are members of these "chain gangs" form a homologous series. Hydrocarbon chains are varied and there are hundreds of them. We shall become familiar with just a few.

THE ALKANE (PARAFFIN) SERIES

Methane (CH_4) is the simplest hydrocarbon. It contains one carbon atom and four hydrogen atoms. Methane is a colorless, odorless gas. It is also the first member of a homologous series.

The second member is ethane (C_2H_6). It is also a colorless gas. Ethane contains two carbon atoms. They form a covalent bond. Ethane contains six hydrogen atoms, all of which are covalently bonded to the carbon atoms.

The above structure represents one molecule of ethane. The lines between the symbols represent a covalent bond. Other members of this series also have the same general formula as ethane, C_nH_{2n+2}, where n is the number of carbon atoms.

The heavier alkanes, $C_{20}H_{42}$ and higher, form waxy solids. Paraffin a mixture of heavy alkanes is a waxy solid. Paraffin means "small attraction." As the number of carbon atoms increase, the more dense the members become. Their boiling points become higher, and their chemical reactivity become more limited. For this reason, the alkane series is called the Paraffin series.

THE ALKANE (OR PARAFFIN) SERIES

NAME	FORMULA	STRUCTURAL FORMULA	PHASE AT ROOM TEMPERATURE
methane	CH_4		gas
ethane	C_2H_6		gas
propane	C_3H_8		gas
butane	C_4H_{10}		gas
pentane	C_5H_{12}		liquid
hexane	C_6H_{14}		liquid
heptane	C_7H_{16}		liquid
octane	C_8H_{18}		liquid

QUICK QUESTIONS

1. How many atoms are there in the ethane molecule?
2. How many carbon atoms?
3. How many hydrogen atoms?
4. Count the number of covalent bonds formed.
5. Why are there over a million organic compounds?
6. What is a hydrocarbon?

Natural Gas

Methane—Auto Fuel of the Future?

Methane is found in the atmosphere of the planets Jupiter, Saturn, Uranus, and Neptune. It is also found on Earth as a result of decaying plant or animal matter. Decaying plant and animal matter deep within the earth form oil. Sometimes when an oil well is drilled, methane gas escapes. You may also find it as tiny bubbles appearing on the surface of a swampy area.

Methane is good fuel. It burns clean and completely. It may be the gas you use in your Bunsen burners. It is used in gas ovens, and water heaters. A trace of a substance with an unpleasant odor is mixed with natural gas. This is done for a purpose—to indicate a leak!

Methane has recently been used as a fuel in experimental automobiles with good results. Used on a large scale, it would reduce smog. Someday when you say, "Fill 'er up," a tank of this compressed gas may be slipped into place on your car. Since the world supply of this gas is not as plentiful as it once was, the use of this gas as an auto fuel may not get beyond the experimental stage.

(© *Universal Oil Products Company*)

Saturated hydrocarbons are in gasoline. (*Atlantic Richfield*)

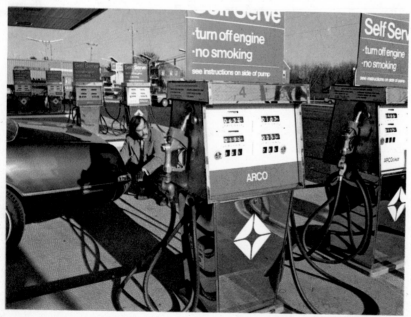

SOMETHING FOR YOU TO DO

1. Write the structural formula for the other members of the alkane series given in the table. It's easy. Try it.
2. Find a pattern in the way the series is formed from one member to the next. *Hint:* Compare how the numbers of carbon and hydrogen atoms change.

RESEARCH PROJECTS FOR THE CURIOUS

3. Look up more information about propane. You may be surprised at what you find.
4. Why is gasoline sometimes called octane? What is an octane rating? Is it important for airplanes and sports cars?

THE ALKENE SERIES

NAME	COMMON NAME	FORMULA	STRUCTURAL FORMULA	PHASE AT ROOM TEMPERATURE
ethene	ethylene	C_2H_2		gas
propene-1	propylene	C_3H_6		gas
butene-1	butylene	C_4H_8		gas
pentene-1	amylene	C_5H_{10}		liquid

THE ALKENE SERIES

The members of the Alkene Series all have a carbon-carbon double bond. The ending "ene" tells us that two carbons share two pairs of electrons between them, forming the double covalent bond. $\overset{\displaystyle H}{\underset{\displaystyle H}{}}C{=}C\overset{\displaystyle H}{\underset{\displaystyle H}{}}$ represents them.

Like the alkanes, the alkenes are chain-like (aliphatic) hydrocarbons, with the general formula C_nH_{2n}. They are named like the members of the alkane series by changing the ending "-ane" to "-ene."

QUICK QUESTIONS

1. Why can't there be a member of the alkene series called methene?
2. Write the structural formula for hexene-1.

Ethylene

The Versatile Gas

Ethylene, C_2H_4, is the first member of the Alkene Series. It is a colorless gas with a sweet odor and taste. It can be used as an anesthetic in hospitals, but, it is flammable, exploding when mixed with air.

Ethylene is derived from petroleum, in the cracking process, and from natural gas.

It is transported by pipeline and stored in cylinders and tube trailers. It has been found in auto exhaust fumes.

Because it is a plant hormone, ethylene is used to ripen fruit and to blanch (whiten) certain vegetables.

It speeds up the growth rate of seedlings, vegetables and fruit trees.

Ethylene has many different uses—in fruit and vegetable processing, medicine, and as a combustible fuel for working with metals, and for processing synthetic alcohol.

THE ALKYNE SERIES

The Alkyne Series is another homologous series of aliphatic hydrocarbons. The homologs of this series each contain a carbon-carbon triple bond —C≡C—. Each member of the series follows the general formula C_nH_{2n-2}.

Ethyne (acetylene) gas is the first member of this series. It's formula is C_2H_2. Acetylene's structural formula is H—C≡C—H.

Acetylene is used as a fuel in welding and cutting of metals. An oxyacetylene flame can reach temperatures as high as 2700°C.

Acetylene burns with a very bright flame. It was used as an illuminating gas before the electric lamp was invented. About 40 years ago, bicycle lamps were equipped with a small acetylene generator. In it was a calcium carbide canister into which water could be dripped as desired through a setscrew valve. Coal miners used this type of lantern in the mines. Now electric lights are used.

Care must be used in the transporting of acetylene. Acetylene may explode when it is compressed. Acetone is added as a solvent. The acetylene dissolves in the acetone and then it is safe to transport it.

Acetylene welding. (*Irene Fertik*)

SATURATED BONDS

When a sponge is filled with water, it is said to be saturated. It can hold no more.

The covalent bonds in the members of the Alkane Series are all single covalent bonds. No more atoms can be added because all the valence electrons on the carbon atoms have formed single covalent bonds with other atoms. The molecule is said to be SATURATED.

SATURATED HYDROCARBONS are those which contain only single covalent bonds between carbon atoms.

UNSATURATED BONDS

An unsaturated sponge can hold more water. Double or triple bonds between carbon atoms can be broken and other atoms added to share the electrons.

UNSATURATED hydrocarbons contain double or triple covalent bonds between carbons next to each other. All members of the Alkene and Alkyne Series of hydrocarbons are unsaturated compounds.

ORGANIC REACTIONS

Substitution

The large variety of organic compounds are made possible by two important types of chemical reactions. The first reaction you studied on page *4/31*, SUBSTITUTION.

SUBSTITUTION is a type of chemical reaction in which one atom or group of atoms is replaced by another atom of group of atoms.

All the members of the Alkane Series have single covalent bonds. These saturated molecules are stable. Their bonds are strong and hard to break. Energy must be added along with a suitable substitution reagent.

$$H-\underset{\underset{H}{|}}{\overset{\overset{H}{|}}{C}}-H \ + \ Cl_2 \ \longrightarrow \ H-\underset{\underset{H}{|}}{\overset{\overset{H}{|}}{C}}-Cl \ + \ HCl$$

| Methane | Chlorine | Methyl chloride | Hydrogen chloride |

Examples:

$$\mathbf{3}\,H-\underset{\underset{H}{|}}{\overset{\overset{H}{|}}{C}}-\underset{\underset{H}{|}}{\overset{\overset{H}{|}}{C}}-O{\cdot}H \ + \ PBr_3 \ \longrightarrow \ \mathbf{3}\,H-\underset{\underset{H}{|}}{\overset{\overset{H}{|}}{C}}-\underset{\underset{H}{|}}{\overset{\overset{H}{|}}{C}}-Br \ + \ H_3PO_3$$

| Ethyl alcohol (ethanol) | Phosphorous tribromide | Ethyl bromide | Phosphorous acid |

Addition

Hydrocarbons with a carbon-carbon double bond (alkenes) and triple bonds (alkynes) are relatively unstable. The extra bonded electrons do not form strong bonds. Other atoms or groups of atoms can be added to these unsaturated compounds.

An ADDITION reaction is one in which one or more atoms are added to a molecule.

The first example transformed an alkene to an alkane by the addition of hydrogen.

$$\overset{H}{\underset{H}{>}}C=C\overset{H}{\underset{H}{<}} \ + \ H_2 \ = \ \left[H-\overset{|}{C}-\overset{|}{C}-H \ + \ H_2 \right] \ = \ H-\overset{\overset{H}{|}}{\underset{\underset{H}{|}}{C}}-\overset{\overset{H}{|}}{\underset{\underset{H}{|}}{C}}-H$$

Ethene (ethylene)   Ethane

This example, shows an alkyne changed to an alkane.

$$H-C\equiv C-H \ + \ \mathbf{2}H_2 \ = \ \left[H-C\!\!\times\!\!C-H \ + \ \mathbf{2}H_2 \right] \ = \ H-\overset{\overset{H}{|}}{\underset{\underset{H}{|}}{C}}-\overset{\overset{H}{|}}{\underset{\underset{H}{|}}{C}}-H$$

Ethyne (acetylene)   Ethane

An alcohol can be made by adding water (hydration) to ethene at 140°C, under pressure, and in the presence of sulfuric acid.

$$\overset{H}{\underset{H}{>}}C=C\overset{H}{\underset{H}{<}} \ + \ HOH \ \xrightarrow[140°]{H_2SO_4} \ H-\overset{\overset{H}{|}}{\underset{\underset{H}{|}}{C}}-\overset{\overset{H}{|}}{\underset{\underset{H}{|}}{C}}-OH$$

Ethene   Ethyl alcohol (ethanol)

Chains Turned to Rings

THE BENZENE STORY
MONKEYS CHASING
THEIR TAILS

Sometimes we wish our dreams could come true. The story of the structure of benzene is a dream that did come true.

Benzene was giving chemists trouble long before the danger due to its vapor was realized. It is a liquid hydrocarbon with a rather pleasant, strong aroma. It is an excellent cleaning fluid, but its fumes, if inhaled, can cause serious damage to the body.

Benzene was discovered in 1825 by Michael Faraday. He isolated it from the oily residue of illuminating gas. He found that there were an equal number of carbons and hydrogen atoms in one molecule.

It wasn't until 1834 that Mitscherlich discovered its formula, C_6H_6.

By 1845, Hofmann found that benzene could be isolated by distilling the tar that came from coal. In those days, coal was converted into coke with coal tar left over. The coke was then used in the iron and steel industry.

The formula for benzene, C_6H_6, was puzzling. It indicated a highly unsaturated molecule like this:

$$\text{H} \quad \quad \text{H} \quad \text{H} \quad \text{H} \quad \text{H}$$
$$\text{C} = \text{C} - \text{C} \equiv \text{C} - \text{C} \equiv \text{C} - \text{H}$$

But this possibility was wrong. Benzene behaved chemically like a saturated compound. What *was* the structure of benzene?

Even its name could not be decided upon. It was first called benzin by Mitscherlich.

Leibig, an important editor of the time, criticized the name. He said it was confusing because it sounded like a chemical having a resemblance to strychnine (a poison) or quinine (a medicine). Leibig recommended benzin be changed to benzol, based on the German word for oil.

Others objected, because alcohols all end with "ol". This strange stuff was clearly not an alcohol.

Another chemist suggested the name pheno, from the Greek "I bear light" because it was first isolated from illuminating gas.

The name benzol was used by the Germans, but in England and France the ending was changed to -ene to avoid confusion with the alcohols.

But, what's in a name? More important findings were at hand.

By 1865, the mystery of the benzene structure was solved.

Friedrich Kekulé (Kay-cool-AY) found that the chemical behavior of benzene could point to only one structure—a ring.

Part of Kekulé's discovery was plain hard work in his chemistry laboratory. Part of it was genius. Still another part was attributed to a dream.

Kekulé had gone to a party. There was good conversation and good wine. In his sleep that night, he dreamed of a string of monkeys chasing each other's tails. They raced faster and faster until the first and last monkey had each other's tail. They formed a ring. And the race went on.

Kekulé awoke with a start. "That is how the bonded electrons are shared."

Who would have dreamed that benzene formed a *ring* of six carbon atoms? Kekulé did.

In the benzene ring, the double bonds between carbon atoms are shared among all the carbon atoms of the ring.

The shape the chemists use for the benzene ring in nature. (*Harry Rogers, National Audubon Society*)

The benzene-ring shape in the American Pavilion at the World's Fair in Montreal. (*Bill Strode, Black Star*)

The knowledge of the chemical structure of benzene opened up a whole new field in organic chemistry. Benzene forms the basis for whole new families of organic compounds.

In 1856, the first synthetic dye was derived from coal tar by Sir William Henry Perkin. Perkin's dye, mauveine, started a new growth in world trade and economics. The synthetic organic chemical industry was born. And benzene led the way with the new class of Aromatic (ring-structured) hydrocarbons.

(a) toluene

(b) phenol

(c) naphthalene

Something for You to Do

Here are some simple aromatic hydrocarbons, based on benzene.

Find out their uses and report back to your class.

ORGANIC ORIGAMI

Isomers

Origami is the ancient Japanese art of paper-folding. Many beautiful and interesting figures can be made by rearranging the corners and edges of a sheet of paper by folding.

Many interesting new structures can be made from a single organic compound by rearranging its atoms.

In Experiment 15.2, *Isomers,* you find that *molecules which have the same number of atoms of each element but different arrangements of these atoms are called ISOMERS.*

Constructing isomers with ball and stick models is an easy way to see structural differences. But are there any other differences between isomers of a molecule besides arrangement of its atoms? The answer is yes. Both the physical and chemical properties of isomers are different.

The straight chain alkane, n-butane, can be converted into ISOBUTANE. Both have the formula C_4H_{10}. The prefix "n" before the straight-chain stands for "normal." The prefix "iso" means that the atoms have been rearranged.

The arrangement of n-butane to isobutane is important in making low-octane gasoline.

Isobutane is also needed for the synthesis of aviation gasoline, high octane gas.

Girl folding paper in the ancient Japanese art of Origami. (*Sekai Bunka Photo*)

TWO ISOMERS OF BUTANE

	MELTING POINT	BOILING POINT
n-butane	a liquid at room temperature	151–152°C
isobutane	−145°C	−10.2°C

HOW TO GET ALONG IN A GROUP

It's been said, "We're known by the company we keep." We identify with our group of friends. Members of a group like the same things, dress somewhat alike, and talk their own language.

Organic compounds have group identity, too. We classify organic compounds by groups. These groups have certain characteristics. Compounds with these groups are easily identified. They all react in a similar way. That is why they are called FUNCTIONAL GROUPS. *A FUNCTIONAL GROUP is that part of the molecule that does the work or enters into characteristic reactions.*

Here are some other famous and important organic functional groups.

"Hi! I'm Alfy Alcohol. Know my kind by the OH group!"

The Alcohols

Characteristic Group: —OH   *hydroxyl group*
Name ending: ol   as in alcoh*ol*

All the aliphatic (straight-chain) hydrocarbons can substitute the hydroxyl group for hydrogen atoms. In such cases alcohols are formed.

In Experiment 15.3, *Alcohol vs. Bases,* you discover the physical and chemical differences between organic bases (alcohols) and inorganic bases (alkalies.)

Examples:

CH_3OH methanol (methyl alcohol, wood alcohol)—poisonous

C_2H_5OH ethanol (ethyl alcohol, grain alcohol) —as a solvent and in alcoholic beverages

$C_3H_5(OH)_3$ glycerol, used to make explosives, such as nitroglycerin, antifreeze and fat

$$\begin{array}{ccc} OH & OH & OH \\ | & | & | \\ H-C & -C & -C-H \\ | & | & | \\ H & H & H \end{array}$$

glycerol

QUICK QUESTIONS?

1. Can an alkane substance undergo an addition reaction?

2. In order for an addition reaction to take place what type bond must be in a molecule?

3. Compare the melting points of the butane isomers.

4. In Experiment 15.3 you compare organic substances, alcohols, with inorganic substances, hydroxides. What is the first thing you notice different about them?

Organic Acids

Many foods we are familiar with have a sour taste. That taste results because they contain organic acids. The formulas of the organic acids are recognized by the presence of the carboxyl group, —COOH. The citrus fruits, oranges, lemons, limes, and tangerines, all contain citric acid. Rhubarb contains oxalic acid, and grapes contain tartaric acid.

Characteristic Group:
$$-C\begin{smallmatrix} O \\ \\ OH \end{smallmatrix}$$
carboxyl group.

A red ant sting is a painful experience. The tiny creature defends himself against his enemies by depositing a small dose of formic acid, HCOOH, under his victim's skin. Swelling and redness are the results. Formic acid gets its name from the Latin word for ant, formica. This acid is also found in the stinging glands of bees. Formic acid is used to make the hard plastic resin, formica.

Some organic acids are called fatty acids. These acids are called fatty acids because fats are made from them. Acetic acid is a fatty acid found in vinegar. Other fatty acids are found in coconuts, peanuts, linseed oil and castor oil. Examine the names, formulas, and food sources of their fatty acids in the chart.

"They call me Fatty Acid. I'm really not fat—only when I get together with alcohol!"

SOME FATTY ACIDS

FORMULA	NAME	FOUND IN
CH_3COOH	acetic acid	vinegar
C_3H_7COOH	butyric acid	butter
$C_{15}H_{31}COOH$	palmitic acid	animal and vegetable fats
$C_{17}H_{35}COOH$	stearic acid	animal and vegetable fats
$C_{25}H_{51}COOH$	cerotic acid	beeswax, wool fat

The Esters

Characteristic Group:
$$-\overset{O}{\overset{\|}{C}}-O-C-$$

An ester is an organic compound formed by the chemical reaction between an acid and an alcohol. This reaction is called ESTERIFICATION.

Example:

$$CH_3COOH + C_2H_5OH \longrightarrow CH_3COOC_2H_5 + H_2O$$

acetic acid   ethanol   ethyl acetate
(fatty acid) (alcohol)   (ester)

$$3C_{15}H_{31}COOH + H-\overset{\displaystyle H}{\underset{\displaystyle H}{\overset{\displaystyle |}{\underset{\displaystyle |}{C}}}}-\overset{\displaystyle H}{\underset{\displaystyle H}{\overset{\displaystyle |}{\underset{\displaystyle |}{C}}}}-\overset{\displaystyle H}{\underset{\displaystyle H}{\overset{\displaystyle |}{\underset{\displaystyle |}{C}}}}-H \longrightarrow (C_{15}H_{31}CO_2)_3C_3H_5 + 3H_2O$$

palmitic acid   glycerol   palmitin
(fatty acid)   (alcohol)   (ester)

In this reaction, the resulting ester, palmitin, is a fat. Fats are formed when the alcohol, glycerol, reacts with a fatty acid of high molecular mass.

Esters are responsible for the pleasing fragrance of many fruits and flowers. The reaction of alcohols with fatty acids can reproduce the flavor and aroma of natural fruits like banana, apple, raspberry, and cherry. Even the disagreeable odor of butyric acid from rancid butter can be converted into a pleasing fragrance by esterification.

The Aldehydes

Characteristic Group $-\underset{\underset{O}{\|}}{\overset{\overset{H}{|}}{C}}$ *aldo group*

Aldehydes are formed by the partial oxidation of alcohols.

One of the most familiar members of this group is formaldehyde, $H-\underset{\underset{O}{\|}}{\overset{\overset{H}{|}}{C}}$

It's strong, pungent odor is not easily forgotten. A solution of this gas in water is used for preserving biological specimens because it is not sensitive to air oxidation.

Dairies add small quantities of formaldehyde to milk to keep it from spoiling by bacterial action.

Formaldehyde reacts with phenol, an aromatic hydrocarbon, to produce bakelite, a hard plastic.

Formalin is a mixture of formaldehyde dissolved in water and methanol. It is used to manufacture rayon.

"I'm Al de Hyde! Let me preserve you!"

The Ketones

Characteristic Group: $\overset{}{\underset{}{\diagup}}C=O$ *carbonyl group*

Ketones are obtained readily by the oxidation of alcohols.

Acetone is a familiar ketone. Its structural formula is:

$$\underset{CH_3}{\overset{CH_3}{\diagdown}}C=O$$

Acetone is often used to dry laboratory glassware. After washing, glass that is rinsed in acetone dries almost immediately. CAUTION: IT IS INFLAMMABLE.

During World War I, acetone was an important ingredient required in making the explosive Cordite. Cordite is a smokeless powder.

Acetone is a product of the bacterial fermentation of sugar.

"Move along!"

The Ketone Kop

The Ethers

Characteristic Group: $-\overset{\mid}{C}-O-\overset{\mid}{C}-$

Ethers are prepared from alcohols. Diethyl ether is the best known member of this group. We shall call this compound simply ether, $H_5C_2-O-C_2H_5$.

It is a good solvent for organic compounds. It dissolves very few inorganic substances and is not miscible (does not mix) with water. It is very volatile (evaporates readily), and is also highly flammable.

The first time ether was used for a surgical operation was by the Boston dentist, Morton. This use took place at the Massachusetts General Hospital in 1846.

Inhalation of ether vapor produces unconsciousness by depressing activity of the central nervous system.

The term anesthesia (meaning insensibility) was suggested to Morton by the poet Oliver Wendell Holmes.

POLYMERS

The Giant Molecules

POLYMERS are the giants of organic chemistry. *POLYMERS are made up of smaller molecules, called MONOMERS, that link together by bonding to each other.*

Proteins are polymers of amino acids. In Experiment 15.4 you learn to form amino acids. The amino acids are bonded together by the removal of water. This process is called DEHYDRATION SYNTHESIS. The resulting bonds formed between two amino acids is called a PEPTIDE Bond. We shall learn more about proteins in Chapter 16.

There are many other important polymers that are found in nature. Starch and cellulose are polymers of the sugar, glucose. Rubber is a natural polymer. We shall study each of these later on.

A knowledge of the natural polymers made it possible for chemists to make synthetic ones that are similar to those found in nature. Synthetic fibers such as nylon, Dacron, acrilan and Orlon offer us fabrics that are strong and long-wearing.

Acrylic fibers are clear and colorless when they are formed. This makes it easy to add dye of any color desired.

Dining room with polyester ceiling. (*John T. Hill*)

(*Courtesy of Nalge*)

Nylon manufacture in Japan has all but replaced the silk industry. Silk worms feed on mulberry trees. The thousands of acres devoted to growing mulberry trees are now free for food crops.

Plastics are polymers. One plastic, Teflon, is made of long chains of carbon atoms covalently bonded to fluorine atoms.

$$-\overset{\displaystyle F}{\underset{\displaystyle F}{C}}-$$

Teflon is a slippery plastic which is resistant to heat and chemical agents. It is used in the home for greaseless frying pans and cookie sheets.

Polyethylene is a plastic made from long chains of ethylene molecules. You may have some polyethylene bottles and graduated cylinders in your lab. It will not react with other chemicals and is unbreakable.

Even synthetic rubber has been synthesized by scientists.

The discovery of these and other polymers have made research in this field an exciting and rewarding activity for the benefit of all.

QUICK QUESTIONS?
1. Why are some organic acids called fatty?
2. Why is acetone used to rinse glassware?
3. Is ether used as an anesthesia today?
4. What is a dehydration process?

Chapter 15
ACTION POINTS

ORGANIC COMPOUNDS include all substances that contain carbon except oxides of carbon and carbonates.

All compounds that contain only the elements hydrogen and carbon are called **HYDROCARBONS.**

Carbon forms long chains with other carbon atoms. Such compounds are called **ALIPHATIC.**

Hydrocarbons can also contain rings of carbon atoms. Such compounds are called **CYCLIC** hydrocarbons.

A **HOMOLOGOUS SERIES** is a listing of organic compounds that are alike except that each successive member differs from the one before it by a small group such as $-CH_2$.

SATURATED hydrocarbons are those which contain only single covalent bonds between carbon atoms.

UNSATURATED hydrocarbons contain double or triple covalent bonds between carbon atoms next to each other.

SUBSTITUTION is a type of chemical reaction in which one atom or group of atoms is replaced by another atom or group of atoms.

An **ADDITION** reaction is one in which one or more atoms are added to a molecule. Molecules which have the same number of atoms of each element but different arrangements of these atoms are called **ISOMERS.**

Compounds that react in a similar way contain the same **FUNCTIONAL GROUPS.**

A **FUNCTIONAL GROUP** is that part of the molecule that does the work or enters into characteristic reactions.

POLYMERS are made up of smaller molecules, called **MONOMERS,** that link together by bonding to each other.

Biochemistry 16

GO POWER

The Weight Watchers

Everybody enjoys good food. French fries, potato chips, coke, and candy bars taste good and satisfy the appetite. A steady diet of these and the pounds begin to show. Sometimes we're just in too much of a hurry to eat a good, balanced meal. All starch and sugar, and no proteins make Jack a fat boy! This is plenty of food, but not the right kinds. Our bodies can actually starve on an unbalanced diet.

In this chapter, we shall learn about carbohydrates (which include starch and sugars); fats, and proteins. These substances are called foods.

All foods supply the body with energy. The energy must be in the form a living cell can use. We must have energy for muscular motion, for carrying of nerve impulses, and for keeping the body warm. The temperature of the average person is about 98.6°F or 37°C. It is measured with a thermometer. This temperature doesn't vary by much. It does not depend upon the weather, hot or cold. Within our bodies, heat is being produced. The quantity of this heat energy can be measured, but not with a thermometer alone. Heat produced by the oxidation of food is measured with a CALORIMETER. You make a simple one in Experiment 16.1.

Read the label on a package of cereal. It tells you how many calories are in an average serving. The calorie is a unit of heat energy. *A calorie* (spelled with a small c) *is the amount of heat needed to increase the temperature of one gram of pure water one Celsius degree.*

The calorie used in nutritional, or food, studies is the large Calorie (spelled with a capital C). *A Food Calorie is the amount of heat needed to increase the temperature of one kilogram of water one Celsius degree.* The Food Calorie is equal to 1,000 small calories.

In Experiment 16.1, *Go Power,* you learn to measure the heat produced by burning small amounts of foods. In the Exercise, *What Is A Calorie?,* you calculate the energy the foods release in terms of calories. When you eat, although there are no small fires in your body, slow oxidation does take place and energy is released.

If you're counting your Food Calories, be sure you're getting enough from the right kinds of foods. Here's to good health!

A steady diet of chocolate cake and the pounds begin to show. (*Burke Uzzle from Magnum*)

INGREDIENTS

Whole wheat, buckwheat, sugar, brown sugar syrup, soy protein, salt, malt syrup, natural and artificial flavors, calcium carbonate, sodium ascorbate, niacin, iron, vitamin A palmitate, gum acacia, calcium phosphate, vitamin E acetate, riboflavin, thiamin, pyridoxine, potassium iodide, vitamin D and vitamin B_{12}. Freshness preserved by BHT.

SPECIAL DIETARY INFORMATION

1 oz. of XXX Wheats provides these percentages of Minimum Daily Adult Requirements:

100% of Vitamin A	4000 USP
100% of Thiamin	1.0 mg.
100% of Riboflavin	1.2 mg.
100% of Niacin	10.0 mg.
200% of Vitamin C	60 mg.
100% of Vitamin D	400 USP
100% of Iron	10 mg.
6% of Calcium	46 mg.
12% of Phosphorus	95 mg.
14% of Iodine	14 mcg.
*Vitamin E	1.7 IU
*Vitamin B_6	.6 mg.
*Vitamin B_{12}	1.6 mcg.

*Minimum Daily Requirements have not been established.

APPROXIMATE COMPOSITION

Protein	10.3%
Fat	1.7%
Carbohydrates	81.2%
Calories per ounce (1 cup)	102

ENERGY EXPENDITURE PER HOUR UNDER DIFFERENT CONDITIONS OF MUSCULAR ACTIVITY

ACTIVITY	CALORIES PER HOUR			ACTIVITY	CALORIES PER HOUR		
	PER 70 KG. = 154 LBS. (AVERAGE MAN)	PER KG.	PER POUND		PER 70 KG. = 154 LBS. (AVERAGE MAN)	PER KG.	PER POUND
Sleeping	65	0.93	0.43	Walking slowly (2.6 miles per hour)	200	2.86	1.30
Awake lying still	77	1.10	0.50	Carpentry, metal working,			
Sitting at rest	100	1.43	0.65	industrial painting	240	3.43	1.56
Reading aloud	105	1.50	0.69	"Active exercise"	290	4.14	1.88
Standing relaxed	105	1.50	0.69	Walking moderately fast			
Hand sewing	111	1.59	0.72	(3.75 miles per hour) . . .	300	4.28	1.95
Standing at attention	115	1.63	0.74	Walking down stairs	364	5.20	2.36
Knitting (23 stitches per				"Severe exercise"	450	6.43	2.92
minute on sweater)	116	1.66	0.75	Swimming	500	7.14	3.25
Singing	122	1.74	0.79	Running (5.3 miles per			
Tailoring	135	1.93	0.88	hour)	570	8.14	3.70
Typewriting rapidly	140	2.00	0.91	"Very severe exercise" . . .	600	8.57	3.90
Dishwashing (plates, bowls,				Walking very fast (5.3 miles			
cups, and saucers)	144	2.06	0.93	per hour)	650	9.28	4.22
Sweeping bare floor (38				Walking up stairs	1100	15.8	7.18
strokes per minute)	169	2.41	1.09				
"Light exercise"	170	2.43	1.10				

(Adapted with permission of Macmillan Publishing Co., Inc. from CHEMISTRY OF FOOD AND NUTRITION by H. C. Sherman, Copyright 1952 by The Macmillan Co.)

SUGARS
Going Into High Gear

You often hear "Eat a chocolate bar for quick energy." Did you know that there is no food value in chocolate? Chocolate is a flavoring, and is really not sweet at all. Try a bite of unsweetened chocolate. The sweetners and the food values come from the added sugar. Sugars are practically pure CARBOHYDRATES. They contain the elements carbon, hydrogen and oxygen.

Carbohydrates are energy-supplying foods. Humans depend upon certain "staple" food for carbohydrate sources. These include cereals, potatoes and rice. The "staple" foods make up over half of our calorie needs. Famine often follows when these foods are in short supply.

When we ask someone to "Pass the sugar," we usually refer to just one particular kind. There are many kinds of sugar. Table sugar is called sucrose. It is white and sweet. Not all sugars are, but they are all crystalline and soluble in water.

We obtain some of our calorie needs from sugars because they are rich in energy-supplying materials. Sixty percent of the sugar produced is used in homes and restaurants. The remainder is used in bakeries, in the canning industries, for flavoring, in soft drinks, by dairies, and in the tobacco industry.

RECOMMENDED DAILY DIETARY ALLOWANCES

	WT.	HT.	CALORIES
	kg	cm	
Men			
25 yrs.	65	170	3200
45 yrs.	65	170	2900
65 yrs.	65	170	2600
Women			
25 yrs.	55	157	2300
45 yrs.	55	157	2100
65 yrs.	55	157	1800
Pregnant (3rd trimester)			Add 400
Lactating (850 ml. daily)			Add 1000
Infants			
1–3 mos.	6	60	kg. × 120
4–9 mos.	9	70	kg. × 110
10–12 mos.	10	75	kg. × 100
Children			
1–3 yrs.	12	87	1200
4–6 yrs.	18	109	1600
7–9 yrs.	27	129	2000
Boys			
10–12 yrs.	35	144	2500
13–15 yrs.	49	163	3200
16–20 yrs.	63	175	3800
Girls			
10–12 yrs.	36	144	2300
13–15 yrs.	49	160	2500
16–20 yrs.	54	162	2400

The Sugar Clubs

Sugars can be grouped according to whether they are simple or complex. See the definition of HYDROLYSIS at the right.

Simple sugars cannot be broken down by hydrolysis into other sugars. Simple sugars are called MONOSAC-CHARIDES. All hexoses, such as glucose, fructose and galactose, are simple sugars.

Complex sugars can be broken down into simple sugars by hydrolysis. A complex sugar that produces two molecules of simple sugars is called a DISACCHA-RIDE. Maltose, lactose and sucrose are disaccharides.

POLYSACCHARIDES are made up of several mono-saccharide units. Polysaccharides are polymers of the $-C_6H_{10}O_5-$ group. Examples of polysaccharides are starch, dextrins, glycogen (animal starch), muscilage (used for glue), and cellulose, which is found in the cell wall of all plant cells.

One of the sources of sugar is maple syrup. (*Grant Heilman*)

Biobriefs of Some V.I.S.'s
(*very important sugars*)

Sucrose—Table Sugar

The sugar we use in cereal, to sweeten lemonade, to bake cookies and cakes, and to make candy is called sucrose. Sucrose is called cane sugar because it comes from the stems of sugar cane. Sugar beets are also an excellent source of sucrose.

Sucrose is a complex sugar (disaccharide). It has the formula $C_{12}H_{22}O_{11}$. The hydrolysis of one molecule of sucrose yields a molecule of glucose and a molecule of fructose. *HYDROLYSIS is a reaction in which a bond is split and oxygen and hydrogen are added in the same proportion as they are in water.*

$$C_{12}H_{22}O_{11} + H_2O \longrightarrow$$
sucrose   water

$$C_6H_{12}O_6 + C_6H_{12}O_6$$
glucose   fructose

Glucose—The One and Only

Glucose is the only sugar the body can use. As we shall see, all other sugars and starch must be converted to glucose by digestion before they can be used for energy by living cells.

Glucose has the formula $C_6H_{12}O_6$. It is obtained from starch but is also found in corn syrup and honey. Glucose is sometimes called dextrose. It is a six-carbon sugar. The Greek prefix for six is *hexo*. The ending given to the names of sugars is "-ose." Glucose is a hexose. It has an aldo group, so we can also say it is an aldo-hexose.

Fructose—Fruit Sugar

Fructose has the same formula as glucose, $C_6H_{12}O_6$. The arrangement of the atoms within the molecule is different. It has a keto-group. That is why fructose is a different kind of sugar. Fructose is a keto-hexose found in fruits like apples, peaches, apricots, pears, oranges, and even lemons.

Reducing Sugars

What sugars will help you reduce? None! But there are some that are called "reducing" sugars.

As you have learned the word "reducing" has a very different meaning in the language of chemistry. A positively charged ion, like the Copper II ion, Cu^{++}, is said to be reduced if it gains one electron. It then becomes a Copper I ion, Cu^+.

REDUCING SUGARS *contain a free or available aldo or keto group for chemical bonding.* These sugars react with a special blue solution containing Copper II ions, Cu^{++}. This reagent is called Benedict's solution.

In Experiment 16.2, *Sugars,* you find that only certain sugars give a positive reaction with Benedict's solution. The positive reaction is indicated by a color change from blue to orange-yellow to red. The red color shows that the Copper I ions, Cu^+, are now present. The Cu^{++} ion has been reduced to the Cu^+ ion.

Glucose, fructose, maltose (malt sugar), and lactose (milk sugar) are reducing sugars. They all contain either a free aldo or keto group to help reduce Cu^{++} to Cu^+.

Sucrose has no free aldo or keto group. Sucrose is not a reducing sugar. Once sucrose has been hydrolyzed during digestion, it forms two reducing sugars, glucose and fructose.

Hydrolysis of Complex Sugars

$$C_{12}H_{22}O_{11} + H_2O \longrightarrow C_6H_{12}O_6 + C_6H_{12}O_6$$

Sucrose (table sugar) $\longrightarrow$
glucose + fructose

Maltose (malt sugar) $\longrightarrow$
glucose + glucose

Lactose (milk sugar) $\longrightarrow$
glucose + galactose

QUESTIONS FOR THE CURIOUS

1. What causes the disease known as diabetes (dye-ah-BEE-tees)? Find out what you can about this disease. Report your findings to your class.

2. What industry can you mention that has not already been named that uses sugar?

3. In Experiment 16.1 you get a rough estimate of how many Calories of heat energy a piece of food gives off. How would you improve the experiment to get a more accurate answer?

Saccharin: A Sugar Substitute

Sugars are not the only substances that are sweet to the taste. Saccharin is 500 times sweeter than cane sugar, sucrose. Saccharin is often used as a substitute for sugar for medical reasons. It is used in the manufacture of syrups, diet soft drinks and in other foods.

Saccharin is not a food. It has no nutritional value. It is a white, crystalline powder. It can be compressed into small tablets. This sweetener has the formula $CHCHCHCHCHCCC(O)NHSO_2$.

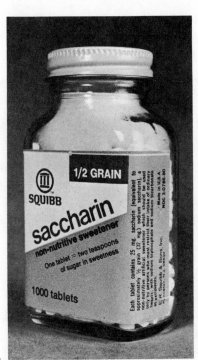

A bottle of saccharin.

Starch—The Mysterious Polymer

The exact formula for starch has not yet been discovered. This is due partly because starch is not soluble in water. Our knowledge of the formula for organic compounds comes from the number of grams of a substance that can be dissolved in a known amount of water. From this, the molecular mass of the compound can be determined.

We do know that starch has a molecular mass close to 50,000. Starch is a polymer of a basic unit resembling glucose, $C_6H_{10}O_5$.

Starch is produced naturally by plants. It is found in grains, such as rice, in fruits and in tubers, such as potatoes. Starch is our main source of carbohydrates.

In Experiment 16.3, you learn about the solubility of starch and how to test for the presence of starch.

The saliva in the mouth contains enzymes (organic catalysts) which help break starch down to glucose molecules by hydrolysis. There are a series of steps involved in this chemical reaction before starch is changed into the monosaccharide glucose. You follow these chemical steps by performing tests on starch as it is hydrolyzed by saliva in Experiment 16.3.

Another type of starch is glycogen. Glycogen has been called Animal Starch because it is found in the liver and muscular tissues. Unlike starch, glycogen is soluble in water and gives a red color with iodine. Glycogen is a polymer of glucose.

Glycogen has recently been isolated from corn. This was an important discovery because it was assumed that glycogen was a typical animal product only.

Chemist watching the process in which hydrogen atoms are being added to fatty acid to improve soybean oil for salads and cooking. (*USDA*)

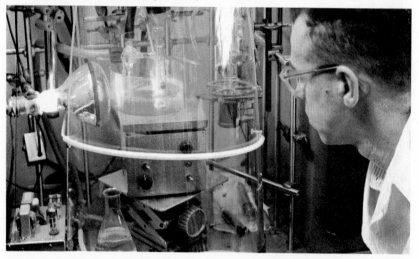

From Oil to Fat
How Shortening Is Made

Take a slice of butter and melt it in a pan. The liquid is greasy. It looks like an oil, but it is not. As soon as the liquid is cool, it turns back to solid butter again. *Oils are liquid at room temperature. Fats are solid at room temperature.*

You learned in Chapter 15 that *fats are formed by the chemical reaction of long chain fatty acids with the alcohol glycerol.*

Oils are formed by the chemical reaction of short chain fatty acids and any simple alcohol.

Oils from plants like olive oil and corn oil are called vegetable oils. Linoleic acid is one fatty acid found in corn oil. This is a polyunsaturated fatty acid because it has two double bonds. Therefore corn oil is called a polyunsaturated oil. If hydrogen is added chemically, the double bonds can be broken and hydrogen atoms are added into the molecule. This is easily done with the aid of a catalyst to speed the reaction. Bits of nickel metal make an excellent catalyst for this process. The result is a saturated solid. The solid is shortening used in cooking.

Vegetable oils are preferred in the diet because there is evidence that polysaturated solid fats form cholesterol in the blood. Too much cholesterol has been known to cause hardening of the arteries (arteriosclerosis) and heart disease. Cholesterol builds up in the blood vessels to block the passage of blood to other organs and cells of the body.

Learning to Live with Fats

Who needs fat? We do. We can't live without it. No one likes too much fat, but it is needed in the diet. Fats, like sugars and starch, are energy-giving foods. Many diets contain from four to five times as much carbohydrates as fats, by weight. Usually, from 20 to 25 per cent of the total Calories we need for good health is fat.

Foods taste better because of their fat content. Meats, eggs, butter, cheese, and oily foods like nuts and peanut butter all contain fat.

Rats react very much like humans in nutritional experiments. It has been found that, *in the absence of fat* in the diet, rats develop a fat deficiency disease, no matter how much carbohydrate is present. This disease is due to the *absence of highly unsaturated fatty acids* from the diet. These fatty acids are present in various fats. Therefore, they are called "essential fatty acids."

On diets *low in protein and high in fat,* rats suffer *liver damage.* This disease is called cirrhosis (sir-OH-sis). Too much fat is deposited in the liver. The liver then becomes fibrous and stringy. This condition can be reversed if the diet is changed and other substances added to the diet.

Fats and fatty acids are found in brain, nerve, liver, lung and spleen tissue. Even the lining of the stomach contains fat. This is partly why the protein portion of the stomach lining is not affected by the hydrochloric acid found in the stomach. The lining of the stomach is not digested, even though proteins are digested in the stomach.

Nutrition experiments provide data on how foods and vitamins affect health, strength, intelligence and growth. *(Courtesy of Merck and Co.)*

PEANUTS •
By Charles M. Schulz

PROTEINS

We Can't Live Without 'em

Proteins are the essential food. Proteins make up for the daily "wear and tear" on our bodies. The body cells are constantly undergoing destruction and must be replaced. An afternoon game of baseball removes thousands of skin cells from the hands. Feet carry us several miles a day. Cells on the soles of the foot are not steel-belted radials. These cells wear out faster than a two-ply tread.

Cuts and bruises require tissue repair. Proteins replace the missing parts in our body shop.

Has anyone told you lately "You've grown"? Proteins have done the job for you.

During digestion about 58 per cent of the proteins we eat is converted to glucose for energy. The remaining 42 per cent is used for building tissues.

Good sources of protein are meat, milk, eggs, cheese and fish. Cooked soybean meal is a good vegetable source of proteins. In countries where fresh meat and dairy products are hard to obtain, soybeans provide a good substitute.

KWASHIORKOR is a disease of infants with protein malnutrition. This disease is common in parts of the world where supplies of milk are limited and where infants are fed mostly carbohydrates.

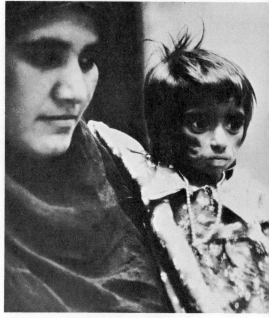

This child is suffering from Kwashiorkor. (*UNICEF PHOTO*)

This is the same child restored to health by the proper diet. (*UNICEF PHOTO*)

Amino Acids

Proteins are polymers of amino acids. All amino acids contain nitrogen. An amino acid must contain two groups of atoms: the amino group, $\begin{smallmatrix} H \\ | \\ N- \\ | \\ H \end{smallmatrix}$, and the carboxyl group, $\begin{smallmatrix} -C=O \\ | \\ O-H \end{smallmatrix}$.

There are about 22 known amino acids. The table shows the light amino acids which cannot be synthesized (put together chemically) in our bodies. These have been found to be essential for normal growth. They must be obtained from the foods we eat.

The general formula for a typical amino acid. R represents some particular chemical group of atoms, such as —CH₃ (methyl) which determines a specific kind of amino acid.

$$
\begin{array}{ccc}
& H & H \\
& | & | \\
R-&C-N \\
& | & | \\
& C=O & H \\
& | \\
& OH
\end{array}
$$

Gerty Theresa Radnitz Cori

In 1947, Gerty Cori and her husband, Carl Cori jointly received the Nobel Prize in Medicine. They worked on the METABOLISM of carbohydrates. *METABOLISM is the chemical process in which elements in foods are changed into body-building materials.*

Insulin, a protein, controls the use of sugar by the body. The Coris fed white rats a known amount of sugar. To some rats they gave insulin, to some they did not. The rats were tested and finally their bodies were analyzed for carbohydrates. The Coris found that half the sugar had been converted to glycogen and stored in the liver and muscles. Some of the sugar was converted to fat and stored as fat. The rest of the sugar was burned to carbon dioxide and water. They found that the insulin decreased the amount of glycogen stored in the liver.

After many experiments, they discovered a process in metabolism, they called this process the "Cori cycle."

Dr. Gerty Cori died in 1957 after receiving many honors for her work in biochemistry done jointly with her husband and independently.

CLASSIFICATION OF AMINO ACIDS

TO GROWTH OF RAT	
ESSENTIAL	NONESSENTIAL
Lysine	Glycine
Tryptophan	Alanine
Histidine	Serine
Phenylalanine	Cystine
Leucine	Tyrosine
Isoleucine	Aspartic acid
Threonine	Glutamic acid
Valine	Proline
Arginine	Hydroxyproline
Methionine	Citrulline

(*Wide World Photo*)

STRUCTURES OF SOME AMINO ACIDS

Glycine—The simplest of the amino acids

$$H-\underset{\underset{\underset{O-H}{\overset{\|}{\underset{}{}}}}{\overset{H}{\underset{C=O}{C}}}-NH_2$$

Alanine—Silk contains about 25% of this amino acid

$$CH_3-\underset{\underset{O-H}{C=O}}{\overset{H}{C}}-NH_2$$

Valine—an essential amino acid

$$CH_3-\underset{CH_3}{\overset{H}{C}}-\underset{C=O}{\overset{H}{C}}-NH_2$$

Leucine—an essential amino acid

$$CH_3-\underset{CH_3}{\overset{H}{C}}-\underset{H}{\overset{H}{C}}-\underset{C=O}{\overset{H}{C}}-NH_2$$

PEPTIDE BONDS

A Protein in the Making

The proteins in a T-bone steak are different from the proteins in a leg of lamb. They even taste different.

A particular protein structure depends upon the number and kinds of amino acids that are bonded together. This bond is formed by a loss of water. The OH group is removed from the carboxyl group of one amino acid. One hydrogen comes from the amino group of the second bonding amino acid. The result is the formation of a molecule of water. This type of reaction is called a DEHYDRATION SYNTHESIS. The word *dehydration* means "water removal." Synthesis means "putting together."

A special kind of bond is formed between the two amino acids. It is called a PEPTIDE BOND,

$$\begin{matrix} O & H \\ \| & | \\ -C-N- \end{matrix}.$$

The resulting compound is called a DIPEPTIDE.

The top photo shows hams from hogs of low protein-high fat diet. (USDA)

In the bottom photo the diet of the hogs was high protein-low fat. (*USDA*)

This biochemist is checking results of test after samples have been run in centrifuge in foreground. (*Irene Fertik*)

Here is an example of the formation of a peptide bond. The two bonding amino acids are glycine and alanine.

$$H-\underset{\underset{NH_2}{|}}{\overset{\overset{H}{|}}{C}}-CO-\boxed{OH+H}-NH-\underset{\underset{COOH}{|}}{\overset{\overset{H}{|}}{C}}-CH_3 \longrightarrow H-\underset{\underset{NH_3}{|}}{\overset{\overset{H}{|}}{C}}-CO-NH-\underset{\underset{COOH}{|}}{\overset{\overset{H}{|}}{C}}-CH_3+HOH$$

Glycine   +   Alanine $\longrightarrow$ a dipeptide   +   water

It is possible to break the peptide bond by hydrolysis. Water can be added to the dipeptide and two amino acids will be formed. This reaction is the reverse of the one above. We shall learn how proteins are digested by hydrolysis to form amino acids later on.

Proteins are complex structures. They are made of long chains of amino acids called POLYPEPTIDES. The prefix "poly" means many. There could be up to 100 peptide bonds in a single protein. These chains come in a single strand that resembles a coiled rope or wire like a slinky. This coil is called HELIX. The coils are linked together by atoms from each strand forming weak chemical bonds between them. These weak bonds are often formed between sulfur and oxygen. All amino acids in proteins contain the elements carbon, hydrogen, oxygen and nitrogen. There are two amino acids that also contain sulfur.

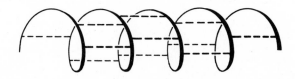

The discovery of the coiled structure of protein was made by Dr. Linus Pauling. He won a Nobel Prize for his work.

There is still much more to learn about the structure and function of proteins. Perhaps you will want to become involved in protein research someday.

QUICK QUESTIONS?

1. When a beam of light from a flashlight is passed through a starch solution what happens?
2. Name two ways in which starch and sugar (sucrose) are different.
3. It is believed that poly-saturated fats may cause cholesterol to build up in the blood vessels. What is the difference between this type fat and fats which are not thought to be connected with cho-lesterol build up?
4. What element do pro-teins have that starches and sugars do not have?
5. List one way to test for each of the following: starch, fat, protein.

Enzymes—Powerhouse Proteins

How would you like some powerful workers to help cut down the amount of energy you need to complete a tough job? You have them, every time you need energy to break chemical bonds during digestion.

DIGESTION is the process that breaks large molecules of food into smaller ones that cells in the body can accept and use.

Enzymes are your powerhouse helpers. Without them, you would not have enough energy to do the job of digestion fast enough to stay alive. It would take a body temperature much higher than 98.6°F to furnish the energy needed for digestion.

Covalent bonds in organic compounds are very strong bonds. Enzymes get into the act of digestion by lowering the amount of energy needed to break these covalent bonds. The process of breaking down foods during digestion can then go faster. The body cells receive the nutrients they need to carry on with the business of living.

A substance that speeds up a chemical reaction by lowering the amount of energy needed to complete the reaction is called a CATALYST.

ENZYMES are organic catalysts. Enzymes have a *protein structure.* This structure is not destroyed during the chemical reactions in which they play a part. There is evidence to support the idea that the enzyme joins with the reacting substances long enough to lower the energy needed to break up the large molecules in food. After that, the enzyme is free to repeat the job.

Enzymes do wear out. Like all body proteins, they must be synthesized (rebuilt) constantly. They are synthesized by some of the molecules they helped to digest!

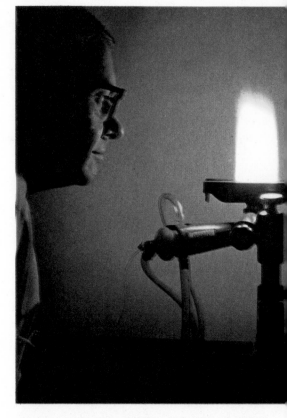

In order to detect an element in biological fluids and tissues which are often available only in small amounts, the biochemist can use flame emission spectrometry. Here the yellow flame indicates the presence of sodium. (*National Bureau of Standards*)

Nurses study biochemistry in order to be more helpful in their duties. (*Irene Fertik*)

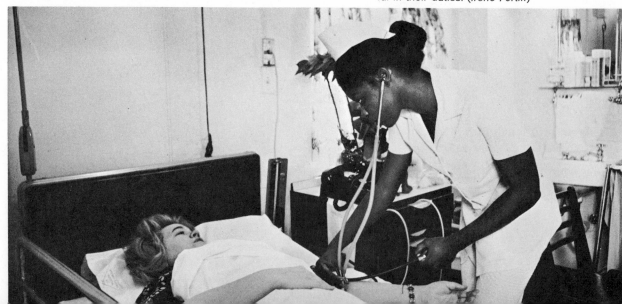

Enzymes Are Fussy

Enzymes are particular about what kind of job they do. In our bodies, each type of chemical reaction depends upon a special enzyme to speed it up. For example, only one kind of enzyme will work in the digestion of fat. Other enzymes are needed to break up large protein molecules into smaller ones. We say that enzymes are *specific*.

Carbohydrate digestion is begun in the mouth. Saliva contains two important enzymes needed for this job. They are ptyalin (TIE-ah-lin), often called salivary amylase, and maltase. These two enzymes are active in changing starch to glucose in a series of chemical steps. In one of the steps, the sugar maltose is formed. This is the over-all reaction of the conversion of starch to glucose. See the equations in the margin.

The conditions under which enzymes will work must be just right, too. Temperature is important. If there is not enough heat, the enzyme may not be able to speed up the chemical reaction at all. If the temperature is too high, the enzyme may be damaged.

The same is true for pH. The enzymes ptyalin and maltase work best when the pH is between 5 and 7.4. The average pH of the mouth is 6.8, slightly acidic. The pH of the mouth is just right for these enzymes to do their work.

Protein digestion begins in the stomach. The pH of the stomach is between 1 and 1.5. This low pH is caused by the presence of hydrochloric acid in gastric juices. Pepsin is the enzyme in the stomach that begins to help break down complex proteins into smaller ones, proteoses and peptones. The conditions of temperature and pH are favorable for pepsin to work.

Other enzymes are required to complete the job begun in the stomach. The hydrolysis of the smaller proteins forming amino acids takes place in a basic environment of the small intestine.

Fats are hydrolyzed to fatty acids and glycerol by enzymes called lipases. Lipases are specific. Some work best in the acid environment of the stomach. Others work best in a basic environment of the small intestine.

There is much more to learn about the work of enzymes in living organisms. Research chemists are working to find out more about the role of enzymes in a chemical reaction. They are discovering new enzymes which had not been identified before. This knowledge enables us to understand the chemistry of the human body. From this new information, researchers are learning how to cure and prevent diseases caused by chemical imbalances and deficiencies.

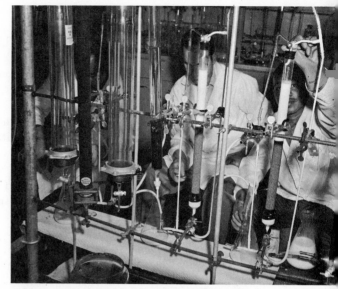

Using the same basic idea as the deionizer column in Experiment 5.4, these biochemists are removing radioactive strontium from milk. (*USDA*)

$$\text{starch} + \text{water} \xrightarrow{\text{ptyalin}} \text{glucose}$$

Maltase converts maltose to glucose.

$$\text{maltose} + \text{water} \xrightarrow{\text{maltase}} \text{two molecules of glucose}$$

$$\text{protein} + \text{water} \xrightarrow[\text{pH} = 1 - 1.5]{\text{pepsin}} \text{proteoses and peptones}$$

QUICK QUESTION?

About what two conditions are enzymes fussy?

Chapter 16
ACTION POINTS

BODY BUILDERS are called foods. They are carbohydrates, fats and proteins.

One calorie (small) represents the amount of heat necessary to raise the temperature of 1 gram of water 1C°.

A Calorie (large) represents the amount of heat necessary to increase the temperature of one kilogram of water 1C° (1 kg = 1,000 g). A Calorie is the unit of heat used in calculating the energy released from food. One large Calorie = 1000 small calories.

A **CARBOHYDRATE** is a compound containing the elements carbon, hydrogen, and oxygen. The hydrogen and the oxygen are in the ratio of two to one.

GLUCOSE is the sugar our body cells can accept and use. It is often called *dextrose*.

HEXOSE is a six-carbon sugar. Glucose and fructose are hexoses.

An **ALDO-HEXOSE** is a six-carbon sugar containing an aldehyde group. Glucose is an example of an aldo-hexose.

FRUCTOSE is a six-carbon sugar which has the same formula as glucose, but a different chemical structure. It is called fruit sugar because it is found in most fruits.

A **KETO-HEXOSE** is a six-carbon sugar containing a ketone group. Fructose is an example of keto-hexose.

HYDROLYSIS is a chemical reaction in which water acts upon another substance to form one or more entirely new substances.

SUCROSE, or table sugar, is called cane sugar because it is extracted from the stems of sugar cane. Sugar beets are another source. When sucrose is hydrolyzed it forms glucose and fructose.

MONOSACCHARIDES are simple sugars. They cannot be broken down by hydrolysis into other sugars.

A **DISACCHARIDE** is a complex sugar molecule that can be broken down by hydrolysis to produce two molecules of simple sugars.

POLYSACCHARIDES are made up of several monosaccharide units. Examples are starch, glycogen and cellulose.

REDUCING SUGARS contain a free (available) aldo or keto group for chemical bonding. These sugars give a positive reaction with Benedict's solution.

SACCHARIN is a sugar substitute. It has no food value.

STARCH is a polymer of glucose molecules of unknown length. It is hydrolyzed into glucose molecules.

FATS are formed by the chemical reaction of long chain fatty acids with the alcohol, glycerol. Fats are solid at room temperature.

VEGETABLE OILS are formed by the chemical reaction for short-chain fatty acids and any simple alcohol. Oils are liquid at room temperature.

PROTEINS are polymers of amino acids. They supply energy and build and repair body tissue.

AMINO ACIDS are the building blocks of proteins. They contain the amino group, $-NH_2$, and the carboxyl group, $-COOH$.

ESSENTIAL AMINO ACIDS are needed for normal growth. The body cannot synthesize these. They must be obtained from the food we eat.

A **PEPTIDE BOND** is formed between two amino acids by dehydration synthesis, $-CO-NH-$.

DEHYDRATION SYNTHESIS is the forming of a chemical bond between two reacting molecules by the removal of atoms between them. The removed atoms will form water.

A **DIPEPTIDE** is a compound made up of two amino acids. The bond between them is called a **DIPEPTIDE BOND.**

A **POLYPEPTIDE** is made up of more than ten but less than one hundred amino acids joined together by peptide bonds.

A **HELIX** is a coiled strand of polypeptide linked by weak chemical bond.

A **CATALYST** is a substance that helps speed up a chemical reaction by lowering the amount of energy needed for the reaction to take place.

ENZYMES are protein structures which act as catalysts for specific chemical reactions in a living organism. Each enzyme works best within its own temperature and pH range.

CHEMISTRY IN THE HOME

Unit 7

Contents

UNIT 7   CHEMISTRY IN THE HOME

Chapter 17   *READER TEXT*   **Chapter 17**   *LABORATORY MANUAL*

THE CHEMISTRY OF FOOD

Chapter 18   *READER TEXT*   **Chapter 18**   *LABORATORY MANUAL*

CLEANSING AGENTS

Chapter 19   *READER TEXT*   **Chapter 19**   *LABORATORY MANUAL*

COSMETICS

The Chemistry of Food 17

IS EVERYTHING FIT TO EAT O.K. TO EAT?

Foods are the Building Blocks of human growth.

Millions of children will grow up with less than the right amount and kinds of foods. As a result, their bodies and minds will never be normal. In some cases a family or even a nation may lack the proper food resources. Often the cause of the trouble is a lack of understanding about the selection of food. A child is not healthy because he or she eats a large amount of food. Remember, it is the kind of food that a child eats that is important. A child must eat enough of the right kind of food to stay healthy.

Children were studied in places where poor diets were known to exist. Some of the problems found in school children who had poor diets (malnutrition) were bone deformities (curvature of the spine, bow legs and knock knees); decayed and crooked teeth; tendency to contract diseases; underweight; and lack of mental alertness.

Unfortunately the damage caused by malnutrition cannot be repaired easily. The child deformed in early childhood due to a poor diet, may carry the results for the rest of its life.

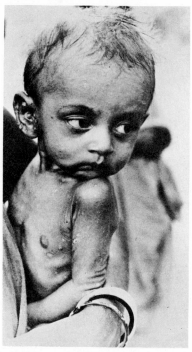

Child with malnutrition. (*Wide World Photos*)

Gathering food and cooking it. (*American Museum of Natural History*)

Food Chemistry, An Old Science

Cooking was probably discovered by accident. It is likely that primitive people ate their food raw. Getting food was not always easy. Finding animals burned in a forest fire was a treat. The burned food saved labor. Something had happened to the burned meat that made it taste better. Wandering primitive tribes started to cook their food. They may have roasted game over fires or buried food in the hot coals of camp fires.

Today cooking is an art. Baking, broiling, stewing, frying, steaming, roasting, and boiling, are a few of the ways used. Seasonings and sauces also add variety.

Whether the meal is simple or a fancy gourmet delight, foods are chemicals. Cooking produces chemical changes and in most cases physical changes as well. These changes are caused mainly by heat energy. Some of the chemical changes may be for taste, but many of the changes are also for health. The heat kills germs and other harmful materials in the food. Often cooked foods are more easily digested than raw foods.

FOOD CHEMISTRY IS ORGANIC CHEMISTRY

In Chapter 15 you learned about the structures of some organic compounds; how the carbon atoms can form long chains to build a variety of compounds. In Chapter 16 the importance of organic compounds to your body was discussed. In Chapter 17 you will be concerned with the chemistry of the foods you eat. How foods are digested and how foods are prepared are important to you in everyday living.

The chemical compounds that you eat to sustain life are made up of organic molecules. These food materials are changed and used by your body (1) for growth and repair, and (2) to keep the body warm.

Food		
Carbohydrates	Minerals	Vitamins
Fats	Proteins	Water

A full course meal which consists of proteins, carbohydrates, vitamins, fats, and minerals. (*Photo Trends*)

Louis Pasteur in his laboratory.

Pasteur Lived: Now You Can Live Longer

Had the people only known, fanfares of trumpets and foot-high headlines would have greeted the year 1822. That was the year Louis Pasteur was born in France. His mother probably feared childbirth. Death following childbirth was common in his day. Surgery and medicine at the beginning of the nineteenth century was so poor that 50 percent of those operated upon died. The local barber doubled as surgeon and the origin and cures for most diseases were unknown.

His parents, poor and uneducated, worked hard for his education, and at 26 Pasteur became a professor of physics. His studies and research led him into physics, chemistry, and biology. It was Pasteur's research of microbes that helped him solve many problems that prevent good health and comfort. He first won the hearts of his countrymen, when he developed methods which saved the silk, wine, and sheep industries from ruinous effects of microbe infections.

Pasteur discovered a vaccine for rabies. He invented the process which bears his name, pasteurization. Through the process of pasteurization many foods (milk, for example) can be preserved for safe consumption.

Pasteur was not a doctor of medicine. He was a scientist, physicist, biologist and chemist, who used the experimental methods of research to discover cause and prevention of diseases.

Joseph Lister, a fellow scientist, once rose to pay respects to Pasteur with these words, "You have raised the veil that for centuries covered infectious diseases."

Today we no longer fear that children will die of diphtheria. We can drink milk without fear of infection; go to a hospital confident of a cure. In his last public statement Pasteur said, "Whether or not our efforts are favored by life, let us be able to say when we come near the great goal, I have done what I could."

In 1895, Pasteur died.

THE DIGESTION FACTORY

The digestive system changes foods into new materials that can be used by your body. There are two ways in which it makes these changes: a physical way and a chemical way. The physical changes are made by breaking the food into small pieces. The factory also serves as the vessel within which the chemistry of digestion takes place. The chemistry way breaks the food down into simpler materials. It also builds them into materials directly useful to the body.

Another Look at Enzymes

As we saw in Experiment 16.6, enzymes are catalysts. They are like the busy little man who starts a fight between two people. He observes the fierce reaction between the two fighters and then walks away from the fight. He is unchanged whereas the fighters lie wounded and remarkably changed. An enzyme "helps" reactions but does not itself change in the process. Each enzyme has a "target" chemical or chemicals which it will serve as a catalyst. The target chemical is called the SUBSTRATE. If the enzyme needs a "helper" chemical before it can go to work, the "helper" enzyme is called a CO-ENZYME.

ACTION IS WHERE THE ENZYMES ARE

All cells contain enzymes. Enzymes in cells start the chemical processes by which life in animals and plants can continue. Pasteur was first to show that certain reactions happen only in the presence of special chemicals now known to be enzymes. He showed that a specific kind of yeast was needed to ferment wine. If the enzyme called zymase is destroyed by heating, the fermentation of wine stops. The reaction showing the fermentation of sugar to produce alcohol is:

$$C_{12}H_{22}O_{11} + H_2O + yeast \xrightarrow{zymase} 4\ C_2H_5OH + 4\ CO_2$$

sucrose (table sugar)   ethanol (ethyl alcohol)

Pasteur also learned that wine would sour, and produce vinegar when exposed to air. Alcohol is changed to acetic acid by an enzyme called dehydrogenase:

$$C_2H_5OH + O_2 + \text{"mother of vinegar"} \xrightarrow{dehydrogense}$$

ethanol   yeast

$$CH_3COOH + H_2O$$

acetic acid

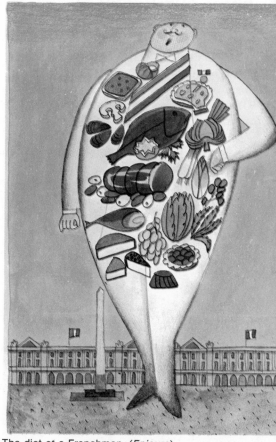

The diet of a Frenchman. (*Epicure*)

Fermentation of wine.

As with some other chemical reactions, when the temperature increases the rate of reaction increases. With enzymes, however, there is a point of no return. With few exceptions, heat in the 80°C to 100°C range destroys enzyme activity. Pasteur found that by raising the temperature of milk, he could prevent the fermentation of the sugars which form lactic acid.

$$C_{12}H_{22}O_{11} + H_2O + \text{lactobacillus} \xrightarrow{\text{lactase}}$$
sucrose

$$4\ CH_3CHOHCOOH$$
lactic acid

Enzymes are destroyed by heat because they are proteins. When proteins are denatured (changed) they become insoluble. Because denatured enzymes are insoluble they cannot enter into solution and react chemically.

Enzymes are compounds and as such can act independently of the living cells that produced them. Enzymes formed in the pancreas are secreted into the small intestine where they digest food. Green fruit separated from a plant ripens because enzymes continue to cause change. Meat becomes tender in storage because enzymes in the meat continue to react with the tissue. In many foods, controlled enzyme activity is desirable during storage. However, too much enzyme activity in storage, can cause food to spoil. Cold storage prevents deteriorization of food because the cold slows the enzyme activity.

Almost all foods contain enzymes. Treatment or refining may remove or destroy enzymes. For example, sugar and shortening (lard) have been purified sufficiently to remove enzymes.

ENZYMES AT WORK

Rennin is obtained from the ground-up lining of calves' stomachs. The enzyme is extracted from the tissue with glycerin and water. Rennin is also produced in the human system by the lining of the stomach and the pancreas. Working as a part of the digestive process rennin has a curdling or clumping action on milk.

Junket is a product made from rennin which is used in a sweet milk desert. Junket can also be used to curdle milk in the preparation of cream cheese.

In Experiment 17.1, you duplicate reactions that occur in a living system and observe the results in a test tube. With rennin you have an opportunity to see how a biochemist can work with enzymes, obtained from a living system.

If raw milk has been added to pasteurized milk, an enzyme, phosphatase will be present. It can be detected by a color test.

Dr. Lloyd A. Hall, one of the outstanding American food chemists, holds patents for meat curing, seasonings, emulsions, baking products, and other food related products. (*Wide World Photos*)

QUICK QUESTIONS?

1. Why is it important to know about foods and proper diets?
2. What is an enzyme?
3. What role do enzymes play in the digestion of food?
4. How do enzymes affect the storage of foods?

THE HAND OF NATURE

$C_{12}H_{22}O_{11}$ is sucrose, the carbohydrate you know as table sugar. It is found in the juice of many plants. It is most concentrated in sugar beets, sugar cane and the sap of maple trees. How does sucrose get to your table and eventually provide energy to your body? It starts first with the "hand of nature" but needs also "the hand of man."

In the leaves of sugar cane and sugar beets, as in all green plants, the reaction called photosynthesis produces sugars. It is a complicated process in which the green coloring chemical of plants plays an important role. Water, carbon dioxide and the radiant energy of the sun interact to organize the sugar molecule. The equation which describes this process is

$$6\ CO_2 + 6\ H_2O + 691{,}000\ \text{calories} \longrightarrow C_6H_{12}O_6 + O_2$$

According to this equation, 691,000 calories of radiant energy are converted into available energy for use in living processes. When, by enzyme activities, the simple sugar formed in photosynthesis is converted to a starch, and then later in a sugar beet it is converted to sucrose, there is a great amount of energy stored into the molecule. This is the energy which you can eventually use in your activities.

Sugar cane harvest.
(*Bjorn Bolstad, Photo Researchers*)

Sugar refinery.
(*Van Bucher, Photo Researchers*)

SUGAR

All green plants make sugar. Sugar cane and sugar beets produce most of the sugar we use.

The crushed tissues of the plant are boiled with water made alkaline with lime. Otherwise, the natural acidity of the sugar solution would cause it to decompose into simpler sugar. The lime also causes the settling out of certain impurities.

As the sugar is heated, crystals form. To separate the crystals from the solution, the mixture is put into a CENTRIFUGE. *A CENTRIFUGE is a piece of equipment that spins causing heavier particles to settle out.*

The crystals which form are raw sugar. To be used for food the raw sugar is further refined. The crystals are redissolved and the resulting colored solution is put through filters usually carbon in the form of boneblack. The solution is then colorless, and when recrystallized, the sugar crystals are white.

Machines package the washed and dried sugar crystals which is then sold to the customer.

Finished candy kisses. (*Hershey Candy Co.*)

Stirring chocolate.
(*Hershey Chocolate Co.*)

Rock candy. (*A. V. Nieves*)

Candy

Sucrose is the sugar usually meant when it is mentioned in cookbooks. Glucose, fructose, and maltose are also common sweetening agents.

When sucrose is used in making candy, INVERT SUGAR is often formed. *INVERT SUGAR is half glucose and half fructose.* It is made by heating sucrose in water. This reaction is called INVERSION.

$$C_{12}H_{22}O_{11} + H_2O \longrightarrow C_6H_{12}O_6 + C_6H_{12}O_6$$
sucrose   glucose   fructose

Although the formulas of glucose and fructose look alike, their structures are different.

The formation of invert sugar is hastened by the addition of an acid substance or the enzyme invertase.

Sucrose alone is not as soluble as a mixture of it with invert sugar. As a result, crystallization takes place more slowly using a mixture. Since the mixture is less easily crystallized, the cook has more control on crystallization. Smaller crystals can be formed. In fudge, the aim is to have smaller crystals to produce a velvety texture. Stirring causes smaller crystals. It prevents the clumping of large groups of crystals.

Temperatures have an effect on the type of candy formed. The higher the temperature of the syrup, the firmer the resulting candy. Syrups cooked to 149°–154°C are used for brittles.

The addition of different materials have various affects on the formation of crystals. You study some in Experiment 17.2. Some materials that delay or prevent the formation of sugar crystals are proteins of milk, or egg, carbohydrates of starch, fat. (Cream and chocolate contribute fat.)

QUICK QUESTIONS?

1. Name three sugars. Write their formulas.
2. Name an enzyme that prevents crystallization.
3. What method did you use in Experiment 17.2 to prevent the crystallization of sugar?
4. In Experiment 17.2 find out how acid substances affect the formation of crystals. Compare this result with the fact that proteins of milk delay or prevent the formation of sugar crystals.

A Study of Eggs

Eggs contain nutrients necessary in the human diet. The chart below gives an idea of how nutrients are distributed in the part of the egg.

The traces of minerals are iron, phosphorous, and calcium. Traces of other materials are also present. The yolk is a good source of vitamin A, thiamine, riboflavin and vitamin D. The white is a good source of sulfur.

The egg is one of the most important items in the human diet because of the high quality and the percentage of proteins present. When heated the proteins coagulate. The coagulation of the egg proteins occurs in two steps. First, the protein molecules break apart. The peptide chains uncoil and unfold. Second, new bonds form between the peptide chains. The new bonds cause the resulting thickening of the yolk and white of the egg. Eggs are more digestible when cooked.

The quality of the egg is judged by CANDLING. The egg is held to a strong light. From the test, experts can tell the freshness and quality of the egg. In a fresh egg, it is hard to see the yolk, and the air packet is small.

Fresh eggs have a high rounded yolk. The white does not spread out much. An older egg spreads out on a dish.

The Browning of Foods

The preparation of foods almost always changes its color. More often than not, food darkens during cooking or processing. The change of color is called BROWNING.

You may have noticed that fruit turns brown after cutting, during freezing and thawing, or after it has been stored for a time. Oxidizing enzymes are probably the cause of this type of browning. Lemon juice which is highly acid interferes with this activity to stop or decrease browning.

Myoglobin is the protein coloring material (pigment) which gives meat its red color. But myoglobin is bright red only when it is combined with oxygen. Meat in the butcher shop, especially if you cut into the center of a roast, has a purplish red color. The deep red hue is caused by the lack of oxygen attached to the myoglobin.

When meat is cooked the protein myoglobin becomes denatured: a new pigment is formed with brownish coloring. The iron in myoglobin changes from iron (II) (Fe^{++}) to iron (III), Fe^{+++}. A chemical change takes place as the red myoglobin becomes a tan or brown-colored denatured protein.

The browning of bread results from the reaction of the aldehyde groups of sugars with the amino groups of proteins.

Candling eggs. (*Grant Heilman*)

PERCENTAGE BY WEIGHT

	WATER	PROTEIN	FAT	MINERALS
White	87	10.9	0.2	0.6
Yolk	49	16	32	1.7

FLOUR STANDARD

REQUIRED	MINIMUM	MAXIMUM
Thiamine	2.0	2.5
Riboflavin	1.2	1.5
Niacin	16.0	20.0
Iron	13.0	16.5

Browning of an apple. (*Clara Aich and George Senty*)

Flour, Leavening—Baking

Flour comes from the grinding the seeds of corn, wheat, rye, or barley. The different seeds produce various kinds of flours. Wheat flour is the kind commonly used in the kitchen.

Wheats are classed as hard, soft, or durum. Durum is a class of hard wheat used in making macaroni products.

The milling of wheat is the separating of endosperm, bran and germ. When no separation is made, whole wheat flour is the product.

A final stage in the production of wheat flour is bleaching. Chemicals including oxides of nitrogen, and chlorine are used.

Instant flour has small particles of uniform size that do not pack. Sifting it is not required for baking.

White wheat flour contains a high percentage of starch and about 10 to 14 percent protein. When flour is moistened and kneaded insoluble proteins form the soluble protein, gluten. The moistened gluten molecules give the dough strength and the ability to stick together.

In Experiment 17.3 you obtain gluten from dough by washing the dough to remove the starch.

In cakes the development of gluten is kept down so that the product is tender.

Fats and oils are used for their shortening power. They are insoluble in water and thus interfere with the development of gluten. They shorten the strands of gluten and in this way increase the tenderness of the product.

Flour which bears the label "enriched" means that certain B vitamins and iron have been added. Calcium and vitamin D are optional.

In order for breads, or cakes, or other bakery products to rise, a LEAVENING AGENT is needed. Yeast plants produce carbon dioxide from sugar. Sodium bicarbonate interacting with an acid ingredient, such as sour milk is another leavening agent. Carbon dioxide is produced.

Any process by which dough is filled with holes which remain after baking is a LEAVENING PROCESS. The objective of the leavening process is to make gas pockets in a sponge-like dough. They make the dough light and fluffy and easy to chew, taste better and easier to digest.

Modern Research

Synthetic Foods

It is believed that synthetic foods can help supply countries with limited natural food supplies with tasty nourishment. *A SYNTHETIC FOOD is one which has one major ingredient which comes from a non-farm source.*

The ingredients are most often used to give color, flavor, texture, or thickness to the food. Petroleum products are the most used synthetic ingredients. Research is being done on obtaining proteins for humans from oil. A problem facing the researchers is toxicity of the oil protein to humans. It will probably be a few years before "food from oil" will be available to the general public.

QUICK QUESTIONS?

1. Proteins can be changed (denatured) by heat, alcohol, strong acids, alkalies, or beating. Which of these methods did you use to coagulate proteins in Experiment 17.3?
2. The next time you use an egg, how will you tell whether it is fresh?
3. Do you think that air in beaten egg acts as a leavening agent?
4. Why does lemon juice stop sliced apples from turning brown?

Leavening of bread.
(*General Mills, Inc.*)

ANY COLLOIDS FOR DINNER?

COLLOIDAL SUSPENSIONS are dispersions of very small particles spread evenly throughout a system. Four important kinds of colloids are SOLS, EMULSIONS, GELS, and AEROSOLS.

In Experiment 17.4 we work with a few colloids found in the kitchen. There is a list of the different types of colloids in the same experiment.

Colloidal suspensions differ from solutions in that the particles suspended are much larger than the ions or molecules dissolved in solutions. The colloidal particles are roughly in a size range of 10^{-7} to 10^{-4}cm. They are too small to be seen by a microscope. Colloidal suspensions also differ from solutions in that the particles are large enough to scatter a beam of light. You saw this effect in Experiment 16.3.

Like solutions, they do not settle. The dispersed particles are spread evenly throughout the system. However, it is possible to make the colloidal particles come together or COAGULATE. Methods to coagulate colloids include changing the temperature, and causing the charge of the colloidal particles be neutralized.

Temperature change: *Colloidal suspensions that seem like liquids are called SOLS. Those which are like solids are called GELS. A gelatin salad is a sol chilled to make a gel. The same reaction happens in the making of jelly. The reverse reaction is true when soup stock is heated to make soup.*

Ice cream contains a gelatin and an emulsifier. (*Eisenberg, Photo Trends*)

Home Lab

Making Mayonnaise. Mayonnaise is an Emulsion of Water in Oil.

In order to maintain the emulsion an EMULSIFIER is needed. *An EMULSIFIER is a stabilizer used to disperse the droplets of liquids which usually do not mix throughout each other.* It is attracted to both substances. In mayonnaise, an egg or egg yolk is an emulsifier.

In a glass container, mix about ¼ cup salad oil with one tablespoon of lemon juice or vinegar. Add the last three ingredients below. Beat the mixture. Set it aside for five minutes. What happens?

In the meantime, get the ingredients to make mayonnaise.

Proportions for Mayonnaise

1 egg yolk
2 tablespoons vinegar or lemon juice
½ cup to 1 cup salad oil
½ teaspoon of salt
½ teaspoon sugar
¼ teaspoon mustard and paprika
Add the last three ingredients to the vinegar or lemon juice. Add to the egg yolk. Mix until well blended. Add the oil one drop at a time. Beat after each addition until an emulsion starts. Then add larger amounts.

Compare the oil and water mixture of the oil and vinegar or lemon juice, with the mayonnaise. List all your observations. What difference does the egg yolk make?

Butter is a colloidal food. It consists of water particles suspended in milk fats. (*Jim Annan, Photo Trends*)

Change in charge: All colloidal systems are electrically neutral. The positive and negative charges may not be equally spread out, however. The surfaces of the suspended particles may have an excess of one charge and the dispersing medium may have an excess of another.

Each colloidal system has a point at which the number of positive and negative charges on the particles are equal. This may cause the colloid to coagulate. Changing the pH by adding an acid or a base or by adding special salts may cause this to occur.

Milk is a colloid. Casein and butterfat particles are suspended in water. When milk becomes acid, it may coagulate.

QUICK QUESTIONS?

1. What kind of colloid is ketchup?
2. Butter is a water-in-oil emulsion. What is needed to maintain the emulsion? Why?
3. Compare colloids to solutions.
4. Is the cornstarch ball in Experiment 17.4, a colloid?

Chapter 17
ACTION POINTS

COOKING produces chemical changes and, in most cases, physical changes in food.

FOOD materials are used by the body for growth and repair of tissue, and to provide the heat that keeps the body warm. Food is broken down by the body's digestive system into **CARBOHYDRATES, FATS, PROTEINS, MINERALS, VITAMINS,** and **WATER.**

The **DIGESTIVE SYSTEM** breaks down foods both physically and chemically.

ENZYMES are proteins that act as catalysts. They are changed chemically (denatured) by heat. The names of enzymes usually have an "ASE" ending. The action of enzymes is affected by temperature change, and by the pH of the system.

A **SUBSTRATE** is the name given to a substance upon which an enzyme acts.

RENNIN is the enzyme that curdles milk. Here milk is the substrate.

SUCROSE is the chemical name for ordinary table sugar. It is usually extracted from maple trees, sugar cane, and sugar beets.

INVERSION is the reaction of water with sucrose to produce **INVERT SUGAR** (a mixture of glucose and fructose).

The formation of sugar crystals is affected by the presence of **INVERT SUGAR, TEMPERATURE, STIRRING,** and certain materials.

FLOUR is a refined product obtained from ground seeds of grains. White flour is made white by a bleaching process.

GLUTEN is a soluble protein that is formed from insoluble proteins when flour is moistened and kneaded. When vitamins are added to flour, it is labelled as **ENRICHED.**

LEAVENING AGENTS are materials added to doughs to produce gas.

LEAVENING PROCESS is the physical action of gases in dough which make it rise in baking breads and pastries.

EGGS are excellent sources of proteins. The proteins in eggs are easily coagulated by heat.

BROWNING of food results from reactions with enzymes.

A **SYNTHETIC FOOD** is one which has one major ingredient added by man rather than by natural means.

A **COLLOIDAL SUSPENSION** is a dispersion of very small particles evenly spread out through all parts of a system. Four important kinds of colloidal suspensions are **SOLS, EMULSIONS, GELS,** and **AEROSOLS.** Colloids may be coagulated by changing the temperature or by changing the charge on the colloidal particles. When a colloidal dispersion of two liquids which do not mix naturally is needed, an **EMULSIFIER** is used. The resulting colloidal dispersion is called an **EMULSION.**

Cleansing Agents 18

Remember when your mother made you scrub your hands before eating? A slippery bar of soap may have been a reason for an argument then. Now you know that it is important to wash off germ-carrying dirt, and that cleanliness is a safeguard to your health. In fact, one of the reasons that human life-span has increased in recent years is cleanliness. A person lives longer when his body is clean and therefore free from infectious germs.

THE ACTION CHEMISTRY OF SOAP

Ordinary soap is either a sodium or potassium salt of a fatty acid. The formation of a soap is a chemical process called SAPONIFICATION. *SAPONIFICATION is the reaction of a fat with a base forming a salt of a fatty acid (soap) and glycerin.* The chemistry is easy:

$$\text{a fat} + \text{a base} \longrightarrow \text{soap} + \text{glycerin}$$

The equation for the reaction is

$$C_3H_5(O-\overset{\overset{\displaystyle O}{\|}}{C}-C_{17}H_{35})_3 + 3\ NaOH \longrightarrow$$

stearin   sodium
hydroxide

$$3\ C_{17}H_{35}COONa + C_3H_5(OH)_3$$

sodium   glycerin
stearate (soap)

To understand the cleansing action of soap you must recognize that a soap molecule has a split personality. Let's look at it more closely.

soap molecule

$$-\overset{|}{\underset{|}{C}}-(\overset{|}{\underset{|}{C}})_{16}-\overset{\overset{\displaystyle O}{}}{C}\diagdown_{O-Na}$$

nonpolar   polar
end   end
(uncharged)   (charged)

soap molecule in water

$$\left[-\overset{|}{\underset{|}{C}}-(\overset{|}{\underset{|}{C}})_{16}-\overset{\overset{\displaystyle O}{}}{C}\diagdown_{O_-} \right]^{-} + Na^+$$

We can compare the action of soap in water to a bridge. In water the Na^+ ion of the soap molecule dissolves. The polar end of the hydrocarbon part of the molecule dissolves in water but the nonpolar end does not. As a result, the hydrocarbon ends cluster together in groups called MICELLES. See figure on the right.

Soap micelle.

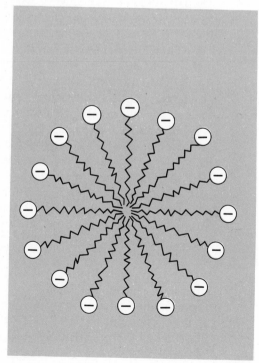

The nonpolar ends dissolve in fats and grease. The polar ends dissolve in water. The water then carries away the particles of dirt surrounded by the soap. This is the bridge action we mentioned earlier. All detergents act in the same way.

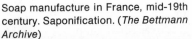

Soap manufacture in France, mid-19th century. Saponification. (*The Bettmann Archive*)

M. E. Chevreul in his laboratory. (*The Bettmann Archive*)

The History of Soap

The word soap comes from the Latin word "sapo". The Roman peasants burned animals as sacrifices to their gods on a hill called Sapo. The animal fat from the sacrifices mixed with the ashes of the burned wood. This mixture formed a crude soap, and women discovered that it could be used to wash clothes.

By the 8th Century, soapmaking had become a profitable industry in Italy. Later, soap was introduced to France, and although a luxury item, it became very popular. Most soap at this time was made from goat fat or tallow. The fat was melted and combined with the ashes of beech trees. This mixture of ashes and water formed a basic or alkaline solution.

Wherever soap was introduced it became popular. For example, in 1500 King James I of England gave special privileges to soap makers in order to encourage growth of the industry. Making soap was considered an art, and possession of fine soaps was a mark of wealth or nobility.

Meanwhile chemists were experimenting with the materials from which soaps were made. In 1783, Scheele accidentally made soap in his laboratory while boiling olive oil with a basic substance. From this reaction he noted that a sweet-smelling product, glycerin, had separated out. Later, the scientist Chevereul studied the composition of animal fats and discovered that a fat is simply a compound made up of an organic fatty acid and glycerin. In soap making, the glycerin part of the fat molecule is replaced by the metal part of an inorganic base.

Eight years later, in 1791, LeBlanc found a method for getting sodium carbonate from common salt. This proved to be an inexpensive way of making lye, a base which could be used to make soap. There was no longer any need for the messy use of ashes which contained many useless compounds.

Today there are many kinds of soaps on the market. Several kinds of synthetic detergents are also popular. Each has its own particular advantages, and we shall study these later in this chapter.

THE MANUFACTURE OF SOAP

There are several industrial processes for the making of soap. The soap maker chooses materials and methods depending on the type of soap he wants. There are different kinds of fats and bases that may be used, and many possible additives such as perfumes which can be used in the process.

Soap making is determined by economy. The choice of fats and oils and their quality is important in determining the quality and price of the product. Most manufacturers blend different kinds of fats and oils in their own special formulas. Firm, hard soaps are made with sodium hydroxide, while softer soaps are made with potassium hydroxide.

Two industrial methods for the production of soap are:

1. *Kettle method*   In this method the fats and oils are boiled with the hydroxide in huge kettles for about a week. At the end of this period the soap has risen to the top. Salt is added to coagulate the soap. Glycerin is a by-product in the process.
2. *Continuous processing method*   In this method steam at about 500°F is injected into the top of a column three feet in diameter and 80 feet high. Hot fat is piped into the bottom. The fats split into fatty acids and glycerin. The glycerin dissolves in the water and goes out the bottom. The fatty acids are mixed with alkalies and make soap. Unlike the Kettle method, this operation is continuous.

Kettle of soap. (*W. R. Grace*)

Warm semiliquid soap is run on a chilled roller which causes the soap to harden and flake.

Soap is cut into bars by wires. The next step is the stamping of the bars with the brand name.

Melted soap can be treated in a variety of ways. It can be poured into molds and cut into bars. It can also be made into chips by cooling on rollers and then finely cut. Powdered soap is made by spraying liquid soap into hot air.

QUICK QUESTION?

Compare the addition of the salt solution in Experiment 18.1, *Making Soap,* to the addition of salt in the Kettle method of making soap industrially.

Liquid spray soap test area. (*W. R. Grace*)

THE DECLINE OF SOAP
. . . THE RISE OF
SYNTHETIC DETERGENTS

There has been a definite decline in the use of soap for laundry purposes. The chief reason for this decline is what happens when soap is used in hard water. A disagreeable scum forms which is difficult to separate from clothes and the washing vats. This is due to the calcium and magnesium ions found in hard water. These ions combine with the long chain part of the soap molecule and form insoluble soaps, or scum deposit. The familiar bathtub ring is an example of this residue. This does not happen when synthetic detergents are used. This accounts for the popularity of detergents in areas where the water is more or less hard.

Synthetic detergents differ from soaps in that they are made with an alcohol in place of the fat. One kind of alcohol used is lauryl alcohol($C_{12}H_{25}OH$). It is made from petroleum. The alcohol is treated with sulfuric acid and the product is then made soluble by adding sodium hydroxide. This product is known as sodium lauryl sulfate and its formula is written as

$$\left[C_{12}H_{25}O-\overset{\displaystyle O}{\underset{\displaystyle O}{S}}=O \right] Na^+$$

Unlike soap, the calcium and magnesium salts of synthetic detergents are soluble. When these detergents are used in hard water no scum forms.

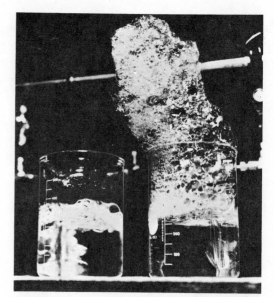

The beaker at the left contains detergent which can be broken down by bacteria in rivers and streams. It is biodegradable. The detergent at the right makes streams foam. It is not biodegradable. (*Standard Oil Co., N. J.*)

Drums are being filled with dishwashing compound. (*W. R. Grace*)

Modern Research

Detergents for Dishes

A dishwasher detergent needs three components in its make-up.
1. Ingredients that soften water and remove dirt.
2. An ingredient that emulsifies fats, has wetting properties, and keeps suds level low.
3. Additives to reduce corrosion and to disinfect.

SOAPLESS SOAPS

It may surprise you to learn that detergents are derived from black, sticky, crude oil. They come from the residues left from the cracking of petroleum. Most synthetic detergents are compounds containing long-chain alcohols. The number of carbon atoms and the arrangement of atoms in the chain give the detergent its characteristics. The cleansing action seems to increase to a maximum when there are 12 to 15 atoms in the chain, and then decreases as the number of carbon atoms in the chain go beyond this number.

All synthetic detergents, like soaps, are surface-acting agents. This means that the molecules of the detergent concentrate between two surfaces and lower the surface tension between them. Like soaps, detergent molecules lift small particles away from the surfaces by their charged (positive or negative) ends.

In Experiment 18.2 you see how soap and detergents act to change the surface tension of water.

Detergents are widely used for industrial purposes, and have annual sales three times larger than that of soaps. The textile industry uses them to wash fabrics. Detergents are also used to degrease metals, to process paper pulp, and in many other industrial cleaning operations. They have now largely replaced soaps for many household cleaning chores, and are used in shampoos and toothpastes as well.

Home Lab

Surface Tension

Have you ever noticed raindrops on the windshield? They form perfect spheres. If there is any grease or oil on the glass, they spread out.

Get a cup filled with water. Run a pin along your fingers in order to get some grease on it. Float a pin on the water. The pin can float on the water as a result of surface tension. Add a few drops of a liquid detergent to the water. What happens to the pin? Does the detergent make the water wetter? (Does the tension become more, less, or unchanged?)

Make a small boat out of a brown paper bag. Tape a piece of camphor to the back of the boat at the water line. Be sure to allow the camphor to touch the water. What happens? Discuss your results in class.

PEANUTS ®   By Charles M. Schulz

HOUSE CLEANING WITH CHEMICALS

Besides personal cleanliness, another important factor in keeping you healthy is a clean environment. Dirt helps the growth and spread of harmful germs. Therefore, the use of some chemicals can help prevent disease in the home.

Products which are used principally to make the floors and walls look like new may also protect against sickness. The dirt and dust removed by waxes and oils rid surfaces from infectious agents. Some materials such as lysol, or phenol (carbolic acid) are used as disinfectants to destroy bacteria. See what this means in Demonstration 18-B *Effect of Disinfectants on Bacterial Growth.*

Germicidal soap goes through filtration operation. (*W. R. Grace*)

The use of Hyamine[R] 3500 controls bacteria in laundering operations. (*Rohm and Haas Co.*)

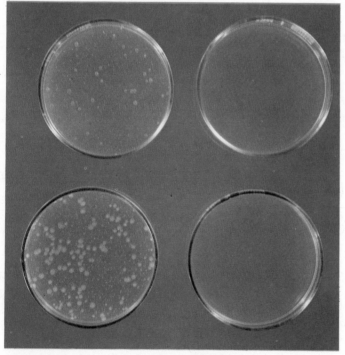

BLEACHING OUT THE SPOTS

Bleaching is a case of "if you can't beat 'em, join 'em!" In the bleaching process, chlorine or active oxygen (O) is released and combines with the spot or dye to be removed. In the reaction, the colored material is changed to a colorless compound. The materials that caused the spot are still present, but in a changed condition.

QUICK QUESTIONS?

1. Compare the properties of (a) soaps, detergents; (b) bleaches, and disinfectants.
2. Some shampoo ads mention that they contain more soap and less detergent than their competitors. Is this necessarily a good feature?
3. Read the labels on the detergents on the shelves in the supermarket. How do the manufacturers list the phosphate content?
4. Read the labels on several brands of disinfectants. Do they list the active ingredients? If they do, what are they?

Some bleaches use a compound, called calcium chloride hypochlorite, $CaCl(OCl)$. It is a white powder with a strong chlorine odor. It is unstable. *UNSTABLE means that it decomposes readily.* This bleaching powder is produced by passing chlorine gas through lime, $Ca(OH)_2$. The resulting chlorinated lime is also known as bleaching powder. The compound decomposes easily in water and is used as a source of chlorine for cleaning, bleaching, and disinfecting. Many swimming pools, for example, are kept sanitary by the addition of chlorinated lime.

Javelle water is a commonly used derivative of bleaching powder. It is prepared by the reaction of bleaching powder with sodium carbonate and produces a solution of sodium hypochlorite.

$$CaOCl_2 + Na_2CO_3 \longrightarrow \underset{\substack{\text{sodium} \\ \text{hypochlorite}}}{NaOCl} + NaCl + CaCO_3\downarrow$$

NaCLO forms NaCl and oxygen which combines with some colored materials and bleaches them.

Many tons of bleaching compounds are manufactured each year. The demand is largely from industry, but is used in the home as well. A large amount of bleaching materials is used in the treatment of wood pulp, a step in the manufacture of paper.

Aerosol cleaner used for spot cleaning. (A-Penn)

Chapter 18
ACTION POINTS

SAPONIFICATION is the reaction of a fat with a base forming a salt of a fatty acid (soap) and glycerin.

The **SOAP MOLECULE** acts like a bridge between a dirt particle and water.

MICELLES are groups of the hydrocarbon part of the soap molecule that cluster together.

Two commercial methods of manufacturing soap are the **KETTLE METHOD**, and the **CONTINUOUS PROCESSING METHOD**.

PRECIPITATE DEPOSITS (better known as scum) are formed when soap comes into contact with calcium and magnesium ions in hard water.

Soaps are detergents. Detergents that are made from alcohol instead of fats are called **SYNTHETIC DETERGENTS**.

SYNTHETIC DETERGENTS do not form insoluble deposits or scum in the presence of calcium and magnesium ions in hard water.

DETERGENTS act also as agents that lower the surface tension of water.

DISINFECTANTS are chemicals that destroy bacteria, especially the disease-causing type of germs.

BLEACHES are chemicals which react with color-producing particles in a material to make them colorless.

Cosmetics 19

SCIENCE BEHIND COSMETICS

COSMETICS are materials used to make the body look younger and more attractive. The production of such materials was once considered an art. Complicated formulas were used to make many products. Today the cosmetics industry is more a science than an art. It is a multi-million dollar business where competition is keen. Cosmetic firms have well-paid specialists, cosmetic chemists.

In general the cosmetics chemist must know about the products already on the market. Feedback from the customer tells the cosmetics people what works, or what improvements could be made. New Products are developed from this kind of information.

When a new product is needed the chemist must analyze what it is the consumer really needs. He has to be careful that no chemicals harmful to the body are used.

Surprising things may happen in the lab leading to important discoveries. Records must be kept. The general steps of the Scientific Method must be followed.

The chemist must understand the chemistry of skin, nails, and hair. He must be an expert in colloid chemistry and in the chemistry of surfaces of chemicals used.

Surfactants

SURFACE-ACTIVE INGREDIENTS or SURFAC-TANTS are substances that can change conditions where one substance comes in contact with another. Soaps are an important class of surfactants.

In Chapter 18 we studied how one part of a soap molecule surrounded grease or oil particles and the other part faced the water molecules. An emulsion of oily substances in water is formed.

Shampoos are soaps or synthetic detergents. Taking away grease and dirt from hair involves liquids (grease and detergent solution) and a solid (hair). The detergent solution must lift the grease from the hair. In order to do this, a detergent must separate the hair and the grease, and the grease must be washed away.

The backbone of cosmetics chemistry is colloidal chemistry. The experiments in this chapter will help you see this. And the reading which will be suggested will also help you to understand why colloids are important. The emulsions formed in cold cream for instance, depend on a surfactant. It is the surfactant which keeps the cold cream in its emulsified condition.

Cosmetics chemist in laboratory. (*Gianni Tortoli, Photo Researchers*)

Egyptian wig. (*The Metropolitan Museum of Art, Excavations, 1907*)

Shaving with bronze razor. (*The Bettman Archive*)

Egyptian princess having her hair dressed. (*The Bettmann Archive*)

QUICK QUESTIONS?

1. Name a cosmetic product that you think needs improvement. What properties would you tell a cosmetic chemist it needs to be improved?
2. Cold cream is an emulsion. Upon what type substance does the emulsion depend?

Cosmetics In The Past

Primitive people used cosmetics. They used colors extracted from plants or earth to decorate themselves.

The Egyptians were the earliest on record as users of cosmetics. The contents of jars found in Egyptian tombs have been analyzed and found to contain 90% animal fat and 10% resin or balsam. Perfume entombed since 1350 B.C. still had an odor in 1928 when the tomb was opened.

During the time of Cleopatra, kohl, a black, shiny galena (PbS) was used to decorate the eyes. Lip salves and henna to color hair were used by fashionable ladies as toilet items.

During the first century A.D. the Romans were using an antimony compound to make the eyelids look lustrous. They also used chalk for whitening the skin, rouge for pink cheeks, and pumice for cleaning teeth.

The Greeks were also fascinated with perfumes. Theophrastus wrote about perfume nearly 400 years B.C. At that time oil was used as a base because it was convenient and retained odors for a long time. It was not until the 14th century A.D. that alcohol was used as a base for perfumes.

The Arabs were the first to extract perfume from flowers by distillation. During the period of the Crusades many of these cosmetics from the Near East were brought back to Europe.

Today, the use of cosmetics is common. The scientific study of cosmetics has led to the development of better, low-cost, products which now form the basis for a prospering industry. You will find that knowing something about the chemistry of cosmetics can be useful and interesting.

Shampoos

One of the characteristics of a shampoo that users insist it should have is that it must lather well. The cosmetic chemist spends much time and effort formulating such a shampoo although he knows that lather has nothing to do with its cleansing action.

Basically, shampoos may be classified as either a *cleansing,* or a *conditioning* preparation. Cleansing shampoos include the specially medicated type such as a dermatologist often prescribes. These are designed to remove, but not completely, the oils and grease that collect on the hair. Taking away all the oil would leave hair brittle and hard to manage. The detergent selected for the job must meet certain requirements such as safety to the eyes, foaming action, and ease of rinsing.

Conditioning shampoos are more gentle in their cleansing action. The after-effects of the detergents used are more important here. Additives such as fatty acid products act as the conditioners.

The detergents used in shampoos may be ordinary soaps, alcohols, and organic sulfates.

Dentifrices

When the diet of early civilizations consisted mainly of food which required a great deal of chewing and less sugar content, tooth decay was rarer. Today, our diet of soft foods with high carbohydrate content has made tooth decay more common. To reduce decay food particles that cling to the teeth must be removed.. To do this we use various preparations. Fluorides are often added to the water supply for more protection.

DENTIFRICES are teeth-cleaning agents. They are made in pastes, powder, liquids, and blocks. Pastes are the most popular. However, the efficiency of food removal with these preparations, depends more on the brushing action than on the dentifrice.

INGREDIENTS IN DENTIFRICES*

B	binder	thickeners
A	abrasives	main parts—to polish teeth (chalk)
S	sudsers	now often detergents
H	humectants	often glycerin—retards reactions within the product—keeps the product from drying out
F	flavors	peppermint, spearmint, wintergreen
U	unique additives	water, preservatives, sodium chloride, stannous fluoride
L	liquids	water

*Adapted from Robert P. T. Young in "Glycerine in Dentrifices (Brochure) Glycerine Producers Association, USA 1960.

Modern Research

New Hair-Setting Sprays

New hair setting sprays which can hold hair in place for several weeks after application are being studied. Setting the hair after shampooing is necessary for this type of spray to work.

The sprays are tested on human hair by setting the hair, and measuring the curl. The hair is then exposed to humid air for a given period of time. The curl is measured again and compared.

Combing, flaking, and adherence of the spray to the hair is also tested. The formulas of the sprays are based on organic compounds which include polymers.

Practical problems such as the length of time the spray stays in the hair even after shampooing, and the physical and chemical effects of the spray on hair and scalp cells are not completely known. Here again, there is a great deal of chemical research necessary.

(Above) Getting oak moss ready for distillation. (*Gianni Tortoli, Photo Researchers*)

(Above, right) Extraction by volatile solvents. (*Gianni Tortoli, Photo Researchers*)

Distillation process set up in laboratory. Picture on wall shows same process in the factory. (*Bannett from dpi*)

Blending room in perfume factory. (*Gianni Tortoli, Photo Researchers*)

Perfumes

Raw materials for perfumes come from three sources: plants such as roses and carnations; animals such as the musk deer and the sperm whale (both of these animals once used are now replaced by chemical sources; chemical sources such as esters, ketones, and aldehydes.)

Methods of obtaining the essence or odor-containing material from plants are:

distillation—the material is heated until the essence is vaporized and then it is condensed.

expression—the pressing out of the oil.

extraction—one method of extraction is the use of volatile (easily evaporated) liquid. The flowers are put into a sealed cylinder. Hot liquids are passed through. In the last container the solvent is distilled off.

QUICK QUESTIONS?

1. Why did early civilizations have less tooth decay than we have today?
2. List the properties you consider necessary in a good dentifrice.

CLASSES OF COSMETICS

When cosmetics are mentioned most people think of materials that are applied to the face. We will take a close look at only a few of them here.

Emulsion Type Products

Vanishing Cream

Vanishing cream is the forerunner of most of the emulsion-type products on the market today. It is called vanishing cream because it disappears when rubbed into the skin. Its purpose is to provide a base for face powder. Vanishing cream is a colloidal dispersion of stearic acid in water. Potassium stearate is formed when stearic acid and water are mixed, and it becomes the emulsifying agent. The pH of the cream is close enough to 7 to make it neutral.

A homogenizer mounted in a vat in which various kinds of liquid face make-up are mixed. (*Jim McGuire, Courtesy of Clairol Inc.*)

Raw Materials of Vanishing Cream

stearic acid potassium hydroxide }	combine to form potassium stearate (the emulsifying agent)
glycerin }	prevents drying out in container and gives pearliness appearance and smooth texture
water }	the medium for colloidal dispersion

Foundation Cream

On today's cosmetic scene, foundation cream is a popular face make-up. Foundation creams contain less free stearic acid than vanishing creams. Alcohols and pigments are some of the additives in this type of cream.

Cold Cream

In Experiment 19.3 you make cold cream, another emulsion-type cosmetic. If you notice a graininess in the cream that you make, it is probably due to an excess of borax in proportion to the amount of beeswax used. Too little borax produces a dull cream. The beeswax serves as the emulsifying agent.

Powder Cosmetics

Powder cosmetics start with a basic loose powder such as you make in Experiment 19.1. Compact powder is similar to loose powder, except that a binder and a lubricant is added. The binder helps hold the particles together in the compact. The lubricant allows the particles to slip and slide over each other.

If the right colors are added, compact rouge can be made from the powder. And by changing the type of coloring agents, eyeshadow can be made. There are strict laws governing the use of coloring agents for the eye area. For example, coal tar colors may not be used for eye makeup.

It is interesting to note that if water is used to put on eye makeup, it is necessary for the makeup to be waterproof once it dries around the eye.

Raw Materials of Powder

talc—basic for the powder
precipitated chalk—absorbent material which minimizes effect of skin moisture and oils on the powder
zinc stearate—slip and stick qualities
kaolin—absorbent material which gives dull (matte) finish
zinc and titanium oxides—covering power
colorants
perfume

The ingredients are weighed out. Next, they are mixed thoroughly. After mixing, they are passed through hammer mills to pulverize the particles.

QUICK QUESTIONS?

1. Compare how you make face powder in Experiment 19.1 to the way it is manufactured by large cosmetic firms.
2. What is the function of the borax in the cold cream you make in Experiment 19.3?
3. Could you sell a large quantity of the cold cream you make in Experiment 19.3? Why or why not?
4. Look at the list of cosmetic products on page 7/28. Can you suggest possible new products? What class of products would they be in? Why?

CLASSES OF FACIAL COSMETICS

Powder Cosmetics

Face Powder
Compact Powder
Rouge Cake
Eyeshadow
Eyeliner
Dusting Powder ⎫ these are not
Talcum Powder ⎰ used on the face

Emulsion Type Cosmetics

Foundation Cream
Liquid Make-up
Souffle Make-up
Liquid Rouge
Eyeliners

Wax-Oil Mixtures

Lipstick
Eyeshadow
Brusher Stick
Eyebrow Pencil
Mascara
Cream Rouge ⎫ not true
Cream Eyeshadow ⎰ creams

Gel Type Cosmetics

Bronzers
Blushes
After Shave

Suspensions

Face Make-up
Liquid Powder
Foundation
Eyeliner

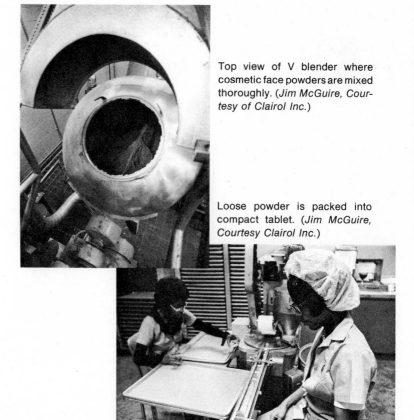

Top view of V blender where cosmetic face powders are mixed thoroughly. (*Jim McGuire, Courtesy of Clairol Inc.*)

Loose powder is packed into compact tablet. (*Jim McGuire, Courtesy Clairol Inc.*)

Shades and quality of powders are tested in the laboratory. (*Jim McGuire, Courtesy Clairol Inc.*)

The mixture is passed through a roller mill to break down dye particles. (*Jim McGuire, Courtesy of Clairol Inc.*)

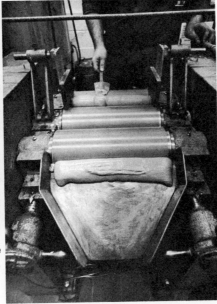

The lipstick is poured into molds. Here the worker is scrapping off the excess material. The molds are then cooled to promote hardening and separated for removal of sticks. (*Jim McGuire, Courtesy of Clairol Inc.*)

Lipstick is a wax-oil mixture that is made in a jacketed tank. (*Jim McGuire, Courtesy Clairol Inc.*)

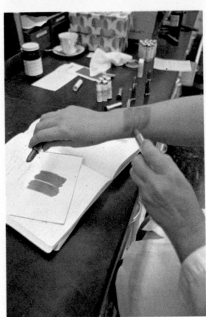

Lipstick colors are tested in the laboratory. (*Jim McGuire, Courtesy Clairol Inc.*)

The worker is putting the lipstick into the case by hand. (*Jim McGuire, Courtesy of Clairol Inc.*)

Aerosol Containers

In chemistry *AEROSOL means a colloidal system in which very small liquid or solid particles are evenly dispersed through a gas.*

In commercial products the term aerosol often refers to products packaged in spray cans. The container has a valve or opening through which the product is forced out. The container holds the product and a PROPELLANT. *A PROPELLANT is a gas used to force the product out of the spray container.*

There are two general types of propellants:

(1) gases that are liquids under pressure at room temperature such as a few alkanes substituted with halogens.

(2) gases compressed into the container such as nitrous oxide (NO), carbon dioxide (CO_2), nitrogen (N_2) and Argon (Ar).

In both types, the general principle is simply that a gas inside a container (the propellant) forces out a product through a small opening. The effect is to spray fine particles into the air (space sprays), or to spread larger particles onto a surface (surface sprays). Hair sprays, suntan oils and deodorants are examples of surface sprays where the coarser particles forced out of the can are intended to coat a surface. Insect repellants are examples of space sprays. The particles must be much smaller to remain suspended in air.

Twentieth-Century Products

History will certainly record that the use of deodorants is a prominent feature of our culture. In this unit we have studied soaps, detergents, and disinfectants. We are very conscious of cleanliness for health and social reasons. Cosmetics have a definite social value. Deodorants and antiperspirants are used by practically everyone.

Human perspiration is composed of water, nitrogeneous materials, and fatty substances. The nitrogeneous materials and fatty substances are often attacked by bacteria and unpleasant odors result.

Two products which help people overcome this problem are deodorants and antiperspirants.

(1) deodorants—suppress odor by attacking the bacteria. Aluminum chlorhydroxide (chlorhydrate) as well as water solutions of other aluminum salts are useful.

(2) Antiperspirants—make use of zinc and aluminum preparations to cut down the amount of perspiration.

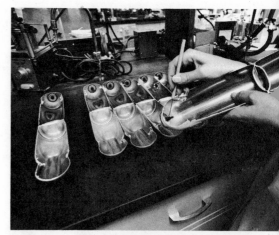

Technician is testing valve inside aerosol container. (*Jim McGuire, Courtesy Clairol Inc.*)

Aerosol cans are filled with nitrogen before testing. (*Jim McGuire, Courtesy Clairol Inc.*)

Laboratory where aerosols are tested. In foreground is constant-temperature bath. (*Jim McGuire, Courtesy Clairol Inc.*)

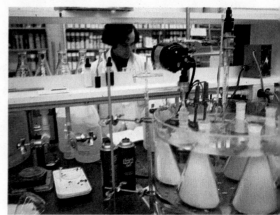

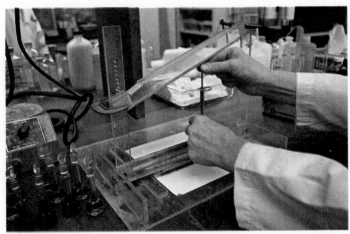

Chromatography test shows percentage of components in various cosmetics. Step One: product is applied to standard glass plate. (*Jim McGuire, Courtesy Clairol Inc.*)

Step Two: glass plate coated with product is put into solution. (*Jim McGuire, Courtesy Clairol Inc.*)

Tests to Evaluate Cosmetics

Quality control tests are conducted by chemists to assure that the cosmetic meets certain standards. Some of the problems that must be checked are

Will the product retain its quality after it stands for long periods of time?

Will reactions occur between ingredients of the cosmetic; or between the product and the container in which the cosmetic is packaged?

Will the solvent evaporate and cause the cosmetic solution to change its concentration?

Is the product free of bacterial contamination?

Does the emulsion, either a gel or sol, break down with high temperatures or cold?

Can the product harm skin, hair, eyes, or the lungs?

Step Three: glass plate is removed from solution. Notice that the product is broken down into parts. (*Jim McGuire, Courtesy Clairol Inc.*)

Step Four: chemist compares test with standard break down. Components are scrapped from glass plate to be analyzed. (*Jim McGuire, Courtesy Clairol Inc.*)

Step Five: components are analyzed on densitometer for exact percentages. (*Jim McGuire, Courtesy Clairol Inc.*)

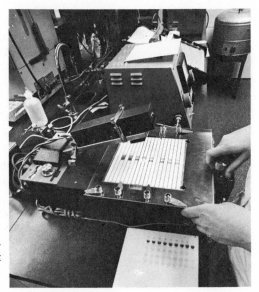

Problems related to performance must also be checked. For example, the cosmetic must live up to the claims that the manufacturer advertises. The product must also meet standards that indicate it will not be harmful to the user.

Each large batch of the cosmetic must be checked to make sure that it contains the right ingredients mixed properly and in the correct proportions.

QUICK QUESTIONS?

1. Compare colloidal aerosol to an aerosol that is packaged in a can.
2. Contrast antiperspirants with deodorants.
3. Trace the steps of the Scientific Method the cosmetics chemist must follow.

Chapter 19

ACTION POINTS

COSMETICS are materials used to make the body look younger and more attractive. The cosmetic chemist must understand the chemistry of the **SKIN, NAILS,** and **HAIR** as well as **COLLOID** chemistry.

SURFACTANTS are surface-acting ingredients, which are substances that can change conditions where one substance comes in contact with another.

SHAMPOOS are detergents used to emulsify the grease and oils on hair to be washed away with water.

DENTIFRICES are teeth-cleaning agents.

Classes of facial cosmetics are **POWDER COSMETICS, EMULSION TYPE COSMETICS, WAX-OIL MIXTURES, GEL TYPE COSMETICS, SUSPENSIONS.**

The term **AEROSOL** is used in two ways. An **AEROSOL** is a colloidal system and it is often used to refer to a spray can. There are two types of aerosol sprays: **SPACE** and **SURFACE.**

DEODORANTS suppress odor.

ANTIPERSPIRANTS cut down the amount of perspiration.

TESTS are made on cosmetics to determine if they meet certain standards.

CHEMISTRY IN THE ENVIRONMENT

Unit 8

Contents

UNIT 8 CHEMISTRY IN THE ENVIRONMENT

Chapter 20 *READER TEXT* **Chapter 20** *LABORATORY MANUAL*

MAN AND NATURE: THE MOST IMPORTANT REACTION

Chapter 21 *READER TEXT* **Chapter 21** *LABORATORY MANUAL*

THE SCIENCE OF AGRICULTURE

MAN AND NATURE: THE MOST IMPORTANT REACTION

20

CHEMICAL REACTIONS WE DON'T SUSPECT

Chemical reactions are going on everywhere. You may not be aware of all the different kinds of reactions that are happening. Some chemical reactions are taking place where you are right now, and you don't even know it! That's how sneaky some chemical reactions can be.

Nothing seemed unusual to thousands of people living in London, England, on December 4, 1952. They weren't aware of some very important chemical reactions that were happening right among them. These reactions were important for one reason. In the next five days, they would kill 4000 people, make 20,000 others sick, and shorten the lives of thousands more. Similar chemical reactions happened in the small town of Donora, Pa., in 1948. Twenty people died then. Two thousand were made sick. Deadly reactions in the atmosphere also happened in Los Angeles in 1950. In the last ten years, New York City has had similar reactions happen four times.

20 DEAD IN SMOG; RAIN CLEARING AIR AS MANY QUIT AREA

Officials Study Cause of Plague Apparently Borne by Heavy Atmosphere in Donora, Pa.

ZINC PLANT CLOSING DOWN

Process Was in Use Since 1917 —Chemist Suggests Deadly Gas Was Responsible

---

Special to THE NEW YORK TIMES.

DONORA, Pa., Oct. 31—Several hundred asthma and cardiac sufferers remaining in this stricken town were evacuated to other areas tonight as a welcome rain helped to clear the air of a smog believed to have contributed to the deaths of twenty residents. The mysterious air-borne plague struck yesterday.

Low-hanging smog over an eight-mile area was considered a factor in the deaths, which were chiefly among elderly persons. A late check indicated that probably two more names would be added to the list of dead.

There also is the threat of pneu-ia wh⋯⋯⋯ght aff⋯⋯⋯⋯r

Air and water pollution.

But these reactions don't just happen in cities. They happen, and are happening, everywhere and all the time. Sometimes the situation is worse than others.

Today, right where you are living, those very same reactions are happening. Experts have estimated that 50,000 people die each year from these reactions. Many others will get sick from them and thousands will lead shortened lives. Symptoms are chronic bronchitis, chronic sore throats, emphysema and other ailments, even heart disease. Sure, people know it is happening. But not enough is known about it. And worse yet, nobody really knows how to stop it. These reactions are being watched and studied. But the reactions are still happening.

What are these killer reactions? Why can't they be stopped? What exactly killed all these people? And will kill more? Where will it hit hardest? How can you be prepared and warned?

Whatever they are, one thing is known. They are in the very air you breathe. The air, of course, is polluted. All the air. Everywhere. Take a look at what really is in that "air."

To Speak, Or Not to Speak!

Two men who were working as window-washers fell off the Empire State Building from the top. One of the men screamed all the way down, while the other admired the changing view. At the 40th floor the quiet one looked at the man who was screaming and asked: "Why're you screaming? We're all right this far."

Some people are always complaining about pollution. Other people feel that as long as environmental disaster has not hit them there is no reason to say anything.

The situation about our environment is different from the window washers' problem because we can still do something.

It is not easy to decide how loud or when to scream about pollution or when to be silent. Few people know about the nature and chemistry of pollutants. Much more research needs to be done to reveal the complete story about pollution. It is no wonder, then, that many people are either screaming about the wrong things, remaining silent at the wrong times, or are just plain bewildered. Your laboratory experiences and reading will help you to understand better your environment and its conditions. As a result you may be more able to see through the haze of pollution. You may be able to make more helpful contributions to the safeguarding of your environment.

QUICK QUESTION?

Do you speak out about air pollution?

CHEMICAL GARBAGE IN YOUR AIR

Air, chemically speaking, is a mixture of nitrogen (about 78%), oxygen (about 21%) and argon (about 1%). The remainder is made up of carbon dioxide and some noble gases. Our atmosphere, in addition to containing air, has quite a bit of water vapor. Through the years, man has had to put up with some other additions to his atmosphere. From the earliest days, wood was burned for warmth and cooking. This burning adds carbon particles to the atmosphere. Natural occurrences such as volcanoes, add other substances. But these additions did not result in pollution problems. Only in the last hundred years did serious problems really begin.

Two factors are responsible: more people and more burning of fossil fuels. Coal, oil and gasoline—the fossil fuels—are used by factories, home furnaces, power plants and motor vehicles. The result is overwhelming.

These sources dump 163 million tons of unwanted gases and tiny particles into our atmosphere every year. That's a lot. If it were all particles, it would cover an area five football fields square and two football fields high! But much of it is gas. And the line-up looks like this:

Cars add 100 million tons
Factories add 28 million tons
Electric power plants add 19 million tons
Home furnaces add 11 million tons . . . . each year.

Here are some of the gases and particles that are added by these sources.

Gases: sulfur dioxide
nitrogen dioxide
hydrocarbons
carbon monoxide
Particles: mercury
lead
carbon

(An idling car will add 100 billion particles to the air every second!)

An erupting volcano is a natural source of pollution. (*J. L. Stage, Photo Researchers*)

Pollution from Motor Vehicles

Motor vehicles account for most of our air pollution. To give you some idea of the amount added, think of this. For every 1000 gallons of gasoline burned, there is released into our atmosphere

3200 lbs. of carbon monoxide
300 lbs. of hydrocarbons
20–75 lbs. of nitrogen oxides
17 lbs. of sulfur compounds

plus those solid particles! All unwanted and unhealthy.

The biggest polluter is the gasoline engine. One type of gasoline has the formula C_8H_{18}. But impurities such as nitrogen, fluorine, lead and sulfur are also in gasoline. One additive in the gasoline is tetraethyl lead, $Pb(C_2H_5)_4$. Of course, air is added to make this mixture of materials explode. This means that nitrogen and oxygen are mixed with the gasoline. The engine exhaust consists of carbon monoxide, carbon dioxide, nitric oxide, and some hydrocarbons.

$$2\,C + O_2 \longrightarrow 2\,CO$$
carbon   oxygen   carbon monoxide

$$C + O_2 \longrightarrow CO_2$$
carbon   oxygen   carbon dioxide

$$N_2 + O_2 \longrightarrow 2\,NO$$
nitrogen   oxygen   nitric oxide

Pollution from Factories and Power Plants

Factories and power plants are the second biggest polluters. They burn coal and oil and natural gas. Here again, nitric oxide, carbon monoxide, and carbon particles are added to the air. Sulfur dioxide is also given off.

$$S + O_2 \longrightarrow SO_2$$
sulfur   oxygen   sulfur dioxide

The sulfur comes from the fuel. If the sulfur is combined with air, the result is sulfur dioxide. Home furnaces burning oil give similar results.

So the atmosphere is loaded with a lot of "unnatural" material—gases and tiny particles from manmade creations. What happens now? Where do these pollutants go? What happens next is more sneaky reactions. These reactions are always taking place. Many times these pollutants are blown to someone else's town. If they take place when weather conditions are a certain way, the atmosphere becomes clogged with those pollutants. They hang around longer than usual. When this happens, people feel as if their town has a lid on it. Actually, it does. For them, they might as well be living in a covered pot. We will look at it as a test tube . . . a natural test tube.

QUICK QUESTIONS?

1. Name one source of natural air pollution.
2. Why have the amounts of air pollutants increased in the last twenty years?
3. Car accidents kill thousands every year. Car exhausts do also. Why do we keep a killer with us?
4. Suppose you had to vote on whether or not to ban all cars. How would you vote and why?
5. Do you think rationing gas and cars is a way of stopping air pollution? Why or why not?

A Natural Test Tube

Weathermen in New York City, on Thanksgiving, 1962, were carefully watching a weather pattern that started to slow down over the East Coast. They were afraid that this particular pattern would create what is called a TEMPERATURE INVERSION. The temperature was right. So were the winds—or the absence of wind. Within a day, their fears were realized. The temperature inversion occurred. Air pollution levels began to rise. An alert was sounded and emergency measures were started. Electric power plants switched to low sulfur fuels. People were asked to drive as little as possible. Buses and taxis were told to cut their idling time. Despite all those precautions, people died from this polluted air, air that became unhealthy because of the temperature inversion. What is it? How does it form? Where does it form? What happens in it?

Temperature Inversion

Temperature inversions can form in many places on the earth's surface. They can form especially easily in a valley or in an area with hills on at least two sides. Los Angeles and San Francisco are prime targets for frequent temperature inversions. In a temperature inversion, warm air hangs over cold, dense air which is closer to the earth. Cold air may also be above the warm air. Any materials in the trapped cold air remain there. Of course, anything added to that air, such as exhaust from autos, and smoke from factories are also kept in that cold layer. This cold air, with the warm air acting as a lid on it, is like a test tube. Reactions take place in the trapped air. The results can be deadly. The arrival of a new cleaner air mass with precipitation or strong winds helps to break up this condition.

Photochemical Reactions

It's awfully hard to breathe in air that is mixed with auto exhaust and factory smoke. It has a lot of carbon dioxide and nitric oxide in it. In addition, the nitric oxide will be changed to toxic nitrogen dioxide.

$$2\,NO \; + \; O_2 \; \longrightarrow \; 2\,NO_2$$
nitric oxide   oxygen   nitrogen dioxide

Nitrogen dioxide is a yellow-brown gas which causes eyes to burn and water. This reaction is caused by the ultra-violet rays from the sun. *Reactions caused by sunlight are called PHOTOCHEMICAL REACTIONS.*

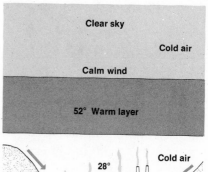

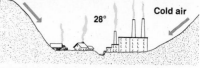

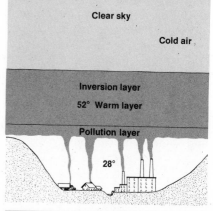

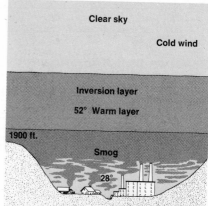

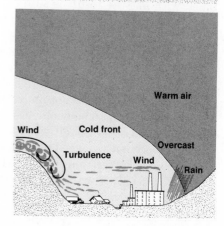

Further photochemical reactions may create ozone (O_3) which is a strong oxidant. It is very toxic and attacks anything organic. Rubber, for example, is especially sensitive to ozone. Due to the open structure of rubber molecules, ozone seeps into the structure and causes the chemical bonds to break.

Some pollutants combine with water. Sulfur dioxide (SO_2) will combine with water vapor to create sulfurous acid (H_2SO_3).

$$SO_2 + H_2O \longrightarrow H_2SO_3$$
sulfur dioxide   water   sulfurous acid

This is also an irritant and will even stain houses and peel paint. Of course, if sulfur dioxide manages to combine with water in your eyes, nose, or lungs, the result is the same: acid. Sulfur dioxide will actually cause acidic reactions in your respiratory system, including the lungs. Even sulfuric acid may form if sulfurous acid combines with oxygen.

$$SO_2 + H_2O \longrightarrow H_2SO_3$$
sulfur dioxide   water   sulfurous acid

$$2\,H_2SO_3 + O_2 \longrightarrow 2\,H_2SO_4$$
sulfurous   oxygen   sulfuric acid
acid

Hydrocarbons with the action of sunlight will create "smog." This causes headaches, watering eyes, infected lungs. It also harms green plants. Nitrogen dioxide, another common pollutant, can also be irritating, especially if it combines with water to form nitric acid.

$$3\,NO_2 + H_2O \longrightarrow 2\,HNO_3 + NO$$
nitrogen   water   nitric   nitric
dioxide   acid   oxide

This can happen in the air or in your lungs. Even the solid particles, like lead and carbon will be harmful to breathing.

Who wants to live in an environment like that? Yet, we all do. Sometimes, it gets really bad. A temperature inversion is an example. Then the very old, the very young and the sick, really begin to suffer. Some die. Some get very sick. It's happening all the time. But sometimes, it makes the headlines.

In Experiment 20.1, you will have a chance to study both gas and particle pollutants. Learn as much as you can. It may save your life!

QUICK QUESTIONS?

1. Why is a temperature inversion like a test tube?
2. What is meant by the term "photochemical reaction"?

The Price of Air Pollution

People are used to thinking about things in terms of money. How much does this or that cost? For some results of air pollution, the cost can be estimated. That sulfurous acid, formed from sulfur dioxide and water vapor in the atmosphere, will make the paint on a house or car look ugly. How much will it cost to repaint? The limestone building becoming gray and pitted, due to the soot and carbonic acid, has to be resurfaced. How much? Rubber, nylon, clothes and metals being attacked by the various pollutants have to be replaced. How much? The car accident, caused by watering eyes due to nitrogen dioxide and other pollutants, may cause a lot of damage. How much?

There are some things that money can't buy. The scenic view of distant mountains is quickly disappearing . . . hidden by the solids and gases thrown into the air. Toxic gases, especially sulfur dioxide, ozone and hydrogen fluoride, make it tough on living things. Plants can take only so much. Their leaves become spotted, blossoms drop, veins show and then . . . death.

What about people? How much is it worth not to have chronic bronchitis or emphysema? Or not to have burning eyes? Or not to die from lung cancer? The average person breathes in about 30 lbs. of "air" every day. Some of the stuff in that air stays in the lungs—and it's not oxygen or nitrogen. The heart works faster, the lungs may become clogged or diseased, and sickness or even death results. Sure, it may take time. But who wins in the end? How much is it worth not to have a shortened life? How much *is* a life worth?

(*Copyright © 1973 The Chicago Sun-Times. Reproduced by courtesy of Wil-Jo Associates, Inc. and Bill Mauldin.*)

"DETERGENT, DEODORANT, DRAIN CLEANER, SCOURING POWDER.... MY, THEY MUST BE VERY NEAT UP THERE."

Home Lab

Diffusion of Pollutants

One of the ways we detect pollution is by odor. You can manufacture and detect some pollution in your home. Pyruvic acid ($CH_3COCOOH$) is a chemical found in the home. It can be formed in the human body and cause bad breath if the body does not have sufficient vitamin B to prevent its formation.

Onions contain pyruvic acid. Different varieties contain a different percentage. Spanish onions have 5.3 micromoles per mole of onion. (Micro moles are one-millionth of a mole.)

Before you start get a wide-mouth jar, a knife, and an onion. Crush a slice of onion. Place it on the bottom of the jar. Cap the jar and wash off the outside of it. Take the jar into another room.

Ask someone to stand three paces from the jar. Record the time it takes the person to smell the onion from the time you remove the lid of the jar.

Do the entire experiment over in another room. How do the times compare?

Think of all of the conditions that could change the results of the experiment. Do you think that these things can affect air pollution?

Rationing Cars and Gas

Some areas of the United States are in for tough times if their air quality isn't improved. Most large cities dump about 8000 to 10,000 tons of solids and gas into the air every day. With the possibility of temperature inversions and the increasing number of cars and people, this can only mean danger ahead. There is a real possibility that only so much gasoline will be sold to each driver. Then no more will you drive into a station and say "Fill it up". Even the number of cars permitted in the city will be limited. The roads would be closed for many cars.

The Federal Environmental Protection Agency, on December 9, 1972, announced that Los Angeles would have their gasoline use cut by 86% from May through October. This plan would begin in 1975. That much decrease means only one thing: rationing. Some experts think that the number of cars permitted in the city will also have to be limited. By 1975, Los Angeles, how long will it be until the whole country has to be rationed? What other action can be taken? Cars account for over 60% of our air pollution. Do we need cars?

Los Angeles Faces Auto Curbs

By GLADWIN HILL
Special to The New York Times

LOS ANGELES, Jan. 13—The Environmental Protection Agency, under court orders, will prescribe drastic measures Monday for alleviating smog in Los Angeles by 1977.

The Federal formula is expected to include stringent gasoline rationing, possibly other restrictions on auto travel and the mandatory conversion of some commercial vehicles to nongasoline fuel.

The order is technically part of a federally imposed "implementation plan" by which the state of California, at least in theory, could comply with the Clean Air Act of 1970 requiring national abatement of air pollution. It may presage similar Federal mandates covering other metropolitan areas that have excessive pollution from automotive or stationary sources.

"This is the crunch," a high-ranking official in Washington said this week. "This is the first dramatic confrontation between the Federal Government and the states on the 1970 act. People have to come to grips with the question of what price to pay fc

Los Angeles Air Basin
Area of Basin: 9,200 sq. miles
Population: 10 million people
Total Automobiles: 6 million

The New York Times/Jan. 14, 1973

Environmental order will affect the Los Angeles air basin, an area bordered by mountains (black line).

be workable, and they think it could lead to Congressional review of the air quality standards set under the 1970 act, or at least of the 1977 deadline for state compliance.

The environmental agency's order will not become final until after public hearings are held in the affected area. Amendment of the order is discretionary with the Federal agency.

Hydrocarbons at Issue

Nominally the focal issue in California is how to reduce the ...nt to b... is one of five basic types of air pollution.

But the situation epitomizes the disagreement and perplexity among Congress, the environmental agency, the states and conservationists about whether the present national abatement program is too tough or not tough enough.

The law required states to submit to the Federal agency by last February comprehensive "implementation plans" for meeting Federal air quality standards by 1975. The law provided for two-year extensions of the ta...

WATER POLLUTION

Rainwater

In Bermuda the roofs of houses are kept clean and in good condition. They are also shaped funny, but for a good reason. Drinking water is scarce in Bermuda. There are very few wells. So the people collect rainwater from the roofs. They just let it run into barrels and other containers. There is nothing wrong with that in Bermuda. Here in the United States it probably wouldn't be wise to drink rainwater, especially after a long, dry spell. That good rainwater is loaded with all kinds of pollutants and is likely to be an acid solution. It is drinkable, but not the best thing for you.

In Experiment 20.2, *Another Detective Assignment,* you study some of the properties of common rainwater.

The Load of Our Streams

You may know that drinking water comes from the ground or from streams. This water may be in worse shape than rainwater. Most large streams are polluted to some extent. It is not likely that most are as bad as the Cayuga River near Cleveland, Ohio. That river caught fire in July, 1969 and burned for 40 hours. Firemen were called to put out the fire on the river!

What made the river burn? What was in it? More importantly, where did the stuff come from?

Any large stream in the United States probably will have in it materials from the three major sources of water pollutants. These sources are:

> sewage (human and liquid garbage)
> factories
> farming chemicals

The stream pollutants include:

acids	organic chemicals
salts	nitrates
grease	phosphates
oil	raw sewage

Also included are old tires, tin cans, and other trash. There is just too much stuff for the streams to carry away, much less do away with it chemically. What happens to the chemistry of the stream when this is the case?

This roof has drainage for rainwater into storage tank in foreground. (*Bermuda News Bureau Photo*)

Many formerly pleasant streams are now polluted. This stream brings pollution to the doorstep. (*Charles E. Rotkin, pfi*)

The pollution travels from the stream into the river. (*Charles E. Rotkin, pfi*)

The Chemistry in the Stream

Raw sewage, and even partially treated sewage, can be broken down by the action of bacteria. All natural organic wastes, such as dead matter, will be acted upon by bacteria. This produces, among other things, nitrates and phosphates. This type of bacteria, called aerobic, needs oxygen to do its job. If there is too much waste to take care of, a lot of oxygen is needed. This oxygen is gotten from the water, where the bacteria live. If the bacteria used too much of the stream's oxygen, other living things don't get enough. And if this happens, the creatures in the stream die. In dying, more natural waste is produced. If there are not enough bacteria to handle the job, it all rots. This rotting is really a job description for a special kind of bacteria, that doesn't need oxygen. They are called anaerobic bacteria. When anaerobic bacteria are at work, certain smelly gases are given off. These gases may include: oxides of nitrogen, hydrogen sulfide, and hydrogen-containing organic compounds.

The burning of the Cayuga River was caused by the waste from refineries flowing into the river. This waste included acids, salts, oils, tars and greases. These materials were packed so tightly in the stream that chemical combustion occurred! Any stream that has a metal or chemical plant on its banks will contain all or some of these substances. If textile or paper mills are on the stream, then various organic wastes will be dumped into the stream. Even food processing plants and slaughterhouses add organic wastes such as blood and animal fat.

The Ocean—the End of the Line

Where does it all end up? Eventually all things go to the sea, our great and wide oceans. Surely the oceans can handle our garbage, but even they are becoming overloaded. Huge areas of the ocean are dead. Nothing is there except garbage, and some types of bacteria. The oceans are really in danger of becoming cesspools. Thor Heyderthal, the explorer, recently crossed the Atlantic Ocean in a *boat made of reeds*. Guess what he found in the middle of the ocean? Large areas of floating garbage and waste!

The Lake Washington Case

Fertilizers with nitrates and phosphates help plants grow in water as well as soil. These chemicals are plant nutrients. They cause water plants called algae to flourish. The decay of the algae is brought about by oxygen-using bacteria. Again the cycle of less oxygen available for the water creatures—more dead fish and plants—decay of materials by anaerobic bacteria proceeds.

Seattle, Washington is a city surrounded by water. On one side is Puget Sound and on the other side is Lake Washington. Even though sewage treatment plants (ten of them) were installed, the pollution of the lake caused an increase of nutrients that support the growth of algae. A growth of green, gummy algae began to cloud the once clear and beautiful lake. Public concern grew and the mayor appointed an advisory commission. It was found that the lake was following a process of deterioration which was typical of many European lakes.

The place where the water from the sewage plants was being piped into the lake was shifted far out into the ocean. The lake cleared almost immediately. It was noted that the amount of algae declined as the amount of phosphates in the lake were reduced. Other nutrients such as the nitrates did not seem to matter as much to algae growth.

About half of the phosphates in sewage come from detergents. Phosphate-free detergents are therefore a partial answer to many water pollution problems.

TESTING FOR POLLUTED WATER

A sample of water may appear clear and sparkling and ready for drinking. Yet, it may cause illness if you drink it. Diseases such as typhoid, dysentery and cholera are due to the drinking of polluted water. Drinking water must be tested to see if it is fit to drink. Some of these test are:

Test for: dissolved oxygen   nitrates
            carbon dioxide   phosphates
            pH   bacteria content

A sample of water can be tested for each of these properties. Your school may even have the necessary chemical or the prepared water test kits. Here are some brief descriptions of the tests.

Test for Dissolved Oxygen

Water (H_2O) is composed of oxygen and hydrogen. The oxygen in the water molecule is not the oxygen described as dissolved oxygen. Dissolved oxygen is needed by the fish and other water creatures. Not enough dissolved oxygen means a sickly body of water.

Tests for dissolved oxygen are complicated and sensitive. Kits prepared for this test make it easy to find out how much is in your sample. Seven to 15 parts per million (ppm) is an acceptable range for dissolved oxygen. The test is usually one that uses sodium thiosulfate and an iodide salt. Iodine reacts with a starch solution to give a blue color as you saw in Experiment 16.3, *About Starch*. Free oxygen ties up the thiosulfate so that the color change is diminished.

Test for Carbon Dioxide

Large amounts of carbon dioxide will be in the water if there is little dissolved oxygen. This carbon dioxide is produced by the fermentation of water life. It is also exhaled by these creatures. Testing for free carbon dioxide is difficult. There are kits prepared for this test also. A titration with sodium hydroxide, using phenolphthalein as the indicator, shows pink in a basic solution. The more free carbon dioxide, the lighter the color, up to a limit. The ideal sample of water contains less than 10 ppm of free carbon dioxide.

Other Tests

The acid character of water should be tested. The range of pH should be 6.5 to 8.5. The methods of determining pH you learned in the laboratory are sufficient.

QUICK QUESTIONS?

1. People have always used streams for dumping. Why shouldn't we do it today?
2. How do aerobic bacteria differ from anaerobic bacteria in their conditions for work?
3. How is each test for polluted water important?
4. In Unit 2 we studied water purification. In Experiments 20.3 and 20.3-A we study floc formation. List the ways of purification of water you know.

(Photograph by The New York Times)

Tests for nitrates, phosphates, chlorides and detergents are usually done on water samples. Again prepared solutions in kits are the best methods. The presence of chlorides is an indication of saltiness of water. Run-off from salt added to highways could increase the saltiness of streams.

A large amount of coliform bacteria in a stream usually means that sewage is leaking into the water system. The coliform bacteria are not dangerous, but certain types that come with them are very dangerous. Sickness can usually result from such contaminated water. See Unit 2 for methods of purifying water.

THE NEW LANDSCAPE

Some of the water problem results from ground water seeping from dumps and run-off from man-made landscape changes. Man is the greatest landscape artist since worms. Highways, tunnels, airports, cities, farming, lumbering, dams—all these have resulted in major changes on the planet Earth. Water drainage has been affected, as well as soil qualities, and heat reflection. By covering the land with cement and other building materials, water storage and ground water drainage has been changed. Also, chemicals such as road salt, have been added to water supplies. But perhaps the biggest problem is what to do with all that solid garbage. The United States makes about four billion tons of solid waste each year. This amounts to each person producing 5 lbs. of garbage each day. This includes paper, bottles, cans, wrecked cars, metal junk of all sorts . . . and so on. Where does it all come from?

Agricultural sources	59%
Mineral sources	31%
(Mine and mine processing)	
City waste	7%
Factories	3%

What is done with all this waste? Some towns bury it. Others burn it. Some ship it out-of-town—to the ocean or to land areas for burning or burying. But one thing is sure: the stuff is still with us. If it is buried, water supplies may become polluted. If it is burned, the air gets it. Better ways are being sought to dispose of all our garbage.

One way is recycling, although this uses more energy than needed to start from raw materials. Another is to use it all for fuel. These are being tried right now. Solutions must be found. If not, our 'ground' may soon be nothing but buried garbage!

Separating trash to prepare to recycle it. (*Fred Ward, Black Star*)

Garbage barge on way to ocean. (*Zubli*)

Cleaning the Environment

All is not bleak for our environment. In 1970 the Environmental Protection Agency was formed. This agency sets pollution standards and tries to enforce them. This is the agency that recently made the decision to ration gas and cars in Los Angeles. It is also the agency that is making car makers put pollution control devices on car engines. Some industries are doing research and trying to stop their air and water polluting. But some can't afford it. So they close down. Many paper mills have done this. That is one reason, our supply of paper is decreasing.

Some industries are still actively polluting our environment, and they are either fined or told to clean up by a certain date. But all that's expensive, and guess who will pay for it? Yet, it's either pay with money or our lives. Certainly an offer we can't refuse!

If you are thinking about what you will do with the rest of your life, think about this. The best job opportunities in the next few decades will be in the field of environmental science: pollution control engineers, weathermen, oceanographers, geologists, chemists, mathematicians, technicians, and a lot more. So think about environmental protection as a career.

Dr. Meredith C. Gourdine developed an anti-pollution device. If it is installed on an apartment building roof, smoke from the incinerator passes through it. It removes over 90% of the particles. The removed particles are charged and put onto metal strips. The strips can be discarded. This is a breakthrough in waste disposal. (*Photo by* EBONY *Magazine*)

Pollution Police

About sixty miles north of New York City, students in many schools are checking water and air purity at locations near their schools. They are making tests similar to the ones described in this chapter. The results of these tests will be sent to a data center which will see that the proper authorities receive the information.

These students are part of a large environmental project called ECOS (Environmental Education Community Opportunity for Stewardship). The project is funded by the U.S. Department of Health, Education and Welfare. It includes nineteen school districts. Frequently, these students and their teachers meet together to discuss problems and actions. One purpose of this program is to monitor or to keep a constant check on types of pollution. Streams may be polluted and people may not know about it. These students may find it. They may even find the source of pollution. Then action can be taken. These students are actually helping the community. Ideally, there should be a team of scientists to cover a small area and keep a check on pollution. Unfortunately, there are not enough scientists, or enough money to hire them. So the students are doing the job.

In fact, in many different parts of the United States, students are monitoring the environment. These students are learning all the different tests for water purity, checking air samples and keeping a look-out for polluters. Since standardized solutions in test kits are used, with similar equipment, the reports can be compared. Many times, the pollution source can be found by using reports from several locations. Computers are even used to summarize all the data. All of this work provides a source of information for people concerned with the environment.

This type of student-teacher activity could become an important source of pollution control. Many students are creating environmental courses or using ideas from pollution problems in other courses. What is your school doing?

Students studying water samples from local streams.

Chapter 20

ACTION POINTS

AIR POLLUTION has increased in the last twenty years as a result of more people and more burning of fossil fuels.

GASOLINE ENGINES are the biggest air polluter.

TEMPERATURE INVERSIONS result from the right combinations of geography, temperature, and wind. Cold dense air is trapped near the ground by warm air.

PHOTOCHEMICAL REACTIONS are chemical reactions caused by sunlight. It is difficult to measure the **COST** of air pollution.

The major sources of water pollution are **SEWAGE, FACTORIES,** and **FARMING CHEMICALS.**

ANAEROBIC BACTERIA do not need oxygen and give off poisonous gases.

NITRATES and **PHOSPHATES** are plant nutrients.

Water is tested for the presence and amounts of **DISSOLVED OXYGEN, CARBON DIOXIDES, pH, NITRATES, PHOSPHATES,** and **BACTERIA CONTENT.**

The major sources of ground pollution are **FARMING CHEMICALS, MINERAL WASTES, CITY WASTES** (garbage), **FACTORIES.**

The Science of Agriculture 21

THE DAWN OF SCIENTIFIC PLANTING AND HARVESTING

The early Stone Age Culture was marked by people who hunted and gathered their food. Eating habits depended on what nature provided. People in the New Stone Age probably began planting food crops before 7000 B.C. The agriculture of primitive man depended for the most part on chance past experiences. Their procedures were more of an art than a science. Times for planting and harvest were closely associated with religious beliefs, and cycles of the moon.

In the years before 1800 there were less than a billion people on earth. Food was produced on small farms. Today, the world's agricultural output has been increased to feed over three-and-one-half billion people! Great changes in the technology of farming methods have made agriculture big business.

Over the centuries some minor changes in basic agricultural techniques occurred. In the 19th century, however, agriculture was affected by great new developments:

(1) the opening of vast new land areas
(2) the invention of new labor-saving machines
(3) a revolution of transportation methods
(4) an increase in the use of power
(5) the application of science to agriculture

Agricultural chemistry is the science that most affects ideas concerning the nutrition of plants and animals. This branch of chemical science dealt with finding new methods in the production of food, which would save in money, labor, and natural resources.

AGRICULTURAL CHEMISTRY

Besides air and water, plants need food from soil. Food production is directly related to the amount of land available for planting, the type of soil, and the enrichment of the soil. *FERTILIZERS are materials which enrich the soil for the production of abundant plant growth.* Many types of fertilizers, both natural and manufactured, are available. Fertilizers are a major product of the chemical industry.

The American Indian used fish for a fertilizer.

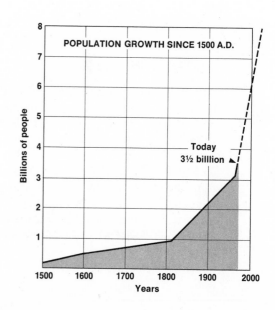

POPULATION GROWTH SINCE 1500 A.D.

Today 3½ billlion

Spraying a fruit tree with an insecticide on an experimental farm. (*The Dow Chemical Company*)

There are many other types of chemical products in the agriculture industry. Such chemicals are called AGRICHEMICALS. *INSECTICIDES, for example, are materials used to destroy undesirable insect pests.* Uncontrolled insect pests can destroy millions of dollars worth of crops. One type of insecticide, DDT, is currently banned. Remains (residues) of the chemical have been found in birds and fish. These residues prevent many types of birds and fish from reproducing. Thus some modern products which have been of tremendous aid in increasing the food supply have brought new problems.

FUNGICIDES are used to control fungus on plants.

HERBICIDES are materials used to prevent growth of undesirable plants. They are used to destroy weeds.

America has an abundant food supply. In some other countries many people live on near-starvation diets. The areas of fastest growing populations are also the areas in which food production is lowest. In many cases the food gap could be bridged by using new products and processes of modern technology.

QUICK QUESTIONS?

1. How has science helped agriculture?
2. Why is DDT banned as an insecticide?
3. Give one reason the United States has a good food supply.

The Ocean: A New Source of Food

You may think that food production has increased with the use of new methods and new kinds of agrichemicals. You are right! It has not increased enough to keep up with population growth however. There is a shortage of food on a per person basis in the whole world.

The growing need for foods has caused us to look to the ocean as a food source. The vast expanses of ocean cover 70% of the earth. But 90% of the oceans are open seas and such areas are considered to be biological deserts. The productive areas of the oceans are close to shores or in areas where there is an upwelling of nutrient rich waters. About 80% of the world's fish catch is obtained in 10% of the ocean.

Farming the ocean by methods similar to those used on land is a reality. Marine cultures, or mariculture, as a food source in offshore ocean areas is quite productive. Methods include stocking fish, keeping fish in running water, and adding food for the fish to the water.

Presently, the technology, economics and politics needed to farm the sea, is, a dream of the future. Our best bet for the immediate future is to increase the productivity of the land.

Harvesting seaweed. (*Sekai Bunka Photo*)

IT ALL STARTS IN THE SOIL

When a clump of grass is pulled from moist earth, the soil clings to the roots. You see a very close physical relationship between soil and roots. What you cannot see are the chemical relationships between the particles of soil and the roots. Soil is active in providing the growing plant with its mineral requirements.

You can compare soil to a very well-stocked and well-equipped laboratory. Almost every known element can be found in the soil. *SOIL is a mixture of mineral matter, organic matter, water and air.* The soil on top, called the topsoil, is richer in organic matter than the soil beneath it. The source of the organic material is animal waste and decayed plants. The principal source of mineral matter is from the rocks found below the soil. The rocks are broken down by WEATHERING. *WEATHERING can be a physical or chemical change. WEATHERING is a physical process when rocks or soil are broken down into smaller pieces by air or water. It is a chemical process when air and water react with the minerals in the rock or soils to form new substances.*

The various sizes of particles in the soil determine its physical nature. Some inorganic particles may be fairly large as pieces of stone, gravel or grains of sand. Other particles are extremely small, less than a hundred-thousandth of an inch. These very small particles of soil are COLLOIDS. The colloids are groups of molecules that are small enough to be suspended in water.

Irrigation is needed to grow grapes in California desert. (*Bureau of Reclamation, Department of the Interior*)

Earth being plowed for spring planting. (*Dole Photo*)

ACTION IN SOIL COLLOIDS

Most of what happens between roots and soil happens at the colloid level. Soil colloidal particles act like a bank. The colloids take up minerals and other plant nutrients from the soil solution which surrounds the particles. The minerals are held to the colloids by differences in charges on the colloidal particles. Then, in times of need, when there is a lack of minerals in the soil solution, the colloidal particle returns minerals to the soil solution. The small size of the colloids causes their large storage capacity. The smaller the particle, the greater is its outside area compared to its mass. The surface attachment of materials to the colloidal particles is called ADSORPTION. *ADSORPTION is the process in which solid, liquid, or gas particles cling to the outside of a solid or a liquid particle.* You may remember how dirt particles were surrounded by parts of soap molecules. The dirt particle could be lifted away from and washed away from the article to be cleaned. The same kind of surface attachment process operates in the soil colloids. The soil minerals are adsorbed on the surface of the colloid.

Humus is composed of dead organic materials found in the soil. The chemical nature of humus is constantly changing as the matter in it is in every stage of decay. The decay of organic materials is caused by bacteria. Complex organic substances are changed to simpler substances. The simpler substances can be used by plants as food.

An example of neglected farmland that is no longer productive. (*Courtesy of the Alaska Travel Division*)

An example of a productive farmland. (*Jim Theologos*)

THE WATER PHASE

You can live without food for weeks, but water becomes critical to life in a matter of days. Plants are equally dependent on water. Plants must obtain the minerals upon which they survive from the water solutions in soils. When there is not enough water, the farmer builds channels to irrigate crops. Where there is too much water drainage ditches carry water away from crop lands.

After water enters the soil either as a result of rainfall or irrigation, much of it drains away. The water that remains in the soil is RETAINED WATER. Plants depend largely on this water for their moisture supply.

Two forces that retain water in the soil are ADHESION and COHESION. *ADHESION is the attraction between the surfaces of two unlike materials, such as between clay particles and water. COHESION is the attraction between the molecules of the same materials, such as one water molecule to another water molecule.*

In Experiment 21.2 you determine the amount of moisture retained in the soil. You find that there are differences in the amount of water soils can retain. You also discover the affects of soluble organic materials on water retention and the differences which soluble salts make on the content of water in soils.

Even after baking soil in an oven, some moisture remains. Such water is closely tied to the crystal lattice structure of the clay particle. Put the dried sample in a humid atmosphere and it takes up a certain amount of the moisture. The water molecules form a very tight adhesive layer close to the soil particles. These closely bound surface water molecules are removed only with difficulty and therefore cannot be used by plants.

The water used by plants is in excess of the amount absorbed from a humid atmosphere. This retained water forms layers of water further away from the surface of the colloids. This water requires less force for removal and may be absorbed by plant roots.

The Kind of Soil = The Amount of Retained Water

The amount of available water in a given soil has a great effect on the agricultural use of that kind of soil. For example soils that contain too much sand do not store water. The water drains to the under-soils carrying with it large amounts of nutrient minerals. *Such removal of plant nutrient minerals by drainage is called LEACHING.*

QUICK QUESTIONS?

1. Compare plant decay with weathering.
2. How do colloids provide food for plants?

Silt loam is a mixture of more than 50% silt with less than 27% clay. It is a very useful soil in agriculture. (*Grant Heilman*)

Topsoil is usually no deeper than a spade. It is rich in humus. Notice the decaying organic material in this photo. (*Grant Heilman*)

Soils that contain clays and loams have an abundance of finer colloidal particles. Such soils retain water that is usable by the plant and also contain a good supply of minerals. Too much clay, however, and the soil retains an excess of water. Heavy clay soils become gummy, difficult to work, and do not support good plant growing conditions.

Some soils repel water in the same manner as a duck's feathers. In regions where there is little rainfall, large amounts of calcium, potassium and sodium remain in the soil. These minerals are not washed out of the topsoil. There is very little leaching. Colloids adsorbed minerals on their surface. Then when such colloids dry, they form colloids that are completely incapable of adsorbing water. Soils containing these minerals are found in Western United States and cannot be irrigated. However, if by leaching the salts are washed out of the top soil, the land becomes usable for agriculture.

In the Eastern part of the United States where forests once flourished, the ground contained rich, organic, humus. With heavy rains and floods organic colloids and colloids with inorganic minerals were washed to the lower layers of soil. The two kinds of colloids formed a concentrated layer in the lower soil. *The combined colloids cemented other soil particles together and formed a solid, dense layer called "HARDPAN."*

QUICK QUESTIONS?

1. Explain the difference between adsorption and adhesion by a drawing.
2. In Experiment 21.2, how do you determine the amount of retained water in the soil?

Acid to Alkaline: The pH of Soils

Some plants are very particular about where they grow. The hydrogen ion concentration, pH, in the soil affects the growth of most plants. Cranberries, for example grow only on soils that are at least moderately acid. They prefer strongly acid soils. Other kinds of plants, as alfalfa and clover grow successfully only in nearly neutral soils.

The usual pH in soils ranges between 4.0 and 11.0. In humid regions the range is 5.0 to 6.8 and in the dry arid regions, 9.5 to 11.0. Many factors determine the pH of soils. Some of the factors are: the original composition of the soil, amount of rainfall, drainage of the soil, type of fertilizer used, the type of crop grown on the soil and even the season of the year and climate affects acid-base soil relationships.

The acidity of soils may result from different kinds of chemical reactions. The colloidal particles have the ability to take part in such reactions known as BASE EXCHANGE. If potassium is added to the soil, part becomes available as ions in the soil solution. Another part of the excess potassium forms a base on the surface of the colloid. Limestone, $CaCO_3$, is often used to neutralize acidity of soils. In the case of lime (CaO) added to the soil, a base calcium hydroxide, $Ca(OH)_2$, is formed on the surface of the colloid.

The Story of Percy Julian

In Montgomery, Alabama, a son, who was to achieve fame and fortune, was born to a railway clerk. His name was Percy Julian.

It was a struggle for Julian to obtain a good education. For a time when he was a student at DePauw University, he worked as a waiter and lived in an attic. He sacrificed for his education but he graduated as valedictorian of his class. He taught at Fisk and Howard Universities and West Virginia State College.

In Vienna where Julian obtained his doctorate degree, he developed an interest in soybeans as a source of useful products. He found it to be an inexpensive source of sterols. Sterols are used to make cortisone, a drug which reduces the pain and inflammation caused by arthritis. Up until his time, sterols were obtained from animals and the cost was high.

He worked as a research chemist and overcame many handicaps. In the first year of operation of Julian Laboratories his profit was *$71.70.* The following year showed good reason for not giving up. The net profit was *$97,000.*

(Photo by EBONY *Magazine)*

In humid climate, soils tend to be more acid. Water reacts with carbon dioxide to form carbonic acid which provides hydrogen ions to surround colloidal particles. The hydrogen ions formed from the acid are held quite closely by the particles of soil. The hydrogen ions thus held by the colloids form the reserve acidity of the soil. At the same time the bases which are formed as carbonates are washed from the top soil by the abundance of water. If there are more hydrogen ions than hydroxide ions in the solution surrounding the colloidal particles, this excess is responsible for the active acidity of the soil.

In Experiment 21.4 you test soil for its pH. It is possible that some samples you test are acid. Others may be basic or neutral. It will be well to remember that there are many factors which determine the pH of soils and many conditions that can change the acidity of soils.

QUICK QUESTIONS?

1. Give one reason why soils have different acidity.
2. How may increased rainfall cause an increase in the acidity of soil?
3. What chemical is added to soil to reduce acidity?

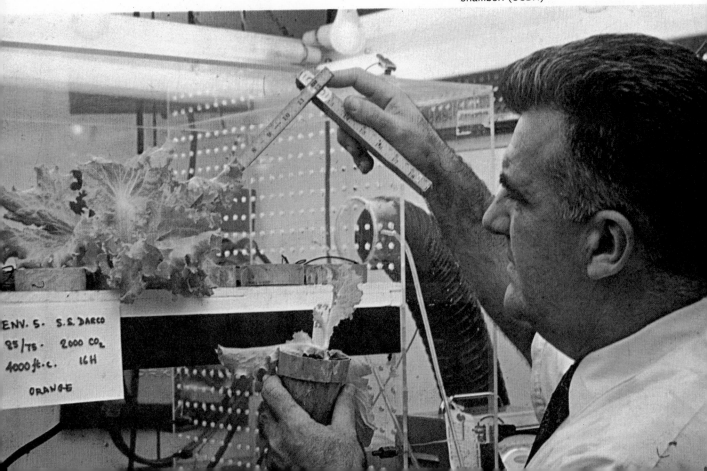

The lettuce grown in the chamber under controlled temperature, light, and carbon dioxide is much larger than the lettuce produced outside the chamber. (*USDA*)

GREEN POWERHOUSES-PLANTS

Do you know how important green plants are to you, and in fact to all of the animals? We and the animals would not survive if it were not for green plants! Green plants can make food from water and carbon dioxide. For this reason animals need plants.

The reactions in which a plant uses carbon dioxide, water, sunlight, and chlorophyll to produce sugar and oxygen is called PHOTOSYNTHESIS. By using the energy in sunlight, green plants can convert water and carbon dioxide into sugar ($C_6H_{12}O_6$) and oxygen.

$$6\,CO_2 + 12\,H_2O \xrightarrow[\text{energy}]{\text{sunlight}} C_6H_{12}O_6 + 6\,O_2 + 6\,H_2O$$

The "Synthesis" of Photosynthesis

SYNTHESIS means making a complex thing from simple parts. In this case, the simple part is the carbon dioxide molecule, CO_2. The complex thing is sugar, $C_6H_{12}O_6$. Through a complicated set of reactions, the green plant changes six carbon dioxide molecules into one molecule of sugar. There is more to it. You may be wondering, for example, where the "H" in $C_6H_{12}O_6$ comes from, or, what role does sunlight play?

The "Photo" of Photosynthesis

The "H" of the sugar comes from water molecules. Within the cells of the green leaf are small structures called chloroplasts. They contain an amazing molecule called chlorophyll. Chlorophyll is green. Since there is so much of it in the leaf, it makes the leaf look green.

Chlorophyll uses the energy in the sunlight to bring about a great change in the water molecule. This change is actually the splitting of H_2O into "H" and "O." Chemists call this process PHOTOLYSIS, photo means light; lysis means splitting. The hydrogen molecules produced by the splitting are added to the carbon dioxide molecules in the conversion to sugar. The oxygen produced is a by-product, and is given off.

The Role of Sunlight

The light energy absorbed by chlorophyll is not all used up in the splitting of water. By a process which is still not clearly understood, some of the sunlight energy is changed into useful chemical energy. In fact, this chemical energy is stored in one of the chemical bonds of a compound called ATP (adenosine triphosphate). When the bond is broken, the energy can be gotten out and used in the synthesis of the sugar from CO_2 and H_2O.

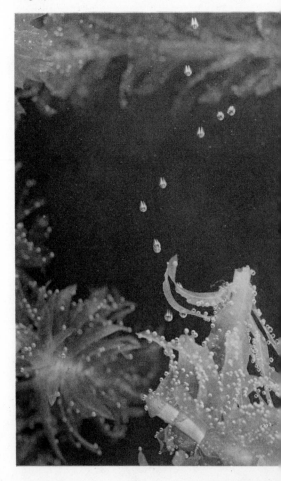

The bubbles of oxygen rising from this water plant were produced by photosynthesis. (*Runk/Schoenberger*)

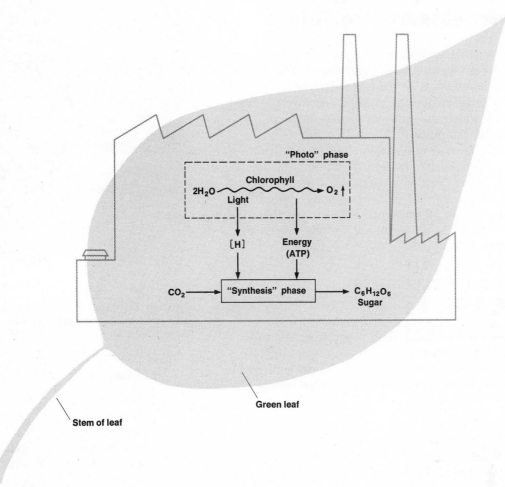

"Photo" phase

Chlorophyll

$2H_2O$ ～～～～～ O_2 ↑

Light

[H]   Energy (ATP)

CO_2 → "Synthesis" phase → $C_6H_{12}O_6$ Sugar

Green leaf

Stem of leaf

Mystery Remains in Photosynthesis

Now we know that in the "photo" phase of photosynthesis, water is split by light in the presence of chlorophyll, and some chemical energy is stored in the bonds of ATP.

In the "synthesis" phase the hydrogen molecules from water and the stored chemical energy are used to make $C_6H_{12}O_6$ from CO_2.

If you put chlorophyll, H_2O, and CO_2 into a test tube and shine light on it, will photosynthesis occur? The answer is no. The chloroplast in the leaf is the only place known where photosynthesis can occur.

The solving of the mysteries of photosynthesis is not complete. Scientists are continuing their research because there are so many unanswered questions. Perhaps one day you will join with them in studying this fascinating process. Without which animals, including ourselves, could not exist.

QUICK QUESTION?

Compare your sample of green plants at work in the laboratory with the photo on page 8/26.

ELEMENTS ESSENTIAL TO PLANTS

By 1860 scientists found that they could grow plants in solutions containing a few familiar salts. *The growth of plants in solutions is called water culture or HYDROPONICS.* The techniques of hydroponics have provided a method by which the minerals needed for plant growth can be determined.

The earth's crust contains about one hundred minerals. Of these only ten are needed by plants in quantity. Five more are needed in trace quantities.

Without these essential elements a plant cannot develop normally. No other element can replace these essential elements. The elements are directly involved in the nutrition of the plant.

SOURCES OF ELEMENTS PLANTS NEED

Some elements are used up or taken from the soil easily. These are nitrogen compounds, potassium compounds, and phosphorous compounds. These compounds need to be replaced in the soil to grow good crops.

Fertilizers

Direct fertilization is a modern method for supplying the soil with minerals plants need. This is done by the addition of manure or ammonium salts such as ammonium sulfate. Dry or anhydrous ammonia gas can be injected directly into the soil. The gas can also be added to the irrigation water. Other modern methods add chemicals for plant nutrition directly to the foliage of plants in the form of sprays.

Rock phosphate $Ca_3(PO_4)_2$, is the chief natural source for phosphates. Ground rock phosphate or bone is treated with sulfuric acid to form a fertilizer, superphosphate.

$$Ca_3(PO_4)_2 + 2 H_2SO_4 + 5 H_2O \longrightarrow Ca(H_2PO_4)_2 \cdot H_2O + 2(CaSO_4 \cdot 2 H_2O)$$

rock phosphate   sulfuric acid   superphosphate

Potassium compounds in the soil result from weathering. This natural supply must be added to for good crops. Large amounts of potassium salts called potash are found at Searles Lake, California. These salts are combined with other materials to make fertilizers. Other sources of potash are wood ashes, seaweed, and wastes from sugar beets.

This fully automated hydroponics system uses no soil. The tomatoes are fed a mixture of inorganic nutrients and water. (*Markow Photography*)

TEN ESSENTIAL ELEMENTS	FIVE TRACE ELEMENTS
carbon	molybdenum
hydrogen	boron
oxygen	copper
phosphorous	manganese
potassium	zinc
nitrogen	
sulfur	
calcium	
iron	

Phosphorous deficient corn. (*Grant Heilman*)

Legumes

Some plants use nitrogen compounds in the soil and other plants restore them. LEGUMES are a family of plants which include beans, peas, and clover. These plants have nodules on their roots. The nodules contain bacteria. These bacteria are called NITROGEN FIXING because they can take free nitrogen in the atmosphere and change it into compounds of nitrogen. They can fix these nitrogen compounds into the soil. It is good farming practice to grow these plants as winter crops to restore the nitrogen to the soil other crops take out. See the role plants play in the nitrogen cycle page 3/26.

Home Lab

Roots of Clover

If it is convenient, dig up a plant of clover and examine the nodules on the roots.

(USDA)

Free . . . . . 100,000,000 Tons
of Fertilizers

Lightning, the destroyer, is also productive. Plants need nitrogen and nitrogen compounds. The nitrogen in the atmosphere is in the form of diatomic molecules. The bonds between the atoms are very strong. The energy from lightning breaks these molecules into nitrogen atoms. The nitrogen atoms combine with oxygen to form oxides of nitrogen.

$$N_2 + O_2 \longrightarrow 2\ NO$$
$$2\ NO + O_2 \longrightarrow 2\ NO_2$$

The various oxides of nitrogen which may be formed are soluble in water. They are washed into the soil by rain. Plants can then use the soluble nitrogen compounds.

$$3\ NO_2 + H_2O \longrightarrow 2\ HNO_3 + NO$$

WHERE DOES IT GO
FROM HERE???

Many agricultural scientists predict the day, within the next twenty years, when many crops will be completely controlled. Acres of glass houses could replace miles of plowed lands. More and better foods will be produced at lower costs. The risks of crop loss will be reduced because natural perils will be practically ended.

Greenhouse in which plants are exposed to radioactivity. (*Brookhaven National Laboratory*)

Plants exposed to gamma radiation show the effects on growth; the more the radiation, the less growth. The tomato plant at the left was not exposed. (*Brookhaven National Laboratory*)

The means for controlled plant growth are now understood. The productivity of plants would be unbelievable, given as much food and light as the plant needs, regulated amounts of water, and carbon dioxide. The fruiting and harvest times can be changed by hormone regulations. Plants have been cross-bred so that the most desirable kinds of fruits, beans, tomatoes, and other crops, are produced.

Biologists, chemists, physicists, and many who work in new areas of science are working on the new methods of agricultural technology. The people of the world can no longer depend upon the seasonal production of crops. Ancient agricultural methods are not able to provide the quantity and quality of food required for the world's growing population.

QUICK QUESTIONS?

1. Why is chlorophyll important?
2. What compounds are involved in the process of photosynthesis?
3. What ways can you test soil pH in the laboratory?
4. List what you consider important to agricultural chemistry.

(*Maurice Sorrell,* EBONY *Magazine*)

Modern Research

Pollution Reduced by No-Till Cropping

Modern tractors have been a major help in farming. One problem that they have helped to enlarge, though, is erosion. They loosen more earth than the old-fashioned horse and plow. The loose earth is washed into rivers and lakes carrying with it nitrates, phosphates, pesticides, and herbicides. These materials add to our growing pollution problem. A new chemical is being developed to reduce erosion from plowing and the resulting pollution. The new chemical called paraquat. It is a weed killer. It is sprayed on the weeds which lay flat on the ground to form a protective covering. The paraquat breaks down into natural compounds and leaves no harmful residues. The new crop is planted into the covering and no plowing is needed.

The chemical works in daylight. The sunlight causes the weed plant to go through the process of photosynthesis. During this process, the paraquat interferes with the vital process and poisons the reaction. The weed plants die as a result.

Chapter 21

ACTION POINTS

AGRICULTURAL CHEMISTRY is the science that most affects ideas concerning the nutrition of plants and animals.

AGRICHEMICALS include **FERTILIZERS, INSECTICIDES,** and **HERBICIDES** and **FUNGICIDES,**

FERTILIZERS are materials which enrich the soil for the production of abundant plant growth.

INSECTICIDES are materials used to destroy undesirable insect pests.

HERBICIDES are materials used to prevent growth of undesirable plants.

FUNGICIDES are materials used to control infections of plants.

SOIL is a mixture of minerals, organic matter, water and air. The minute particles of soil are colloids.

WEATHERING is the natural process by which rocks are broken down to soils.

ADSORPTION is the process by which the soil particles, colloids, hold various kinds of plant nutrition materials to their surfaces.

HUMUS results from the decay of organic matter and usually provides negative charged ions to the soil.

The colloid reactions in soil is called the **SOLID PHASE** and the water solution reactions in soils is called the **WATER PHASE.**

The various qualities of soil to retain water is an important difference in kinds of soils. The water holding properties of soil are related to the character of the colloids found in the various kinds of soils.

Plants will grow or not grow in various kinds of soils depending on the pH of those soils. The pH or acid properties of the soils is dependent upon various reactions of minerals and water with colloids.

CHLOROPHYLL is the green coloring matter of plants. It is needed for the process of photosynthesis.

PHOTOSYNTHESIS is a complex series of reactions in green plants, in which carbon dioxide and water, with the help of chlorophyll and the sun's energy produce sugar and oxygen.

New methods of **NO-TILL CROPPING** may provide increased agricultural production.

FERTILIZERS, both natural and those made by modern technology, are important to the growth patterns of plants. Certain minerals and elements are critical to the life of plants.

NEW DEVELOPMENTS may change the character of farming considerably and may be needed to feed the increased population of the earth.

CHEMISTRY IN INDUSTRY

Unit 9

Contents

UNIT 9   CHEMISTRY IN INDUSTRY

Fuels 22

Materials known as fuels are used by humans to make themselves more comfortable; to do work for them; and to enable them to travel easily.

The oldest source of energy known is the chemical energy in fuels. The energy is locked within the chemical bonds. The energy is POTENTIAL. *POTENTIAL ENERGY is that energy not being used.* It is stored. Fire releases the energy.

Fuels are substances that are reactants in an exothermic reaction. Usually they react with oxygen. Energy in the form of light, heat or electricity are given off in these reactions. Most elements can be used as fuels.

Only oxidation-reduction reactions usually are used for energy production. The fuel is the reactant oxidized. See Chapter 13 for a review of oxidation-reduction reactions.

Sometimes energy must be used for a reaction to take place. This is an endothermic reaction. The products have taken in this energy during their formation. The products, then, are more useful as fuels than the reactants.

Oil well in Alaska. (*Courtesy of Atlantic-Richfield*)

Chemistry and the fuel industry are directly related. (*Courtesy of The M.W. Kellogg Company, a division of Pullman Incorporated*)

QUICK QUESTIONS?

1. List ways in which fuels make your life more comfortable.
2. Name three fuels which may be used for heat in the home. What are the advantages of each over the others?

Elements As Fuels

Most of the fuels we use are carbon-containing materials. Oil, natural gas, coke, peat and various forms of coal, contain carbon. Some other materials would be just as good or better as carbon containing materials. Even though many elements or compounds are more plentiful they are not as convenient to use as fuels.

If a high temperature or high intensity of heat is needed such as in a flashbulb, magnesium is used. Never touch a flashbulb right after its been used. Why? Aluminum may be used as a fuel in high altitude flight. The above are two examples of metals used as fuels. As we shall see in Chapter 25 most metals exist in the earth in ores as sulfides, carbonates, or oxides. There is an expense in obtaining the pure element. If the element is to be used as a fuel, it must first be refined. This expense must be considered when a fuel is needed. Is the purpose worth the time and money? In special cases as above it is.

Fuels such as coal and oil are called fossil fuels. The decay of plants and animals throughout the ages formed layers. Pressure caused these layers to change gradually into fuel forms. (*Courtesy of the AMERICAN MUSEUM OF NATURAL HISTORY*)

ENERGY MAKES THE WORLD GO

In this age of technology, our whole way of life depends on our having a steady supply of power. According to the findings of researchers at the United Nations, world power demand has doubled in the twenty-year period from 1943 to 1963. The prediction is that by 1983 this demand for power will have doubled again. Man gets his power from three major sources: 1. forces in nature—gravity, wind, or solar energy; 2. forces resulting from reactions going on in the nucleus of the atom—nuclear energy; 3. forces resulting from the burning (combustion) of solid, liquid, or gaseous fuels. At the present time, the burning of fuels is by far the most important source of power in the world.

FRACTIONAL DISTILLATION is the separation of a mixture of liquids by their boiling points. As crude oil is heated, the low boiling point liquids boil. Then the temperature is raised until the various liquids boil at different temperatures.

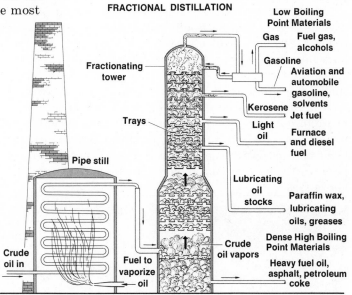

FRACTIONAL DISTILLATION

Combustion

COMBUSTION, or burning, is a chemical reaction in which a fuel, usually one that contains carbon, reacts with oxygen. The reaction forms a product (an oxide) and gives off heat as it does so. Some of the largest industries of the world are completely engaged in making fuels. These fuels are used by other industries to produce heat energy. This heat energy, in turn, is used to heat matter (like heating water to make steam) producing still other forms of energy such as mechanical or electrical energy. Energy in these forms is then used to run machines that do man's work, and help him manufacture all sorts of goods. So, the activity of prospectors, miners, petroleum engineers, and chemists continues. There is an endless search for and processing of the product that is to be destroyed by fire. This is destruction with a purpose—to provide the heat energy so important to man.

Home Lab
Combustion of a Candle

Check to see how complete the combustion of a candle is. Assemble a candle, a white dish, a soda straw, and kitchen tongs. Light the candle. Observe the flame. With the tongs hold the dish in the flame. Let the dish cool.

Squeeze the soda straw into a jet. Blow into the candle flame. What happens?

Wipe off the bottom of the dish. Was there anything on the bottom of the dish?

If you have a gas stove, put the burner on low. Hold the dish in the flame for a few minutes. Let the dish cool. Wipe it off. Are the results the same as with the candle? Why?

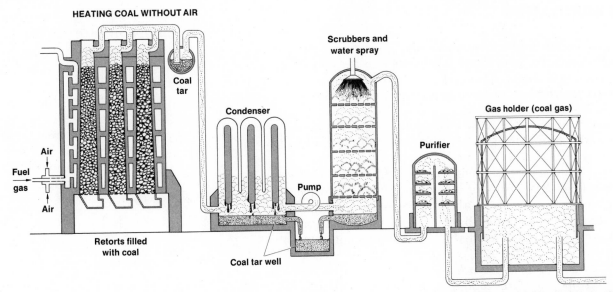

HEATING COAL WITHOUT AIR

Coal tar

Condenser

Scrubbers and water spray

Gas holder (coal gas)

Purifier

Air

Fuel gas

Air

Pump

Retorts filled with coal

Coal tar well

DESTRUCTIVE DISTILLATION is the process of decomposing a substance in the absence of air. Coke, ammonia, coal, tar, and coal gas are formed from the destructive distillation of soft coal.

Fuels for combustion may be in the form of a solid (coal, wood, peat), or in the form of a liquid (oil, kerosene, alcohol), or in the form of a gas (propane, natural gas, butane). Whatever type of fuel is used, the purpose is always to release as much potential heat energy as possible. This heat energy is released by combustion. This can be done by making sure that the combustion of the fuel is complete. Just the right amount of air must be used in the process. If combustion is incomplete much of the fuel escapes and the potential energy stored in it is lost. When combustion is complete, only a small amount of air is used. The products are very nearly all carbon dioxide and water. If too much air is used, the excess air which is not oxidized escapes along with the exhaust gases. Some of the heat energy is then lost because it is used in heating up this excess air.

The Combustion Reactions

Fuels are composed principally of carbon and hydrogen. We can write an equation for the combustion reaction as follows

$$C + O_2 \longrightarrow CO_2 + heat$$

and

$$2\,H_2 + O_2 \longrightarrow 2\,H_2O \text{ (vapor)} + heat$$

These two reactions represent the *complete* combustion of a fuel. In cases of incomplete combustion, carbon monoxide, CO, is one of the products formed along with carbon dioxide.

QUICK QUESTIONS?

1. In Experiment 22.2, *Fuels and Heat Energy*, you calculate the amount of heat energy in "canned heat." For which of the following would you need more "canned heat?"
   (a) To warm a bathtub of water to 30°C
   (b) To warm a cup of water to 30°C
2. Which contains more heat energy, a three-gallon tub of water at 30°C or a cup of water at 30°C?
3. What are the products of combustion?

LUBRICATION

Run your fingers across the desk top or drag your foot along the floor. There is resistance to the movements, isn't there? Whenever there are objects rubbed together, there is a force called friction which opposes the movement. Friction is an everyday experience. What would happen if we walked across the floor and there were little friction? Did you ever walk on a pond of ice? There is less friction between your boot and the ice than there is between your boot and the floor.

In many cases surfaces allowed to rub against each other can damage each other. This is especially true of metal surfaces. Engines have metal surfaces which are moving parts. In order that the surfaces do not damage each other LUBRICANTS are rubbed on the surface. *LUBRICATION is the addition of a material called a lubricant to surfaces to keep them from rubbing together.* Lubricants are usually oils or greases. Thousands of hydrocarbon compounds are among the most used lubricants. The different properties of various lubricants help in the selection of one for a particular job.

QUICK QUESTIONS?

1. Name two other lubricants you use besides motor oil.
2. Next time you visit a gas station notice the motor oils. Find out which type motor oil is most used in automobiles in your region.

Inventory must be taken of the various products used in the fuel system of an automobile. (*Irene Fertik*)

Viscosity of Lubricants

In the laboratory you study VISCOSITY. *The VIS-COSITY of a liquid is a measure of the resistance of a liquid to flow.* It is a very important property of lubricants. It is important that the lubricant is viscous enough to spread on a surface, but not run off a surface.

The flow of any liquid can be compared with the flow of water. The comparison can give us the relative viscosity of the liquid.

The viscosity of liquids change with temperature. The lower the temperature the higher the viscosity. Hot liquids flow better than cold liquids. In other words, if motor oil is to flow through a cold engine, it will flow more slowly than it will in a hot engine.

Oils for engines are rated for their viscosity by the Society of Automotive Engineers (SAE). The oils are assigned a number which we ordinarily call the "weight." The numbers like 5, 10, 20, 30 are not exact viscosity values, but it is true that higher "weights" are more viscous. Oils used in cars and trucks usually have their viscosity measured at either 210°F(99°C) or at 0°F(−18°C). Those measured at 0°F are given a number and a W such as 10 W. An oil with the number 10 W 30 means that it has a viscosity like a 10 weight oil at 0°F and a viscosity like a 30 weight oil at 210°F.

To avoid slow starts in the winter, some people use 10 oil, and they use 30 oil in summer. Some people simply use 10 W 30 all year.

Technician checks feedback from an experiment on the viscosity of various lubricants. (*Irene Fertik*)

Chapter 22

ACTION POINTS

FUELS contain potential energy locked within their chemical bonds.
FIRE releases the energy of fuels.
OXIDATION-REDUCTION reactions are used for energy production.
Most **ELEMENTS** can be oxidized, therefore, most elements can be used as fuels.
Man gets his power from three sources: **NATURAL FORCES; ATOMIC ENERGY;** or **COMBUSTION** of **FUELS.**
LUBRICANTS, usually greases or oils, are rubbed on surfaces to decrease friction.
VISCOSITY is an important property of a liquid. It is the measure of the resistance of a liquid to flow.

Rubber and Plastics 23

RUBBER

Rubber is one of the most remarkable substances we know about because it is ELASTIC! Rubber can be shaped into a great number of products, useful in our everyday lives. All of these products are elastic, long wearing and water-resistant. Natural rubber is made by a number of different plants and trees, which grow in the tropical areas of the world.

Natural Rubber

Natural rubber has been known for many centuries. The Mayan civilization, which dates back at least to the 11th Century, is known to have used products made from natural rubber. Even so, natural rubber was not widely used by industrial nations until around 1850. Before that time, rubber products melted at high temperature, were brittle at low temperatures. In 1839, Charles Goodyear, discovered a process which greatly improved rubber's usefulness. *The process consists of adding sulfur to the natural rubber, and is called VULCANIZATION.*

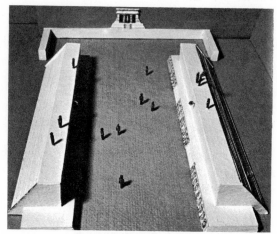

The Mayan people used a rubber ball in a game like basketball on a court similar to the one above.

Tappers make a fresh cut in the tree daily from which the latex will flow. (*UNIROYAL INC.*)

What is rubber? In the plants and trees from which rubber is obtained, a watery suspension of rubber particles is found. The suspension is called LATEX. Proper processing of the latex gives the solid substance we recognize as natural rubber. The main ingredient of this solid material is a hydrocarbon polymer. The basic unit or monomer is isoprene (C_5H_8). The long hydrocarbon chains are not hooked together (or cross-linked) in natural rubber, but the vulcanization process causes sulfur bridges to form between the chains.

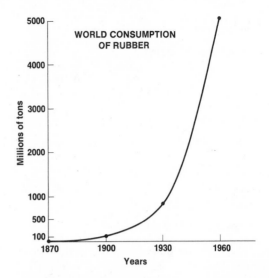

Synthetic Rubber

In the past 70 years or so, scientists have learned a great deal about polymerization reactions. Polymers can now be made from one monomer, or two or more different monomers. A number of polymers resembling natural rubber in their properties have been made, and these are called "synthetic rubbers." Some of the hydrocarbon monomers used in making synthetic rubber are butadiene, isoprene, and chloroprene. The products of the polymerization of these substances are given many trade names in different countries like Neoprene often used for shoe soles in the U.S.A. They are all elastic, some can be vulcanized just like natural rubber, and some have rubber-like properties superior to the natural material.

At the present time, world rubber consumption exceeds six million tons annually. More than 60% of the rubber produced is used to make tires. As yet, no good way to recycle used rubber has been found. Discarded bits of this useful substance are threatening to become a serious waste problem. Just as with other materials, thought must be given as to what to do with material after it has served its purpose.

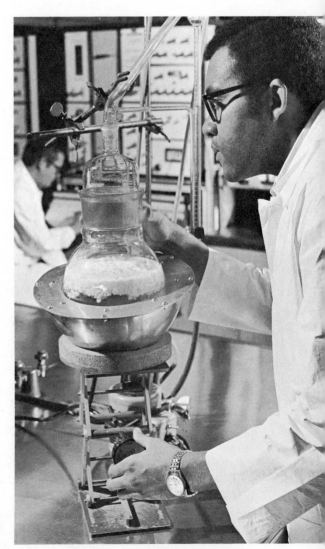

This laboratory technician is checking rubber crumb samples for quality.
(*Goodyear*)

PLASTICS

What are Plastics?

Plastics are polymers like natural or synthetic rubber. To be called a *PLASTIC a product must be sold in a finished state and it must have been shaped by flow at some point in its manufacture.* Even so, the distinction between some plastics and some synthetic rubbers is not always clear. In addition to the polymer substance, plastics contain other materials. These materials include fillers to improve the strength and plasticizers to improve the flexibility of the plastic.

Forming of Plastics

Most of the plastics to be used in products are formed into fibers such as rayon and nylon; films such as Saran Wrap; and foams. Certain plastics like the urethanes can be made into foams. They are made fluffy by putting air or other gases into their structure. These foams are used for cushions and for insulation against heat, cold, and electricity.

Different Kinds of Plastics

From your own experience you know that there are many, many different kinds of plastics. They are made into containers, wrapping films for foods, handles and cabinets for a variety of machines and appliances, floor coverings, racks, hangers, and many other uses.

Most of the basic varieties of plastics are different from one another because they contain a different polymer. Many plastics called *THERMOPLASTICS soften when heated and harden again when cooled.* This large group of plastics includes many familiar ones such as nylons (polyamides), rayons (cellulose plastic), plexiglass (acrylic plastic), polyethylenes, and sarans (polyvinylidene chloride plastics). These are used in such common products as clothing, clear plastic coverings or containers, and food wrapping films like Saran Wrap.

Another important family of plastics called *THERMO-SETTING PLASTICS become permanently hard when heated to a particular temperature.* Examples of these are: epoxy plastics, such as are found in Epoxy adhesives; the phenolic plastics used in shoe soles, bowling balls, and battery casings; the Bakelite phenolics used to make phonograph records.

Polyester plastics are thermosetting. They are often made with substances added to improve their hardness or resistance to shock or chemicals. A common reinforcer is glass. The glass-containing materials are then used to make such things as luggage, skis, protective helmets, and many other things.

Synthetic resins used in polyvinyl chloride plastics. (*Charles E. Rotkin, pfi*)

Bubble of Saran Wrap. (*The Dow Chemical Co.*)

Modern Research
What's Happening in Plastics?

Scientists and engineers are constantly trying to develop new polymers for plastics, and new uses for existing plastics. In coming years more and more of our world will be made of plastics. Plastics containing fire-retardants for fire-proofing will be used in building construction and for fixtures within buildings. Before long the milk we buy may be in plastic bags rather than in paper cartons.

Even an automobile muffler has been made. It is currently being used in Europe. It is only one-third as heavy as a metal one. The muffler is expected to last longer and be cheaper than a metal one also.

A spectacular application of modern science is the 350,000 pounds of cast acrylic used to cover the baseball stadium in Houston, Texas—the Astrodome.

The potential of plastics is limited only by our knowledge of polymers and our imagination!

The plastic roof of the Astrodome. (*Tom McHugh, Photo Researchers*)

Modern Research
Plastics and the Environment

Everyday more and more products are packaged in some form of plastics. Once used the container is thrown away. Mountains of plastic containers pile up in dumps. These dumps become eyesores and sources of land pollution. If the plastics are burned, the air is polluted with poisonous gases. The disposal of plastics is a problem.

Several methods of building in "self destruct" qualities in plastics are being researched. In one method a ketone group is inserted in the polymer chain. When the plastic is exposed to sunlight, rain, and wind, it becomes brittle. The plastic becomes granular. It starts to de-compose into the soil where it is further degraded. The end result is carbon dioxide and water. The time for decomposition takes from a few days to six months. Factors such as the type plastic, its thickness, and the exposure to sunlight, rain, and wind help to determine the time of decomposition.

If the plastic is kept out of the ultraviolet rays of the sun, it remains stable. Storekeepers will have no trouble in displaying the plastics in store windows because the windows remove enough of the sun's ultraviolet rays.

When these plastics are used widely, there will be sure to be some interesting results.

QUICK QUESTIONS?

1. What is a disadvantage of nautral rubber before it is vulcanized?
2. What is a good use for a thermoplastic?
3. Give three new uses of plastics in the last ten years.

Chapter 23

ACTION POINTS

Natural rubber is a polymer, made from a substance called **LATEX.** The monomer of rubber is **ISOPRENE** ($C_5H_8^-$).
VULCANIZATION is a process to make rubber more useful by adding sulfur.
SYNTHETIC RUBBER is a polymer like natural rubber. There are many monomers used to make synthetic rubber.
PLASTICS are products that are polymers that are shaped by flow during manufacture. Plastics are sold in the finished state. They may contain fillers and plasticizers. Two of the many kinds of plastics are **THERMOPLASTICS** and **THERMO-SETTING PLASTICS.**
Plastics come in many forms including:
FIBERS, FILMS, and **FOAMS.**

Natural and Synthetic Fibers

THREADS OF LIFE
AND LABORATORY: FIBERS

The many kinds of fibers are very important to you. A chemist may tell you about the elements in fibers and how they are bonded together, but you don't need a chemist to tell you about the importance of fibers in your life. Muscle fibers move your body, and nerve fibers carry the messages that make your body function. The fibers discussed in this chapter are those that can be twisted into threads and woven into cloth, or twisted into cords to make into ropes. Natural and synthetic thread-like fibers are important to your life and comfort.

Fiborama: The Many Kinds of Fibers

In Experiment 24.1 you examine the physical properties of different kinds of fibers. In Experiment 24.2 you test the chemical nature of fibers. From your laboratory experiences you might note that materials which have similar chemical structures will also have similarities in their physical properties.

A simple classification of fibers will help you understand some of your experimental findings. All fibers can be grouped into four general types which relate to their origins: animal fibers, plant fibers, mineral fibers and synthetic (man-made fibers).

Animal Fibers
Silk and wool are the two major sources of animal fiber. Chemically, all animal fibers, are proteins. (Review the chemical characteristics of proteins, Chapter 15).

Plant Fibers
Cotton and flax are the most important fibers that come from plants. Cotton and linen are mainly cellulose.

Man-Made Fibers
There are a wide variety of man-made fibers. They are produced by chemical treatments of certain raw materials. Some of the raw materials include: wood pulp, cotton linters (fuzz left on cotton seeds), coal and petroleum by-products, casein (a milk protein), air, water, and salt.

Home Lab

Both cotton and linen are largely cellulose. To distinguish cotton from linen, place a drop of olive oil on a sample of each. Blot it and place over a dark background. If the fabric seems to become clearer, it is linen; if it just looks a little damp, it is cotton.

ORIGIN OF FIBERS

ANIMAL	**silk** **wool**	
PLANT	**cotton** **flax**	
MINERAL	**asbestos** **glass**	
	Regenerated—rayon	
	cellulose derivative	**acetate** **arnel**
	acrylic	**A—Acrilan** **Creslan** **Orlon**
	Modacrylic	**dynel**
	olefin	**polyethylene**
MAN-MADE		**polypropylene**
(a selection)		**polyurethane**
	polyamide	**nylon**
	polyester	**Dacron** **Kodel** **vycron**
	glass fibers—fiberglass	
	metallic—lamé	
	rubber—lastex	
	saran—	

Wool is still spun by hand in Romania. This woman is pulling the wool that had been sheared from a sheep and washed. She twists the wool and spins it onto a stick. (*Jim Theologos*)

American loom used to weave material in the 18th and early 19th centuries. (*Linda Lindroth*)

Navajo Indian woman using traditional loom to weave a rug. This folk craft is still done today. (*Library, State Historical Society of Colorado*)

Textiles Find A Place in Civilization

Some 6000 years ago the last ice age came to a close. About that time nomadic, hunting tribes began to settle into villages. As dependence on hunting gave way to agriculture, some inventive people twisted animal hairs or vegetable fibers into thread. Threads were woven into cloth. Clothes of woven threads made animal skins out of style. Cloth coverings were soft and more comfortable. They became a mark of a more advanced civilization.

Various civilizations used different kinds of fibers to make cloth. In Egypt the earliest textiles were woven from a plant fiber, flax; in India from cotton; and in southern Europe wool was used.

Chinese legend and recent discoveries confirm that silk originated in China in the 27th Century B.C. The secret of the precious silk fibers were kept from the Western World until the 6th Century A.D. Then silk worm eggs were smuggled out of China and the silk fiber was introduced into Europe.

The first man-made fiber was artificial silk. A French chemist, Count Hilaire de Chardonnet, invented a process for producing it. A viscous (thick) fluid was forced through the small openings of a machine called a spinneret and hardened into a thread by immersion in a chemical bath. This process continues to be a basic method for producing man-made textile fibers.

Artificial silk was recognized by the U.S. Federal Trade Commission in 1927 by the name of rayon. During the 1930's, research was done in developing other man-made fibers. These fibers were developed for their own properties rather than imitating natural fibers. In the New York's World Fair of 1939, a new material, nylon, stronger than silk was introduced to the textile industry. The introduction of many more man-made fibers quickly followed.

Today, research is directed toward improving existing fibers for special purposes.

Biobriefs of Some V.I.F.'s (very important fibers)

Cotton: Universal Textile Fiber

Cotton is about 95 percent cellulose. The fibers start from a single cell that grows about the seeds of a cotton plant. When it is living the cell fiber is full and shaped like a bulb. When it is dead it looks like a flat, twisted ribbon.

To improve its properties, cotton is treated in several ways. Look on a spool of cotton thread to see if it says "mercerized." Cotton yarn that is stretched is placed in a solution of sodium hydroxide. It is then taken and neutralized with a dilute solution of sulfuric acid. This treatment is called MERCERIZING. Mercerized yarns have a silky luster, dye more easily, and do not shrink as much as untreated cotton.

Absorbent cotton, used in medical work, has been cleaned and treated with ether to remove the natural wax.

Cotton provides fiber for textiles, paper, and cellulose for explosives and the plastics industry.

Cotton plant. (*National Cotton Council*)

Silkworm cocoon. (*Russ Kinne, Photo Researchers*)

Silk: The Fiber of Kings

The production of "natural" silk starts with the larval stage of a moth. The eggs of the moth hatch into a caterpillar, called the silkworm. The silkworm feeds on mulberry leaves and as the worm matures it reaches a pupal stage (or cocoon). Just before reaching the pupal development the silkworm spins a protective coat of fibers about itself. This is the silk fiber and it is as strong as a strand of steel the same diameter.

The worm manufactures silk fibers in two glands located in the upper part of its body. The glands secrete a protein, fibroin, which squeezes out through a small hole located in the head of the worm. Like the clotting protein in human blood, the fibroin solidifies when it comes in contact with air to form two slender threads of silk. Another protein, sericin, is secreted at the same time. The protein, sericin, binds the two strands of silk into a single fiber.

Silk, just as all large polymer protein molecules, is made up of amino acids. Nine amino acids have been identified in the proteins of silk.

Fibers That Are Mineral

What happened when you pulled melted glass apart in the laboratory? You observed a fine strand, fiber, of glass stretching between the solid glass. Produced in mass quantities for commercial use the glass threads are called glass silk, glass wool, or fiber glass.

Glass cloth or fiber glass is often used with a plastic. The glass serves as a reinforcement just as steel is used in concrete and a very rigid structure of plastic and glass is obtained. The hulls of boats, pipes and furniture can be constructed from such plastic-fiber glass materials.

One of the best known mineral fibers obtained from nature is asbestos. It is found associated with volcanic formations. Asbestos, like glass wool, is used for insulation and for fireproof materials used in stage curtains, suits for fire fighters and for laboratory safety blankets.

Fine metal wires, as fine as silk, can also be used for fiber. Steel and copper wire fibers are used in the form of a metallic fiber cloth which serve as window screens. A metallic cloth made from highly heat resistant metal mixtures, is used for re-entry parachutes which lower space capsules back to earth.

Metallic cloth is used in parachutes used to return space capsules to Earth. (*NASA*)

CHEMICAL AND PHYSICAL PROPERTIES OF VARIOUS MAN-MADE FIBERS

Acetate

Acetate has cellulose for its base. The cellulose from cotton linters or wood chips are treated with acetic anhydride. Cellulose acetate is formed.

Acetate melts, when burned. It may give painful burns. The odor given off is similar to vinegar. Concentrated acids cause acetate to decompose. It dissolves in acetone. (Watch fingernail polish remover!) It dries rapidly, does not deteriorate from salt or mold, and does not rot.

Acrilan

Acrilan is a polymer of acrylonitrile. It has good resistance to acids, bases, and bleaches. It is not harmed by organic solvents or sunlight. It does not melt, but burns leaving a hard black bead. It blends well with other fibers. It washes and dries easily and resists wrinkling. It should be ironed at rayon setting.

Nylon spinning plant.
(*Charles E. Rotkin, pfi*)

Dynel

Dynel is a COPOLYMER. *A COPOLYMER is a polymer with two or more different molecules as units.* The units in the dynel polymer are acrylonitrile and vinyl chloride.

Dynel burns on contact with an open flame, but the burning stops when the flame is removed. It does not melt or drip.

It will begin to shrink and stiffen at 215°F. For this reason it should be ironed below the acetate setting on an iron. Sunlight bleaches the fabric slightly.

Nylon

The basic substances from which nylon is produced are made from coal-tar, or from oil products. In a burning test there is no flame, but there is melting and dripping. There is a residue, a very hard black bead.

Nylon melts above 400°F and is resistant to bleaches. It is generally insoluble in organic solvents. Bases have very little affect on it. Nylon washes easily, dries quickly. If ironing is needed, use a low setting on iron.

SOMETHING FOR YOU TO DO

1. Check tags in department stores to determine the care required for products of man-made fibers.
2. Check the dial on an automatic washer to see the temperature range at which various fabrics should be washed.

DYES

DYES are coloring substances. Until the middle of the 19th century dyes were made from plants and animals. Today dyes are almost entirely man made.

Thousands of man-made dyes are in use. Coal tar is the basic source of these products. Coal tar is fractionally distilled to produce substances like benzene, naphthalene, and anthracene from which dyes are made.

A good dye gives a color that is FAST. *FAST means it resists fading by water, light, perspiration, and other factors.* A dye must be soluble in some solvent or form some soluble compound so it can be applied to the material to be colored. After the material is colored, the dye must be insoluble so that it is fast. Dyes become insoluble by either combining with the material; by being adsorbed by the material; or by being used with a MORDANT. *A MORDANT is a substance which forms an insoluble compound with a dye to produce a fast color.*

Sir William Perkin made the first synthetic dye. (*The Bettmann Archive*)

This is a laboratory in which dyes for leather and tanning chemicals are tested. (*Charles E. Rotkin, pfi*)

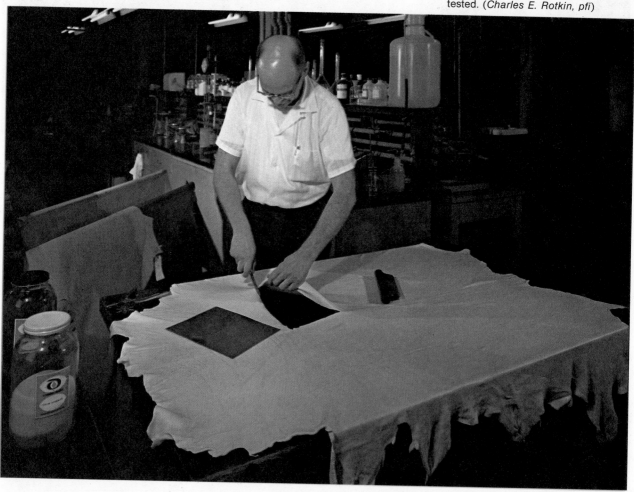

Fibers and Dyes

There are a great variety of dyes and many methods of dyeing. The same dye does not react the same way with all fibers. Nor can all fibers be dyed under the same conditions.

Cotton, linen, and rayon are made from cellulose. It is a carbohydrate and is neutral. Silk, wool, leather, and fur are proteins. Proteins have both acid and basic character. They are composed of amino acids. These acids have an amino group which can give basic qualities. Cellulose fibers take dyes less readily than protein fibers.

The action of the dye depends upon the chemical nature of the fiber and the dye itself. Acid dyes color fibers that have a basic nature. Basic dyes color fibers that have an acid nature. Cotton and linen must be made either acid or basic by mordanting before dyeing. Both acid and basic dyes color silk and wool directly.

QUICK QUESTIONS?

Some dyes you have used in the laboratory are: methyl orange, phenolphthalein, and methylene blue. For what purpose did you use them?

Chapter 24

ACTION POINTS

FIBERS can be classed by their sources: **ANIMAL, MINERAL, PLANT,** and **SYNTHETIC.**
COTTON is 95 percent cellulose. One treatment to improve the properties of cotton is **MERCERIZATION.**
SILK is a polymer of proteins.
Important mineral fibers include: **GLASS** and **ASBESTOS.**
The origins and properties of **MAN-MADE** or **SYNTHETIC** fibers are varied.
DYES are coloring substances. Coal tar is a source from which many dyes originate.
Some dyes **DIRECTLY** color a material.
Some dyes **INDIRECTLY** color a material by using a **MORDANT.**

Metallurgy 25

Metals in History

It was getting dark and the cry of a wolf pack made the caveman family jumpy. Joe Stoneflint went over to his fire and piled on more wood. Tonight, a big fire was needed for protection. Flames reached high into the air. And the small family settled down for the night.

In the morning, one of the women went over to the smoldering fire to add more wood. Something shiny and gray in the embers caught her eye. She knew it wasn't there last evening. Where did it come from? Maybe it was from that shiny stone that was used to build the base. Tonight, she would find another one of those stones and build the fire over it. Maybe more of that shiny stuff would appear.

Joe Schmidt waited for the signal to break the plug on the blast furnace. After a day in the mill he was ready to go home. Now it was his turn to act. The melt should be ready to pop soon. Now! He pulled a yellow lever and 400 tons of liquid iron poured out of the furnace while he retreated behind his safety shield.

The time between the Stoneflint cave family and Joe Schmidt, our steelworker, could be about 20,000 years, maybe even longer. For the first evidence that man used metals is 8000 years old. It is a long way back to the day when people of ancient times squeezed a few pounds of copper out of the rocks. They hammered them into the desired-shape piece of jewelry, a shield, a tool or a weapon. The ancient Hittites, 2000 years ago, were taking the iron from rocks to make iron utensils. An iron sword found in Iran is over 4000 years old. Not only practical things were made however. The bronze vessel shown was cast about 4000 years ago.

Bronze vessel from Iran made about 2000 B.C. (*The Metropolitan Museum of Art*)

The Bronze Age

Before metals were discovered, man had only stone and wooden implements. Spear points, bowls and axes were all made from the most common materials available, stone or wood. The first metals used were probably copper, gold and silver. These are easily hammered into various shapes. Eventually, a mixture of the metals copper and tin melted together was used to make everyday implements. This mixture is called bronze and, when humans began to use bronze instead of stone or wood to make his instruments, they entered the Bronze Age. This was about 5000 years ago, in Mesopotamia. About 1000 B.C., the widespread use of iron then replaced bronze. As you can see, the metal workers began their trade a long time ago.

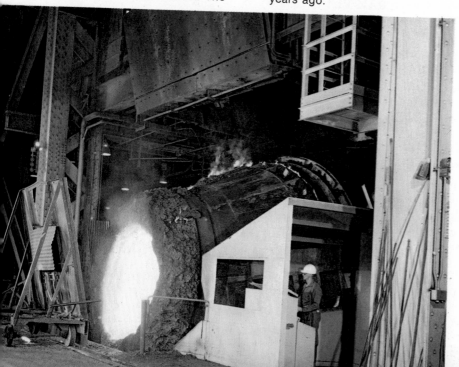

Steelworker behind shield at basic oxygen furnace in a modern steel plant. (*Charles E. Rotkin, pfi*)

MODERN METALS

In our time, metals have become a very important re-
source. Think of all the things that are made of metals:
cooking utensils, nails, wire, cars, planes, washing machines, furnaces, even the antennae that bring the world
into your home. The list is endless. From jewelry to
bridges, printing presses to tall buildings, metals are
necessary for our standard of living. It would be very
difficult, if not impossible, to live without metals.

From Where Do We Get Our Metals?

From ORES in the earth. *An ORE is a material that
has enough metal in it to make it worth mining. The
study of metals, called METALLURGY,* began when
ores were discovered. From the time it is taken from the
earth and a finished metallic product is made, a lot is
done to an ore. Metallurgy began to grow into a science
when methods were discovered that let men get the
metal out of the ore. The whole process, from ore to
product, follows these steps: from the mine, the
ore is taken to a mill nearby. At the mill, the ore is separated into the useful ore (concentrated ore) and the
useless rock that comes with it (called gangue). The
concentrated ore may then be treated in several ways,
depending on what ore you have. This step is an at-
tempt to separate the desired metal from anything else
with which it may be combined. After the metal is obtained, then it may be mixed with another metal. Pure
metals have remarkably few useful properties. Other
metals are usually added to make ALLOYS. From
there, the alloy is shipped to manufacturers who will
make your finished product.

Seems like a long journey from deep in the earth to
your home, and it is. So, let's start at the beginning,
when the ore is taken from the earth.

Metal is used in suspension bridges. It is strong
and can be pulled into wires. (*Mackinac Bridge
Authority, Photo by H.J. Bell*)

Open pit iron ore mine near Hibbing, Minnesota. (*Standard Oil Co. (N.J.)*)

Digging It: Getting the Ore Out

What are the major metals that are used today? Some common ones are iron, aluminum, zinc, copper and lead. These metals are usually found chemically combined with other substances in minerals. Some of the minerals that contain these metals are:

Metal	Mineral	Composition
Iron	Hematite	Fe_2O_3
Aluminum	Bauxite	Aluminum oxide, hydrated
Zinc	Sphalerite	ZnS
Copper	Chalcopyrite	$CuFeS_2$
Lead	Galena	PbS
Tin	Cassiterite	SnO_2

Once an ore is located, and if it's worth it, mining it from the earth begins. This can be done by either strip mining or by actually tunneling into the earth. Strip mining is done if the ore is close to the earth's surface. Huge shovels and bulldozers strip away the cover of the earth. The huge iron mine in Mesabi, Minn. is a strip-mining operation. If the ore is deep within the earth, tunneling then has to be done. The iron ore mine in Morgantown, Pa. is an example of a shaft and tunnel operation.

Some ores, such as native copper, may be found as a pure metal not combined with anything. Gold is found in this native state, also. Most ores are compounds of the metal combined with substances such as sulfur or oxygen. For example, iron ore is usually found as iron oxide. Iron is combined with oxygen. Aluminum and tin are also found as oxides. Sulfur is frequently in combination with lead, copper, nickel, or zinc. These metals are found as sulfide ores. To free the metal from these chemical combinations, the ore must be treated chemically. But before that is done, the ore and the gangue must be separated.

SOMETHING TO THINK ABOUT

Metals are important in our everyday life. Describe a room without any metal in it. What materials could you substitute for metals?

Leaving the Gangue Behind: The Concentration Game

The ore taken from the earth usually contains impurities. *The unwanted rocks that are mined with the wanted ore is the GANGUE.* The gangue and the wanted ore are usually separated right near the mine. This separation process concentrates the ore. When ores are as rich as some iron ore, it may contain 60 percent iron. Rich ores do not require much concentration, but many of today's ores are far from rich. Copper comes in ores that contain as little as 0.6 percent of the metal.

There are several machines that are used to get the ore concentrated. First, the ore is crushed. Then the crushed ore is screened and sorted according to size. The smaller ore particles are then sent through a grinding process to be made even smaller. It's easier and cheaper to treat smaller-size particles than larger ones. The wanted ore particles usually break apart from the unwanted particles, but they are all mixed up. So the mixture has to go through further separation processes.

The small particles of ore can be separated in several ways. Two of these methods are GRAVITY SEPARATION and FLOTATION. Both processes use water and both result in metal-rich minerals in tiny bits being separated from the gangue particles. After the separation process, the concentrated ore is then sent to the furnaces.

Separation by Gravity

In this method, the ore particles are dropped into a large tank of water. The tank is shaken constantly. The lighter, non-metallic particles (the gangue) are pushed out of the tank, but the heavier metallic ore sinks to the bottom. The ore concentrates are then collected from the bottom of the tank. This process is usually repeated several times. Then the "saved" material is placed in shaking tables. This table has a current of water moving over it which washes the light waste material away. The heavier metallic matter flows into another tank.

Separation by Flotation

Metallic mineral particles (usually sulfides) cling to oil droplets in water. If the particles are small enough, and if bubbles are formed by air blown through the mixture the particles float to the top of a water bath. These oily bubbles, with the metal particles clinging to them, form a scum which then can be scraped off the top of the water. The scum is then washed clean of the oil, leaving the wanted metal ore behind.

Home Lab

Can you "recover" heavy minerals from your backyard?

Collect some tiny pebbles and dirt and place them in a large pie pan. If you live near a shallow stream, collect the material from the bottom. Place enough water in the pan to cover the materials. Now swish it around and see if you can separate the "lights" and "heavies." Try to wash the light material out of the pan while keeping the heavy stones in it.

What materials did you keep?

Describe them. (If you found anything that is gold-colored and soft, send it to us at Holt, Rinehart and Winston.)

Flotation separation of copper ore. (*Courtesy of Kennecott Copper Corporation*)

METALS FROM ORES

Once the ore has been concentrated, the next step is to remove the metal from the ore. Most ores are oxides, sulfides, or carbonates of the wanted metal. Usually, if an ore is a carbonate or a sulfide, it is ROASTED to an oxide. *ROAST means to heat the ore in air.* In DEMONSTRATION: *Roasting A Carbonate* Ore, copper(II) carbonate is heated in an open evaporating dish.

$$CuCO_3 \xrightarrow{\Delta} CuO + CO_2$$

The reason that ores are roasted is that it is easier to obtain the metal from an oxide than from a sulfide or a carbonate. The step in which the metal is obtained from the metal ore is REDUCTION. In Experiment 25.1, *Reduction Of An Ore,* lead oxide is reduced. (Remember Oxidation-Reduction Reactions from Unit 5.) The lead oxide is heated with carbon which reduces it.

$$2\,PbO + C \longrightarrow 2\,Pb + CO_2\uparrow$$

This is a view of Dow cells where magnesium chloride is electrolyzed to magnesium metal and chlorine gas.

Refining Copper

It pays to refine copper. Impure copper, though 99% pure contains impurities of gold, silver, iron and other metals. The gold and silver can be removed as metals and are valuable by-products. The iron and zinc lower the ability of copper to carry electric current and are therefore undesirable impurities. In Experiment 25.2 *Refining Copper, Pay Dirt!,* you see how copper can be refined by ELECTROLYSIS. *ELECTROLYSIS is the breaking apart of a compound by passing an electric current through it.* When the current is turned on the impure copper at the positive electrode (anode) forms ions of copper and ions of the impurities of zinc and iron.

$$Cu - 2\,e^- \longrightarrow Cu^{+2}$$
$$Zn - 2\,e^- \longrightarrow Zn^{+2}$$
$$Fe - 2\,e^- \longrightarrow Fe^{+2}$$

The low voltage sends copper ions through the solution to the negative electrode (cathode). At the cathode the copper plates out. The ions of the other metals stay in solution.

$$Cu^{+2} + 2\,e^- \longrightarrow Cu \quad \text{(metal)}$$

The gold and silver are in a sludge at the bottom of the container. The industrial process is similar to what you see in the laboratory.

Copper anodes. are being removed from solution. The anodes are left in solution 28 days for the pure copper to build up on the cathodes. (*Charles E. Rotkin, pfi*)

QUICK QUESTIONS?

1. Electrolysis is an oxidation-reduction reaction. When copper ore is refined is the copper oxidized or reduced?
2. Name two ways of obtaining metal from an ore.

INDUSTRIAL PRODUCTION OF STEEL

We have read about and perhaps seen in the laboratory the various steps ores must go through before the metal is obtained. Iron is our most useful metal. Let's look at how iron and steel are produced in industry.

Pure iron is not strong enough for many of the uses required of it. So, steel is made, by adding carbon to it.

How is iron gotten from the ore concentrate so that steel can be made?

After most of the gangue is left behind, the iron ore is put into a blast furnace. It is called a blast furnace because strong blasts of hot air are shot into the lower part. Inside the blast furnace, there is the fuel, coke, and limestone. In this blast operation, coal gas and ammonia gas are given off. The coke is used in the making of iron. Coke, being carbon, will combine with the oxygen in the iron ore, which is melted in the furnace. Most of the iron ore in this country is an oxide of iron (Fe_2O_3). The basic reactions in a blast furnace are

$$Fe_2O_3 + 3\,C \longrightarrow 2\,Fe + 3\,CO\uparrow$$

$$Fe_2O_3 + 3\,CO \longrightarrow 2\,Fe + 3\,CO_2\uparrow$$

You can see this is a reduction process, as in Experiment 25.1.

Even though the oxygen is taken out of the iron ore, there are usually other impurities in it. The goal is to obtain iron as pure as possible. Many of these impurities have a melting point higher than that of iron. To separate the melted iron and the other impurities, all of the material must be melted. That's where limestone enters the scene. Limestone is calcium carbonate, mostly. Limestone combines with the remaining impurities in the melt so that the melting point is lowered. One typical reaction involves the impurity silicon dioxide, a commercial mineral called quartz.

$$CaCO_3 + SiO_2 \longrightarrow CaSiO_3 + CO_2\uparrow$$

To go through this process, it takes about 1.5 tons of coke, and one-half tons of limestone, for every three tons of iron ore. Huge quantities of air and water are also needed.

Home Lab

Metal ores are not as plentiful as they once were, though we still have quite a bit. The supply is being used up. Recycling used metals is a big business. Over half of our "new" steel is really recycled scrap steel.

Make a survey of all the metal objects in your home.

1. How many are absolutely necessary?
2. Could the metal objects in your home be made of other materials? What ones?
3. List the metal objects in your home that are used once and then discarded.

Purification Processes

The melted impurities float to the top of the liquid metal forming slag. This slag is poured off and beneath is melted iron. The resulting pig iron contains up to five percent of carbon, and traces of manganese, phosphorous, and sulfur. To get rid of these impurities, the pig iron is drained from the blast furnace and processed further.

Pig iron can be changed to steel in several ways. We shall describe the basic-oxygen type furnace.

A huge bowl made of steel is lined with heat-resisting fire-bricks. Liquid pig iron from a blast furnace is poured into this furnace. A protected hollow (so it doesn't melt) oxygen lance is lowered into the center of the bowl and oxygen at high pressure is forced out and into the liquid iron. Fire works! The oxygen combines with the impurities of the pig iron. Carbon and sulfur form carbon dioxide and sulfur dioxide which escape as gases. Other oxides that are solid are caught in a slag that covers the melted metal. After most of the impurities have been removed, the correct amounts of carbon, manganese, and other ingredients can be added to make the kind of steel needed.

Pig iron from blast furnace being poured into basic oxygen furnace. (*Charles E. Rotkin, pfi*)

IRON AND STEEL ALLOYS AND THEIR USES

METAL	ADDED METAL	PROPERTIES	USES
Cast iron	2–5% carbon	Very hard; can be cast	Bases, castings, columns
Steel	Carbon (low) 0.2%–1%	Soft, can be cast, welded, or forged	Rails, sheets, nails, structural parts
Steel	Carbon (high) 1%–2%	Hard, can be cast, forged and tempered	Springs, tools, dies, permanent magnets
Manganese steel	About 12% manganese	Hard, tough	Safes, rock-crusher jaws
Chrome steel	About 3% chromium	Hard, tough, elastic, corrosion resistant	Ball bearings, files
Nickel steel	Up to 6% nickel	Hard, tough, elastic, corrosion resistant	Armor plate, steam engine parts
Tungsten steel	Up to 6% tungsten	Very hard	Cutting tools
Silicon steel	About 3% silicon	Hard, flexible, high magnetic permeability	Car springs, cores for transformers, electromagnets
Molybdenum steel	About 5% molybdenum	Very hard, tensile strength, corrosion resistant	Axles, lathe tools
Vanadium steel	Up to 3% vanadium	High elasticity, tensile strength, shock resistant	Auto parts

Using the Other Metals

The other metals as well as their alloys are useful. Copper, for example, is used in its non-alloyed form for electrical wiring and for water pipes. Sheets of copper can be used for roofing. Many pieces of cast items in the hardware store are made of copper. Important alloys of copper include brass (copper and zinc); and bronze (copper and tin).

Aluminum metal has many uses. Aluminum alloys are also useful. Chromium-aluminum alloys are used on automobiles, brass and aluminum alloys for kitchen utensils, bronze-aluminum alloys for ships.

Zinc is used to coat iron (galvanized iron).

An interesting type of alloy is the FUSIBLE alloy. Such an alloy is used in automatic sprinkling systems to put out fires. The next time you see such a sprinkler, look at it closely. The plug in the nozzle is a low-melting point alloy. Alloys have melting points that are lower than that of the pure metals of which they are made. *FUSIBLE alloys have melting points lower than the boiling point of water.* These alloys are usually made of lead, tin, cadmium and bismuth.

Millions of dollars of metals and metal products are ruined each year by corrosion. (*J.V.A.F. Nea, Photo Researchers*)

MIXING THE METALS—ALLOYS

Think of a metal object that you have in your home. Chances are that it is an *ALLOY, a metallic object containing two or more metals.* You observe the properties of alloys in Experiment 25.4. Metals in a pure state may not have the strength or other properties required for a particular job. As we have seen, iron usually has carbon added to it to make steel. Most steel, in addition to carbon contains various other metals. The kind of metal added to the iron depends on why you need the steel. For example, nickel is added to increase the heat and acid resistance of the steel. Chromium may be added to help prevent rust. Some steel in your car may contain fifteen different kinds of metals. As you might guess, there are many different recipes for steel, each depending on the job it has to do.

High temperature alloy casting.
   (*Charles E. Rotkin, pfi*)

Titanium: The Rediscovered Metal

Titanium is a very abundant metal in the earth's crust. It was discovered in 1791 by Reverend William Gregor. Then it was forgotten. Until 1948 only small quantities were produced at costs over $3,000 per pound. Today over two million pounds a year are used in space engineering and jet airliners. The frame and support of the Apollo missiles are made of titanium. The metal is heat-resistant and light-weight.

One of the reasons it was forgotten was that it is hard to handle. The melted metal is so active chemically that it dissolves just about anything used to hold it including the linings of furnaces and forms into which it is poured. As better methods of handling the metal are developed, titanium will become a metal we use everyday.

As a compound, titanium oxide, TiO_2, titania is used in paints. It has more covering power than lead pigments and is not poisonous. Over one billion pounds of titania are used in laundry detergents to make "whites whiter."

QUICK QUESTIONS?

1. What is the purpose of a blast furnace in steel making?
2. Trace the path of a metal from earth to finished product.
3. What is an alloy?

Chapter 25

ACTION POINTS

ORES are materials containing compounds of metals found in the earth.

Steps in the obtaining of a metal include: **DIGGING** the **ORE; CONCENTRATING** the **ORE; REDUCING** the **ORE: PURIFYING** the **METAL.**

Two methods of concentrating the ore are: **GRAVITY SEPARATION** and **FLOTATION.**

ROASTING an ore is done by heating it in air.

IMPURE copper is made pure by **ELECTROLYSIS.**

ELECTROLYSIS is the breaking apart of a compound by passing an electric current through it.

Iron ore is reduced in a **BLAST FURNACE.**

The resulting pig iron is purified in **BASIC-OXYGEN FURNACE.**

An **ALLOY** is a mixture of two or more metals.

PROPERTIES of alloys are slightly different from those of the pure metals combined in the alloy.

INDEX